21.
7101

ORCHIDS—Their Description and Cultivation

MILTONIA MAIDEN'S BLUSH

ORCHIDS

Their Description and Cultivation

by

CHARLES H. CURTIS

With a Foreword by

LORD ABERCONWAY, C.B.E., V.M.H.

LONDON

PUTNAM & COMPANY, LTD.

42, GREAT RUSSELL STREET, W.C. 1

First Published, 1950

Printed by HARRISON & SONS, Ltd., Printers to His Majesty the King, London, Hayes (Middx.) and High Wycombe

To My Wife, HELEN MARY CURTIS,
who patiently endured many long,
silent evenings, while this book was
being written; and to the many
friends with whom I have been
associated during the past forty-two
years on the Orchid Committee of
The Royal Horticultural Society.

CONTENTS

LIST OF ILLUSTRATIONS

Titles in capitals indicate colour plates.

FOREWORD

TO write a book on Orchids that is not only of service to those who grow and admire this wonderful race of plants, but that is also an outstanding milestone in their history, requires an author who not only knows how to express his views, but, above all, has a deep and intimate knowledge of the plants themselves.

Mr. Charles H. Curtis, F.L.S., V.M.H., is already the author, among many other books, of that well-known volume " Orchids for Everyone," which has long been out of print. Hence this new volume, with its thirty full-page illustrations in colour, forty-eight in half-tone, and beautiful type and printing.

It deals with Orchids from every point of view—their history, descriptions of genera and species of horticultural and of botanical interest (with cultural notes), their hybrids and even a section on Orchid Bibliography.

As might be expected, hybrids occupy a prominent place in this volume, and there are hybrids now which are not only primary, but bigeneric, trigeneric, and even quadrigeneric.

But Mr. Curtis is not only a writer—he is a man who thoroughly knows Orchids. For more than forty years he has been a member of the Royal Horticultural Society's Orchid Committee, and now for some time a Vice-Chairman of this Committee. He probably holds the record for attendance at these meetings, where the soundness of his judgment on the plants submitted is well recognized by all his colleagues.

He has, of course, grown Orchids himself and many of them; in his earlier years he had charge of the collection at Kew, but, unluckily, as it happens, he has twice had his own private collection destroyed by war attacks—once during the first world war, and again during the second.

There is none more capable than Mr. Curtis of writing a really first-class book on Orchids, and all those who love these plants are deeply indebted to him for the two years of intense work, and more than a half-century of experience, which are embodied in this volume.

ABERCONWAY.

ORCHIDS—Their Description and Cultivation

INTRODUCTION

THE chief reasons for the production of this book are found in the growing demand for publications on Orchids and Orchid cultivation, and the fact that practically all books of this kind are out of print and high prices are being paid for second-hand copies. Horticultural journals, however ably they may deal with Orchids, do not provide such a ready means of reference as a book which finds a place on a grower's bookshelf. No important books have appeared since *Orchids for Everyone* was published prior to the first World War, and as second-hand copies now sell at £7 7s., the present contribution appears desirable.

The earliest known book on Orchids was a small one written by Mr. T. C. Lyons of Ladiston, Ireland. The first edition was printed and bound by the author, who gave copies to all Orchid cultivators he knew. The second, and enlarged, edition was published in 1845, in London by Mr. J. Ridgway, and in Dublin by Messrs. Hodge and Smith. Copies of both editions are extremely rare.

A larger book, by Mr. B. S. Williams, of Holloway—who had been gardener to R. Warner, Esq., of Broxbourne, Hertfordshire, famous for his fine collection of Orchids—appeared in 1852 and, under the title of *Orchid Growers' Manual*, ran into numerous editions, each larger than the previous one and indicating the growing popularity of Orchids. Thomas Appleby, who had been manager of the Orchid department in the nurseries of Messrs. A. Henderson and Co., Pineapple Place, Maida Vale, London, wrote a small book entitled *The Orchid Manual*, of which the second edition was published by the *Journal of Horticulture*, Fleet Street, in 1865.

Large, splendidly illustrated and often sumptuously bound Orchid books followed, notably Robert Warner's *Select Orchidaceous Plants* (1862–91), and James Bateman's *A Monograph of Odontoglossum* (1874), but the high water mark was reached by the four weighty folio volumes of *Reichenbachia*, by Mr. F. Sander, St. Albans, with hundreds of full-page, finely coloured illustrations reproduced from paintings by

3

Mr. H. Moon, and descriptions in three languages. A good set may realize £100 to £130 ; publication commenced in 1888 and ended in 1894. The work was dedicated to Queen Victoria.

The Orchid Album, conducted by Robert Warner, with the assistance of B. S. Williams, and Thomas Moore, Curator of the Chelsea Botanic Gardens, commenced publication in 1882, and ran into eleven volumes. *L'Orchidophile*, by A. Godefroy-Lebeuf, with the collaboration of Comte du Buysson, at Argenteuil, Seine-et-Oise, France, was first published in June 1881 and continued until 1892 ; there are ten volumes of it in my collection. *The Orchid Review* holds the record for the longest continuous run of any monthly journal devoted to Orchidology; it was founded in 1893 by Mr. R. Allen Rolfe, A.L.S., who was then the authority on Orchids at the Herbarium, Royal Botanic Gardens, Kew. He continued as Editor until his demise in 1920, when publication was suspended for six months; he was followed by Mr. Gurney Wilson, then Secretary, and now Chairman, of the Royal Horticultural Society's Orchid Committee, who retired at the end of 1932, and whom I succeeded as Editor in 1933.

A particularly valuable work, in two thick volumes, the *Manual of Orchidaceous Plants*, was published by Messrs. James Veitch & Sons, Chelsea, in 1887–94, and is a mine of information concerning the discovery and introduction of Orchids, but has long since been out of print; the large-paper edition is extremely rare. This fine work, and those previously cited, together with *Sander's Orchid Guide*, *Sander's List of Orchid Hybrids* and the Royal Horticultural Society's *List of Awards to Orchids*, have been consulted during the preparation of the present work.

Frequent reference has also been made to works not wholly devoted to Orchids, the most important of these being Curtis's *Botanical Magazine*, Edwards's *Botanical Register*, and Paxton's *Magazine of Botany*.

To Mrs. Malby, Southgate, for her painstaking work in connection with the preparation of the coloured plates; to Miss Annice Walkden, for the privilege of reproducing photographs of Orchids she has grown at The Raft, Derbyshire Road, Sale; to the Proprietors of *The Gardeners' Chronicle*, for permission to reproduce numerous illustrations; and to Mr. E. Cooper, St. Albans; Mr. H. G. Alexander, Westonbirt; Mr. B. Hills, Exbury; and Mr. David Sander, St. Albans, for kindly assistance, I am particularly grateful.

My own association with Orchids, Orchid growers, Orchid collectors and raisers of Orchids, has been a long one; it began at Messrs. W. D. Thomson & Sons' nurseries at Wimbledon and was continued at Oakfield, Wimbledon Park; the nurseries of Messrs. James Veitch & Sons, Chelsea; and the Royal Botanic Gardens, Kew.

Long service as Sub-Editor and Editor of *The Gardeners' Magazine*, and subsequently as Editor of *The Gardeners' Chronicle* and *The Orchid Review*, has enabled me to maintain contact with amateur and professional growers, while forty-two years of continuous service on the R.H.S. Orchid Committee have kept me *au fait* with the production and increase of hybrid Orchids. My private and modest collection of Orchids suffered considerably during the war of 1914–18 and was entirely disposed of by enemy action in the recent war. These experiences and the success of *Orchids for Everyone* encourage me to hope that the present publication may prove equally useful and acceptable to Orchid growers in the British Isles and far overseas. I cannot expect that no errors of any kind occur, but trust mistakes are few, and that readers will tolerate them, remembering that "to err is human" and that it is easier to be critical than correct. Writing this book has entailed much work, but has given me much pleasure and I console myself with Pliny's observation that "no book was so bad but some good might be got out of it."

CHARLES H. CURTIS

Chestergate, Brentford,
January, 1949

HISTORICAL

THE progress made in the importation and cultivation of exotic Orchids is one of the most remarkable developments that horti-culture can show. As in so many other instances —Dahlias, Sweet Peas, Carnations, Chrysanthemums, Delphiniums, Michaelmas Daisies and Pelargoniums —the beginnings of the development were small and insignificant and the pioneers could not possibly have envisaged the present world-wide enthusiasm for Orchids.

Peter Collinson received Bletia verecunda from Providence Island, one of the Bahamas group, West Indies, in 1731 and it flowered under cultivation in the following year, and so the history of Orchid importa-tion and cultivation began. Nearly fifty years elapsed before Dr. Fother-gill imported Phaius grandifolius from China, but it became known as Limodorum Tankervilliae and was figured under this name, in colour, in the first edition of *Hortus Kewensis*, published in 1789. This fine old terrestrial Orchid became an established favourite and was a popular subject in collections of stove plants upwards of fifty years ago, but a particular interest attaches to it, inasmuch as Francis Bauer, a famous draughtsman, studied its biological make-up and made the wonderful discovery that each plant cell has a nucleus.

When Kew was Crown property, and long before it became a National Institution, it had a modest collection of Orchids. Aiton, the Garden Superintendent in those far-off days, listed fifteen exotic Orchids in 1789, but by the time that the second edition of *Hortus Kewensis* was published, in 1813, the collection consisted of eighty-four exotic species, belonging to thirty-nine genera. Epidendrum fragrans flowered at Kew in 1782 and E. cochleatum in 1787. Later, Dr. Roxburgh sent various Orchids to Kew, from India, and these included the first Aerides, the first Vanda and the first Dendrobium ever seen in an English garden. The Kew "Records" also show that between 1823 and 1825 numer-ous species were sent to Kew, from Trinidad, by David Lockhart and the collection contained the first examples to reach this country of Stanhopea insignis, Oncidium Papilio, Lockhartia elegans, Catasetum tridentatum and Ionopsis pallidiflora. Lockhart sent specimens grow-ing on portions of branches of trees and these suggested a method of cultivation that eventually proved successful with many epiphytic species.

But while the Kew collection was being built up steadily, the Horticultural Society of London (subsequently "Royal") was engaged in the same way at its gardens at Chiswick, while several prominent patrons of horticulture found great pleasure and interest in a similar proceeding. Earl Fitzwilliam, at Wentworth, and the Duke of Devonshire, at Chatsworth, had large and excellent collections quite early in the nineteenth century and both noblemen were fortunate in having head gardeners who did not fear to experiment in various methods of cultivation. Joseph Cooper, at Wentworth, and Joseph Paxton, at Chatsworth, had unusual opportunities as their employers were wealthy noblemen who were helpful in every possible way and took great pride in their gardens, gardeners and collections. Paxton (afterwards Sir Joseph) was employed at Chiswick and attracted the attention of the Duke of Devonshire, who owned the gardens, and much of the surrounding property, including Chiswick House and grounds—now maintained as a public park by the Corporation of Brentford and Chiswick. The Duke so greatly admired Paxton's appearance, skill and initiative that he offered him the charge of the Chatsworth Gardens. With immense financial resources at his disposal Paxton took full advantage of his opportunities and the magnificence of his lay-out and the ranges of glasshouses still remain. The fine collections of Orchids and other exotic plants, however, have long since passed away. Gibson was employed as a collector of Orchids, in India, and his success helped to make the Chatsworth collection the most notable of its kind.

At this period Dr. Lindley was an outstanding figure in horticulture and in botany. As Secretary to the Royal Horticultural Society, and a founder and first Editor of *The Gardeners' Chronicle*, Lindley came into close contact with all the famous horticulturists of his time and as new Orchids were sent to him he described and named them, with the result that he became the authority for hundreds of species. He also took a keen interest in the cultivation of Orchids and in 1830 laid down general cultural rules, but the experience of growers in later years showed that the high temperature, excessive humidity and intense shade he advised were by no means essential. In those early years the altitudes at which Orchids were found in several tropical countries did not always receive due consideration.

CHYSIS BRACTESCENS

Paxton and Cooper, thoughtful, studious and skilful men, introduced a cultural system that allowed for lower temperatures and more ventilation, and as they were successful cultivators their more rational methods were gradually adopted. Nor must it be overlooked that the pioneers of Orchid cultivation had to house their plants in flue-heated structures, and, consequently, their successors started with the advantages of hot-water heating and were able to grade their Orchids in separate houses according to the temperature that appeared to be desirable.

Many of those who formed collections of Orchids in the past century bore names that are familiar to present-day growers. Mr. William Cattley, Barnet, was a notable grower and introduced many new species to cultivation. Mrs. Arnold Harrison and Mr. Richard Harrison, Liverpool, were famous for South American Orchids sent by their brother, Mr. Wm. Harrison, who resided at Rio de Janeiro; the collection was dispersed in 1842. The collections at Chatsworth and Wentworth have already been referred to. The Rev. J. T. Huntley grew Orchids in Huntingdonshire and frequently corresponded with James Bateman, who was famous over a long period for his collection at Knypersley Hall, Cheshire. George Ure-Skinner, a merchant trading with Guatemala, sent many very fine Orchids to Mr. Bateman and is commemorated by Cattleya Skinneri.

The Rev. John Clowes formed a collection at Broughton Hall, Manchester, and introduced some novel features of interior construction in Orchid houses; he died in 1846 and, by his bequest, his Orchids passed to the Kew collection. Mr. Thomas Brocklehurst, The Fence, near Macclesfield, and Sir Charles Lemon, Carclew, Cornwall, had collections of note. Mr. Sigismund Rucker maintained a collection for about thirty-five years and it was one unusually rich in rare species and varieties, all cultivated with great success and exhibited frequently as fine specimens; he died in 1875. Mr. George Barker, Springfield, near Birmingham, specialized in Mexican Orchids, sent one of his gardeners to collect plants, and also contributed to the expenses of J. Linden's expedition to Colombia.

Mrs. Wray, Oakfield, Cheltenham, and Mrs. Lawrence, Ealing Park, Middlesex, cultivated Orchids, but the latter lady will be best remembered in this connection as the mother of Sir Trevor Lawrence, who had one of the finest collections in the country, at Burford Lodge, Dorking,

Surrey, and was President of the Royal Horticultural Society for many years. Unfortunately, his Orchids were dispersed soon after his death.

Two names stand out conspicuously in the records of their time—Mr. Robert Warner and his gardener Mr. Ben Williams, whose splendid collection at Hoddesdon, Hertfordshire, was famous over a long period. Warner's *Select Orchidaceous Plants* is a handsome reminder of the Hoddesdon Orchids. Mr. Williams founded the firm of B. S. Williams & Son, at Holloway, where Orchids were a speciality, and he was the author of *The Orchid Grower's Manual*, which increased in size with every edition. Mr. Donald Beaton had charge of a considerable collection at Shrubland Park, the home of Sir William Middleton, and his correspondence with Sir William Hooker—the first Director of the Royal Botanic Gardens, Kew—with his contributions to the current horticultural literature of his time, show that he was a thoughtful and skilful cultivator, and not afraid to take risks when making experiments. It was about the same time that Mr. S. Rucker gathered together a fine lot of Orchids at West Hill, Wandsworth, where his capable gardener was Mr. John Mylam. As might be expected, the Horticultural Society of London was not behind the times and the collection founded while Mr. George Gordon was Superintendent at Chiswick was maintained for many years after his decease, as contemporary records show. Gordon wrote a lengthy treatise on Orchid cultivation and this may be found in the *Journal* of the Society (now the R.H.S.) for 1849.

In 1821 Messrs. Conrad Loddiges & Sons, of Hackney, London, a famous nursery firm, began to cultivate Orchids on a commercial scale and continued to do so until the business ceased forty years later. The name of Loddiges will be remembered so long as Orchids are cultivated, as large numbers of species were introduced to cultivation by them for the first time and not a few bear their name (Cattleya Loddigesii and others). But Messrs. Loddiges are also commemorated by the twenty quarto volumes of the *Botanical Cabinet*, with coloured plates, produced by them from 1813 to 1833, in which many Orchids are illustrated and described.

Many nursery firms that specialized in Orchids, and thereby won a foremost place in British horticulture, have long since passed out of existence, but their names are kept in happy memory by their introductions and by their improved methods of cultivation. Messrs. C. Loddiges & Sons, of Hackney, have been referred to already, but not less famous in later times were Messrs. James Veitch & Sons, Royal Exotic Nurseries, King's Road, Chelsea. This grand old firm sent collectors to those countries where Orchids abound, and were instrumental in introducing many fine species, while their clever hybridist, Mr. John Seden, raised many of the finest of the earlier hybrids, including Brassocattleya Veitchii, or as it was first called, Bc. Digbyano-Mossiae. When Sir Harry Veitch retired the business ceased, and the Orchid Department, together with the hybridizing section, at Langley were taken over and carried on by Messrs. Black & Flory.

Also in the King's Road, Chelsea, and quite close to the Veitchian nursery, Mr. William Bull had his establishment; he was a great advertiser and every year held an exhibition of his own, to which he invited all the fashionable people of London, and usually persuaded some notability to open it. An awning, in brilliant colours, extended from the entrance out over the path, so that visitors alighting from their horse-drawn equipages could enter without fear of getting wet if it rained, or of being scorched if the sun shone brightly. Needless to state, the daily press and the horticultural press received invitations and their representatives were received royally.

Cymbidium Lowianun and Renanthera Lowii are reminders of Messrs. Hugh Low & Co., of Clapton, London, a firm famous over a long period for the many splendid new Orchids they introduced to cultivation. Although this firm has ceased to be, the business it conducted eventually passed into the hands of Mr. Stuart Low and is continued under the title of Messrs. Stuart Low & Co., at Enfield, Middlesex, and at Jarvis Brook, Crowborough, Sussex.

The establishment of Messrs. Sanders, St. Albans, Hertfordshire, was founded by Mr. F. H. Sander, who was an enthusiast, a great cultivator and an astute business man. For a long period he was aided by Mr. Godseff, as general manager; Mr. Godseff had previously occupied a similar position with Mr. William Bull. Those were the days when Orchids were imported in considerable quantities. Mr. Sander employed numerous collectors and sent them to all parts of the world in search of beautiful, new and rare species. The firm exhibited freely and consistently, and the R.H.S. lists of *Awards to Orchids* show how successful these collectors were. The raising of Orchids from seeds, and the production of fine hybrids followed and a branch establishment was founded at Bruges. There were three sons, and on the death of their father, Mr. Fearnley Sander took charge at Bruges, who, on his retirement, was succeeded by the late Mr. Louis Sander, whose wife became a clever raiser of Orchid hybrids. Mr. Fred K. Sander succeeded to the management of the St. Albans nursery, where he is assisted by Mr. David Sander, while Mr. Roger Sander presides at Bruges. These two last represent the third generation of a family intimately associated with the commercial development of Orchid culture.

Another instance of the change of venue, but without change of title, is that of Messrs. Charlesworth & Co. Mr. Charlesworth founded the business at Bradford, and is commemorated by Cypripedium Charlesworthii and many other Orchids. The business grew and, under Mr. Charlesworth's personal supervision, hybridising was carried on extensively under the best scientific methods. Subsequently, the whole establishment was transported to a sunnier site at Haywards Heath, where Orchid seedlings, chiefly of hybrid parentage, are still raised in large quantities. One of their finest achievements was the raising of a splendid strain of Odontoglossum crispum, obtained from the very finest of imported varieties. Odontioda Charlesworthii, Odontocidium Smithii, Miltonia Charlesworthii, and Charleswortheara nobilis are four Orchids that made Orchid lovers their debtors. When Sir George Holford died, his Orchid grower, Mr. H. G. Alexander, formed a company to continue the Westonbirt collection as a commercial proposition; he has raised many fine Orchids and is recognized as the creator of the modern race of hybrid Cymbidiums.

Within the last sixty years many private collections have been dispersed, usually after the death of the owner. A few that come to mind include those formed by Mr. R. I. Measures, at Camberwell; Mr. R. H. Measures, at Streatham; Mr. G. D. Owen, Rotherham; Sir Frederick Wigan, Clare Lawn, East Sheen; Mr. Norman Cookson, Wylam-on-Tyne; Mr. Samuel Gratrix, West Point, Whalley Range, Manchester, whose collection realized £7,369; Mrs. Carl Holmes, The Node, Welwyn, Hertfordshire; Mr. H. Worsley, Harlingden, Lancashire; Sir George Holford, Westonbirt, Tetbury, Gloucestershire; Mr. A. T. Cussons, Oaklands, Kersal, Manchester; Mr. W. E. Lee, Plumpton Hall, Lancashire;

Major C. Drummond, Cadland Park; Dr. Craven Moore, East Grinstead; Mr. G. F. Moore, Chardwar, Bourton-on-the-Water, Gloucestershire; Mr. H. J. Elwes, Colesbourne, Gloucestershire; Sir Jeremiah Coleman, Gatton Park, Reigate; Sir Trevor Lawrence, Burford Lodge, Dorking; Mr. Warburton, Vine House, Haslingden; Mr. Robert Paterson, Ardingly, Sussex; Mr. J. McCartney, Bolton; Mr. H. T. Pitt, Rosslyn, Stamford Hill, London; Mr. F. J. Hanbury, Brockhurst, East Grinstead; Major J. J. Joicey, Witley, Surrey; Mrs. Bruce and Miss Wrigley, Bridge Hall, Bury, Lancashire; Mr. B. J. Beckton, Daisy Hill, Irlams-o'-th'-Height, Manchester; Mr. Brooman White, who grew Odontoglossums splendidly at Arddarroch, in Scotland; and Mr. de Barri Crawshay, Sevenoaks, who specialized in Odontoglossums. Baron Sir Henry Schröder's collection at The Dell, Egham, remains in the family.

The foregoing list, however lamentable it may appear, could be extended considerably and is compiled solely for the purpose of recording some of the many private growers who, in their day and generation, were generous patrons of horticulture and assisted nobly in advancing the interest in Orchids. The Royal Horticultural Society's *List of Awards to Orchids* shows how great was their success in acquiring new species, outstanding varietal forms, or new and improved hybrids.

It must not be imagined, however, that these past-masters are without successors. Not by any means. Some of the principal British collections in this year of grace are those of Capt. Edmund de Rothschild, Exbury, Southampton; Sir William Cooke, Bart., Wyld Court, Hampstead Norris, Newbury; Mr. H. W. B. Schröder, Dell Park, Egham, Surrey; Mr. Guy P. Harben, Colbury House, Totton, Hampshire; Mr. H. P. Lawson, Woking, Surrey; Dr. W. Stirling, Whatcroft Hall, near Northwich, Cheshire; Miss Annice Walkden, The Raft, Derbyshire Road, Sale, Manchester; Lord Aberconway, Bodnant, Tal-y-Cafn, North Wales; The Hon. H. S. Tufton, Castle Hill, Englefield Green, Surrey; The Hon. H. R. Broughton, Englefield Green; Mr. E. R. Ashton, Broadlands, Camden Park, Tunbridge Wells (recently dispersed); Mr. Clive Cookson, Newcastle; Mr. H. S. Wharton, Temple Avenue, Hampstead; Lt.-Col. F. E. Griggs, Chislehurst; and Mr. N. M. Jensen, Woldingham, Surrey.

But these modern collections differ very considerably from the private collections that have passed away; they consist very largely of hybrid

Orchids—Cymbidiums, Cypripediums, Cattleyas, Odontoglossums, Odontiodas, Miltonias, a few Oncidiums, Calanthes, a few Dendrobiums and Vandas, and examples of the hybrid genera Vuylstekeara, Lowiara, Odontocidium, Miltonioda, and Wilsonara—whereas in the past the collections included far larger numbers of true species, the stronger-growing Vandas of the V. suavis type, long-stemmed Dendrobiums, Coelogynes, Maxillarias, Stanhopeas, Saccolabiums, Renantheras and many others, for those were the days when the more popular Orchids were imported annually in large quantities, and replacements could be made easily and cheaply. During the period under consideration colour variations were greatly prized and scores of varietal names were given to forms of Cattleya Mossiae, C. labiata, C. Trianae, C. Dowiana, Laelia purpurata, Odontoglossum crispum and Dendrobium nobile that showed some difference in colour from what was considered to be the type.

Similarly, the old commercial establishments do not lack notable successors and those that occupy a high position to-day include Messrs. Sanders, St. Albans, with a branch establishment at Bruges, Belgium; Messrs. Charlesworth & Co., Haywards Heath; Messrs. Stuart Low & Co., Jarvis Brook, Crowborough, Sussex; Messrs. A. J. Keeling & Sons, Bradford, Yorkshire; Messrs. Armstrong & Brown, Tunbridge Wells, now owned by Mr. Clint McDade, who has a large establishment at Chattanooga, Tennessee, U.S.A.; Messrs. H. G. Alexander, Ltd. Westonbirt, Tetbury, Gloucester, founded on the collection made by Sir George Holford and cared for by Mr. H. G. Alexander; Messrs. Black & Flory, Langley, Slough; Mr. D. Cowan, Surbiton, Surrey; Messrs. Mansell and Hatcher, Leeds; and Messrs. Harry Dixon & Sons, Spencer Park, Wandsworth Common, London, S.W.18.

Commercial Orchid establishments in the United States of America are of comparatively recent origin, but nevertheless very important, and the chief are those of the L. Sherman Adams Company, Wellesley, Massachusetts; Messrs. Clint McDade & Sons, Rivermont, Tennessee; and Messrs. E. W. McLellan & Co., Colma, San Francisco, California.

On the continent of Europe the passage of time, war and other conditions have reduced the number of commercial Orchid establishments, but Messrs. Sanders, at Bruges, and the Flandria Company, also at Bruges, Belgium, have immense nurseries, but the nurseries of Chas.

CYMBIDIUM SWALLOW VAR. ORIOLE

Vuylsteke, Linden, and many others are but memories. In France, Messrs. Vacherot-Lecoufle keep the flag flying at Boisy Saint Leger, Seine et Oise, as do Messrs. Cholet & Son.

Several modern developments remain to be placed on record. The cultivation of Orchids to supply the cut-flower industry has increased amazingly in the British Isles, in the United States and in Australia. Certain growers, in Sussex, grow large quantities of Cypripedium insigne and C. i. var. Sanderae solely for the purpose of providing marketable flowers during the Winter. Most of our commercial growers found the sale of cut flowers a profitable proceeding during the war years and this side-line, together with the sales of plants, exported to America and Australia, enabled them to surmount the difficulties incidental to a nation at war. Extra fuel was allowed them, and also to the principal private growers, as the Government appreciated the desirability of maintaining these Orchid collections, with their innumerable and valuable seedling hybrids, until the return of happier times.

One other development must suffice to indicate the world-wide appreciation of Orchids. In the Far East, and notably at Singapore Botanic Gardens, many hybrid tropical Orchids have been raised for the enrichment of gardens where the plants can be grown entirely out of doors. Vanda, Arachnis, and other genera have been pressed into service with excellent results. In California, and in some parts of Australia Cymbidiums are cultivated on a large scale out of doors, or under lath-roofing and without the aid of artificial heat.

GEOGRAPHICAL DISTRIBUTION

THE geographical distribution of Orchids provides a most interesting study. Climate is by no means the sole governing factor, otherwise Vandas, Aerides and Phalaenopses might be found in certain parts of tropical America; these genera, however, are confined to Asia and found chiefly in Siam, India, Malaya and the Philippines, and, even so, are more or less confined to particular areas of these vast, Far-Eastern regions. Similarly, Odontoglossums are not found in the Far East, although climatic conditions in the highlands of India and Burma approximate to those obtaining in the highlands of parts of South America.

The genus Aerides, for instance, is represented in Southern and even Northern India, Upper Burma, Annam, the Malay Peninsula, and farther east, in the Philippines, with an odd species or two in Java, Borneo and Celebes, but why none in Sumatra ?

The Vandas are equally selective. A few are found in Southern India and Ceylon and a few more, including the lovely V. teres, away up in Nepal. Many more are natives of Siam, the Malay Peninsula and Java, but they are scarce in Borneo, Timor and Amboina, and the collector must journey farther east to find the magnificent V. Sanderiana in Mindanao.

No less interesting is the range of the genus Phalaenopsis throughout Eastern Asia. It appears to dislike the Indian Continent. A few species are found in Assam, Cambodia, the Malayas, and Sumatra, but more in Borneo, and the Philippines, where the beautiful P. Schilleriana and P. Stuartiana are found, while the delightful P. amabilis strays from Java to Northern Celebes and farther east to Amboina and the Tenimber Islands, indeed P. amabilis has the widest distribution of any member of this genus.

Angraecums find their principal home in Madagascar, whence come A. sesquipedale and A. eburneum, nevertheless several species are found in West Africa, and East Africa, one from the Cape and another far away in Japan—A. falcatum.

Saccolabium is largely a Burmese genus, but Java, the Sikkim and Khasia Hills, Northern Borneo and Cochin China have made modest contributions to it.

Calanthes have a wide range, from Japan, Cochin China, to Australia (New South Wales), Southern India, Moulmein, Java and Fiji.

The particularly extensive genus Epidendrum is confined to the New World, but finds its chief expression in South America, with extensions in Central America, the West Indies, Mexico, and even in the U.S. States of Louisiana and Carolina.

Although the splendid Cattleyas are found only in South America, the distribution of the various species is particularly interesting as the allied Laelias are freely associated with them throughout Southern Brazil and particularly in the vast country that includes the Provinces of Bahia, Minas Geraes, São Paulo and down to the Rio Grande. But there is another very wide area where Cattleyas are found, although in fewer numbers—and without their erstwhile associates, the Laelias. This area extends across Venezuela, and then down the western side of the South American Continent, through Colombia and into Ecuador, with a few species scattered in other parts of these countries, but north of Brazil, and more in the centre of South America. The popular Labiatae group is in no sense centralized; for instance, C. Trianae, C. Warscewiczii and C. Dowiana var. aurea are found in the far west of South America, whereas C. labiata and C. Warneri come from the east side, and C. Mendelii, C. Mossiae much farther north. One species, C. Dowiana, has strayed still farther north, and may also be found in Costa Rica, while C. Skinneri and C. Bowringiana are found in Nicaragua and Honduras, with C. citrina in Southern Mexico. Remembering this wide range—from about 18° lat. N., to 30° lat. S., and between 40° and 105° long. W.—and that most species are found in mountainous country, their various needs under cultivation are explained.

Considering the comparatively few species it contains, the genus Phaius has a remarkably wide range. Some species are found in the comparatively cool climate of China and Japan, whereas others come from Madagascar, Africa, the Malay Archipelago, Assam, Burma and Ceylon.

The genus Laelia is more or less mixed up with Cattleya in the matter of distribution. L. anceps and L. (Brassavola) glauca occupy the northern outposts in southern Mexico; L. autumnalis and L. majalis are found somewhat farther south, with L. rubescens and L. superbiens lower down, in Mexico, with L. (Brassavola) Digbyana farther east, in Guatemala, and the pretty little L. monophylla more eastward still, in

Jamaica. Southward still, L. pumila and its varieties are found in British Guiana and Brazil, while the home of the robust and variable L. pur-purata centres in the Santa Catherina province of southern Brazil, probably the most southern location of the genus.

Coelogyne, a genus of considerable horticultural value, is most largely represented in Nepal and Sikkim, but several species are found in Bhutan and Moulmein, with C. speciosa in Java and the remarkable C. pandurata in Sarawak. The allied, alpine, deciduous Pleiones are found in the Khasia Hills, Sikkim, Nepal and almost to Moulmein.

Probably in no other genus of Orchids is the tufted habit of growth so consistent throughout as in Masdevallia. Numerous species, without pseudo-bulbs, are found in the Cordilleras on the western side of South America, but the range is through the mountainous regions of Brazil, British Guiana, the Peruvian Andes, Colombia and northward to Mexico. Practically all grow where the atmosphere is heavily charged with moisture, at considerable altitudes and often where the temperature may rise to 82° by day and fall to freezing point at night.

Dendrobiums belong to Asia, with outlying species in Australasia. For the most part they are grouped in four large areas—South Western India and Ceylon, Upper and Lower Burma (especially the Moulmein region), along the southern side of the Himalaya, from North India to China, and in the Philippines. A few species are found in Borneo, Sumatra, Java, Celebes, Timor and the extreme north of Australia.

Sophronitis is Brazilian and Schomburgkia is native to Honduras.

Cypripediums are able to retain and increase their popularity chiefly because the great majority of modern hybrids flower during the Winter season and therefore have few competitors. Were they Spring-flowering, they would have to compete with Cymbidiums. Except for one or two hardy species, from Canada, and the extreme north of the U.S.A., there are no Cypripediums in the whole of the American Continent. A somewhat small group of species, however, have their home in Colombia, Venezuela and Peru, but although they are regarded as Cypripediums by horticulturists, the botanists label them Selenipediums ; they include C. caudatum, C. longifolium, C. caricinum and C. Schlimii, all rather robust and green-leaved species.

The true Cypripediums (i.e., Cypripedium proper, Phragmipedium and Paphiopedilum) are found in the Far East, North-East India,

Burma, the Malay Peninsula, Annam, Sumatra, Java, Borneo, the Philippines and New Guinea, with one species in Southern India.

The charming species of Platyclinis (formerly Dendrochilum) all come from the Philippine Islands.

Pleurothallis, an extremely large genus, all very interesting botanically, but of small horticultural value, finds its home in the mountainous regions of Bolivia, Mexico, Brazil and the West Indies. The lowly yet beautiful Restrepias inhabit the mountains of tropical America, from Mexico to Brazil.

It is of interest to observe that Odontoglossums are distributed far more widely than is generally believed. Many species are found in Mexico and Central America, where numerous Laelias and Cattleyas are also natives, but there is a parting of the ways when South America is reached, for whereas these two genera are plentiful on the Brazilian side, the Odontoglossums continue down the Pacific side, along the Andean country, ranging from Bolivia through Colombia—the great centre of the genus—to Ecuador and on down to Peru. The most northerly species are O. maxillare and O. citrosmum, but a few unimportant species occupy the "farthest South" position, in short, Odontoglossums are found between 10° north of the Equator and (with one or two exceptions) 7° south of it; nevertheless, owing to the altitudes occupied, and the moist conditions, the great majority of species are, horticulturally, cool-house Orchids.

The vast majority of Cymbidiums now in cultivation are hybrids raised, for the most part, in England, but their progenitors range over Khasia, Nepal and Sikkim, with outliers in Japan. The fine old Cymbidium Lowianum is found in Burma and has also been collected in the Khasia Hills; the beautiful C. eburneum also finds its home in the Khasia Hills, as does the pendulous C. Devonianum, but C. giganteum is found in Nepal, Bhutan and Sikkim, and the comparatively newcomer, C. insigne, is a native of Annam.

Although the majority of Oncidiums are found in Southern Mexico, on through Colombia and Ecuador to Peru, there are groups located in central, western and southern Brazil. The popular O. tigrinum is the most northerly species, and found 20° north of the Equator, while the no less popular O. varicosum, O. crispum and O. sarcodes, and the interesting O. Jonesianum, occupy country on the opposite side of South

America, in Southern Brazil, about 23° south of the Equator. A few species find homes in the West Indies, while O. Papilio hails from the north of Venezuela and the long-stemmed O. macranthum and O. serratum are found far across the sub-continent, in Ecuador.

Lycastes have a distribution somewhat akin to that of Odontoglossum, from Mexico to Bolivia, but are found at lower altitudes. The popular, variable and easily-grown L. Skinneri is at home in Guatemala and Honduras.

It will be gathered from the foregoing notes on the more popular genera that the majority of Orchids known to cultivation are natives of tropical countries and are found in that immense and encircling band of the earth that lies between the tropic of Cancer and the tropic of Capricorn, and if the band were widened to 30° of latitude north and south of the Equator it would include the homes of practically all Orchids of horticultural interest. The land area in such a band is comparatively small compared with the water area, and, for the most part, the rainfall ranges from sixty inches to one hundred inches per year.

Why is it that this particular region is so thickly populated with Orchids? And why is it that there are no counterparts of tropical Orchids in temperate climates? The hardy Orchids are beautiful but do not attract like tropical species. The latter are not found spread out like Buttercups in a meadow, or Heather on the moors. They are abundant in various parts of the world, and although the homes of certain popular species of Odontoglossum, Dendrobium, Cypripedium and Phalaenopsis have been ravaged by collectors, nevertheless they had to be sought for and the older collectors endured many hardships to obtain them. Nature hid her chief floral treasures and man had to search for them with the same keenness and risk of life and limb that have been endured by those who harnessed steam power and electrical energy for the use of mankind, those who have given us the internal combustion engine, aeroplanes, wireless broadcasting, television, and discovered the power of radium and released atomic energy. Nature entices and attracts, she also resists and repels; only those who seek can find, therefore, when enjoying the splendour within the Orchid Tent at a Chelsea Show, the spectator should be mindful of those who, in the past, made such magnificence possible.

CYPRIPEDIUM HELLAS, WESTONBIRT VAR.

p. 100

MILTONIA REINE ELISABETH

BOTANICAL

FOR purposes of classification, the great botanical family of Orchidaceae has been divided into several large Tribes, and these again have been divided into Sub-tribes, each containing a certain number of genera, which, in turn, contain the species.

As outward appearance is no guide to natural affinity, it follows that the basis of classification is founded on much more than meets the eye. Style of growth, form of inflorescence and flowers, leafage, pseudobulbs (or their absence), and the manner in which the pollen masses are formed—their number and method of attachment, and the pollen itself, and methods of fertilization—have all to be taken into consideration.

Much confusion arose in the early days of Orchid nomenclature and botanists of considerable standing not infrequently placed a species in its wrong genus. Miltonias were sometimes placed in Odontoglossum and even in Oncidium, Aerides in Saccolabium, Scuticaria in Bifrenaria, Lycaste in Maxillaria, therefore one can find excuses for Linnaeus who, when he first saw herbarium specimens of what we are now familiar with as Phalaenopsis amabile, named it Epidendrum amabile ! New genera were created when previously unknown Orchids did not fit easily into any genus then known, but in later years, aided by more and better herbarium specimens, and by growing plants, botanists were able to make more critical studies and thus many of the older genera (based on insufficient material or erroneous diagnoses) have become obsolete.

The following is the general scheme of classificatory arrangement used by Bentham and Hooker, but includes only those Orchid genera that are, or have been, in more or less general cultivation. Other schemes of classification have been proposed by Pfitzer and by Schlechter.

TRIBE EPIDENDREAE

Sub-tribe Bletieae	Acanthophippium, Bletia, Chysis, Limatodes, Phaius, Spathoglottis, Thunia.
Sub-tribe Coelogyneae ..	Arundina, Calanthe, Coelogyne, Pleione, Trichosma.
Sub-tribe Dendrobieae ..	Bulbophyllum, Cirrhopetalum, Dendrobium.
Sub-tribe Erieae	Coelia, Eria, Ipsea, Pachystoma, Spathoglottis.

Sub-tribe Laelieae ..   .. Barkeria, Brassovola, Broughtonia, Cattleya, Diacrium, Epidendrum (including Nanodes), Laelia, Laeliopsis, Schomburgkia, Sophronitis, Tetramicra (Leptotes).

Sub-tribe Liparieae ..   .. Dendrochilum, Liparis, Mesospinidium, Platyclinis.

Sub-tribe Malaxeae ..   .. Microstylis.

Sub-tribe Pleurothalleae   .. Arpophyllum, Cryptophoranthus, Masdevallia, Pleurothallis, Restrepia.

TRIBE VANDEAE

Sub-tribe Cymbidieae   .. Ansellia, Cymbidium, Cyperorchis, Dipodium, Grammangis, Grammatophyllum, Polystachya.

Sub-tribe Cyrtopodieae   .. Acacallis, Acropera, Aganisia, Anguloa, Batemania, Bifrenaria, Colax, Cyrtopodium, Eriopsis, Eulophiella, Gongora, Govinia, Koellensteinia (Aganisia), Lycaste, Paphinia, Warrea, Zyopetalum (including Bollea, Huntleya, Kefersteinia, Pescatorea, Promenaea and Warscewiczella).

Sub-tribe Eulophieae   .. Eulophia, Lissochilus, Galeandra.

Sub-tribe Maxillarieae   .. Maxillaria, Schlimia, Scuticaria, Stenia.

Sub-tribe Notylideae   .. Ornithocephalus.

Sub-tribe Oncideae ..   .. Ada, Aspasia, Brassia, Cochlioda, Comparettia, Gomeza, Helcia (Trichopilia), Ionopsis, Miltonia, Odontoglossum, Oncidium, Ornithocepalus, Pilumna (now Tricopilia), Rodriguezia (including Burlingtonia), Trichocentrum, Trichopilia.

Sub-tribe Sarcantheae   .. Aeranthus, Aerides, Angraecum, Arachnanthe, Camarotis, Cleistostoma, Esmeralda, Euanthe, Luisia, Phalaenopsis, Renanthera, Rhyncostylis, Saccolabium, Sarcochilus, Stauropsis, Trichoglottis, Vanda.

Sub-tribe Stanhopieae   .. Acineta, Coryanthes, Cycnoches, Houlletia, Moorea, Mormodes, Neomooria, Peristeria, Polycycnis, Stanhopea.

TRIBE CYPRIPEDIEAE

Cypripedium, Paphiopedilum, Phragmopedium, Selenipedium, Uropedium.

TRIBE APOSTASIEAE

Neuwiedia.

TRIBE OPHRYDEAE

Sub-tribe Gymnodenieae .. Habenaria, Gymnadenia, Stenoglottis.
Sub-tribe Satyrieae .. .. Disa, Satyrium.

TRIBE NEOTTIEAE

Sub-tribe Spirantheae .. Anoectochilus, Cystorchis, Dossinia, Goodyera, Haemaria, Macodes, Physurus, Spiranthes.
Sub-tribe Vanilleae .. .. Epistephium, Sobralia, Vanilla.

Botanists figure prominently in the history of Orchids, and although we may be exasperated when any one of them alters a name with which we have grown familiar to one that was given to the same species by an older botanist, we have to remember that priority of publication is a particularly important rule in the realm of nomenclature. Orchid nomenclature is full of these pitfalls and growers have to reckon with them. The names of hybrid Orchids are sometimes mislaid or given erroneously, but these are horticultural rather than botanical errors. Moreover, the records of the Royal Horticultural Society invariably include the parentage of a hybrid that receives an Award of Merit or a First Class Certificate, and similar records are published with unfailing regularity in *The Gardeners' Chronicle* and *The Orchid Review*. Further, lists of new hybrids, with parentage and the name of the raiser or exhibitor, appear in the last-named publication, and such lists are issued only after they have been scrutinized by Mr. Fred K. Sander—to whom the Orchid world owes a great debt of gratitude for this splendid work over a long period of years. And, also, Mr. Sander's monumental *List of Orchid Hybrids* is so arranged that it is an easy matter to determine whether any two species or two hybrids have been mated and what name the progeny received originally, therefore there is no excuse for giving a new name to the results of a combination previously raised and named.

Linnaeus did not describe and name many Orchids, and those for which he is the recognized authority are chiefly terrestrial species, natives of European countries. John Lindley probably holds the record for a botanist who specialized in Orchids, but the two Reichenbachs, especially the younger Reichenbach, were responsible for the determination of very large numbers. Later Robert Allen Rolfe was the principal authority for naming Orchids for many years. Professor Oakes Ames, in the U.S.A., made a valuable contribution to the botany of Orchids, while R. Brown, Dr. J. J. Smith, Sir Joseph Hooker, E. Rodigas, Blume, Bentham, Bateman, Dr. Kränzlin, Dr. Schlechter, Pfitzer, and V. S. Summerhayes have had a share in the botanical classification, description and naming of Orchids.

WHAT IS AN ORCHID?

WHAT is an Orchid? I expect every horticulturist has been asked this question and found some difficulty in giving a satisfactory answer. Probably the general reply is that in an Orchid flower there is a "column" instead of stamens and stigma, and a more or less prominent "lip," while the growth of most species develops a bulbous appearance. Not an entirely satisfactory description, for the Calceolaria and the Antirrhinum have lipped flowers and the Water Hyacinth (Eichhornia crassipes) has swollen stems.

Charles Darwin answered the question and we cannot do better than quote him: "From the analogy of other Monocotyledonous plants we might expect the hidden presence of fifteen organs in the flowers of the Orchideae, arranged alternately in five whorls; and in these flowers we find fifteen groups of vessels exactly thus arranged. Hence there is a strong possibility that the vessels . . . which enter the sides of the labellum, not in one or two cases, but in all Orchids seen by me, and which occupy the precise position which they would have occupied had they supplied the normal stamens, do really represent modified and petaloid stamens, and are not lateral vessels of the labellum which have wandered from the proper course."

Darwin continued: "Can we feel satisfied by saying that each Orchid was created, exactly as we now see it, on a certain 'ideal type'; that the omnipotent Creator, having fixed one plan for the whole Order, did not depart from this plan; that He, therefore, made the same organ to perform diverse functions—often of trifling importance compared with their proper function—converted the organs into mere purposeless rudiments, and arranged all as if they had to stand separate, and then made them cohere? Is it not a more simple and intelligible view that all the Orchideae owe what they have in common, to descent from some Monocotyledonous plant, which, like so many other plants of the same class, possessed fifteen organs, arranged alternatively, three within three, in five whorls; and that the now wonderfully changed structure of the flower is due to a long course of slow modification—each modification having been preserved which was useful to the plant, during the incessant changes to which the organic and inorganic world has been exposed?"

VARIATION OF GROWTH

IT must be remembered that Orchids are found growing in every country, everywhere, even within the Arctic but not the Antarctic circle ; consequently, in adapting themselves to climatic conditions, they have assumed widely different types of growth. Very many people who think about these matters consider that, when Orchids began to take their part in the flora of the world, they were all terrestrial, but finding insufficient light and sunshine on the ground level, and also experiencing severe competition from the more vigorous lowly plants in tropical countries, they ascended trees or made a home on rocks : in other words, they became epiphytes. It is a common mistake among the general public to regard Orchids as parasites and in this connection I remember listening to a preacher, famous in his day, who, pointing out that beauty of form and colour *might* cover a multitude of sins, used Orchids as an example and said that notwithstanding their attractiveness, and that men died to win them, "they were parasites." Later, when told the difference between an epiphyte and a parasite, he was "not afraid with any amazement."

Within the two great groups of Orchids—terrestrial and epiphytic— there are wide differences of habit. The great majority of terrestrial Orchids are deciduous and tuberous-rooted and found chiefly in cool and temperate countries, where there is a distinct Winter season—as in the case of native British Orchids; or in countries where there are distinct dry and wet seasons—as in many parts of Australia and South Africa. The tuberous roots are store-houses wherein food is stored ready for use when kindly conditions excite growth and the production of flowers. Their plan of life is, therefore, very much like that adopted by Nerines, Lilies, Daffodils, Tulips, certain Begonias and Anemones, and other bulbous or tuberous-rooted subjects.

By far the widest range of form and habit is to be found among the epiphytes. Some are tiny, creeping plants, while others grow in robust masses, like the Cattleyas. Some, as in the case of certain Epidendrums, have long, slender, flexible growths, that clamber among or over other plants that afford the needful support. Very many kinds of Orchids that are popular with cultivators have pseudo-bulbs and these are formed by

CYMBIDIUM SUSETTE

the swelling and consolidation of the base of each new growth. These pseudo-bulbs are not composed of scales, as in the case of the Lily and the Onion, but are masses of firm tissue clothed in a stout, often very hard, protective "skin." Pseudo-bulbs are amazingly varied in form and size. Some are small and squat, as in Pleione; others more or less oval, with a short stem by which they are attached to the rhizome, as in most Cattleyas; others may "sit" on the rhizome, and may be smooth, angular or corrugated; while others, as in Schomburgkia, are of large size and very tough, although occasionally hollow. The genus Dendrobium is remarkable in that it contains species with short pseudo-bulbs (e.g., D. aggregatum); stout, terete stems (e.g., D. Brymerianum); tallish, clavate, four-angled stems (e.g., D. densiflorum); three-inch, fusiform stems (e.g., D. capillipes); and long, flexuose, terete, knotted (nodose) stems, a yard or more in length (e.g., D. Wardianum); with other species showing gradations between all these forms of growth.

Calanthes of the C. vestita group have stout, bluntly angular, large pseudo-bulbs that are covered prettily with a silvery-grey skin. These lose their leaves before the flower-spikes appear. In Odontoglossum and Oncidium, and some other genera, the stoutly-textured leaves are retained on the pseudo-bulbs for several years. Pseudo-bulbs contain a store of food that assists the development of the new growth, or a flower spike, but if old, leafless pseudo-bulbs are allowed to remain they become a nuisance and may rot and cause disease, therefore they should be cut off when no longer useful. In passing, however, it may be pointed out that an old—not too old—pseudo-bulb, if severed, with a small piece of the old rhizome attached, and placed in a propagating case, it is quite possible that a latent bud may develop into a growth, new roots formed and a new plant produced.

Numerous tropical Orchids produce aerial roots that help to anchor the plant as it extends upwards. Vandas and Aerides are examples and the grower takes advantage of them—when the plants become too tall and "leggy"—to re-establish the upper portion and, in due course, to dispense with the lower and leafless portion. Vanda teres produces aerial roots so freely that cutting down and replanting the upper portions is common practice.

For the most part, Orchids are evergreen, but some are deciduous, notably the Calanthes and Pleiones. Others are semi-deciduous; they shed the leaves from the older stems when the new growths have partly or wholly developed. Certain growers of an older generation used to cut out the old stems of Dendrobium nobile so soon as the new growths were extending freely.

Orchids that make their homes on trees obtain sustenance from the decay of parts of themselves, from the decaying leaves of their hosts, and also from the decay of detritus which collects around and among their own growths. The excrement of birds cannot be entirely ruled out as a possible addition to the material on which such Orchids exist. An observation made by collectors is that healthy Orchids are not found on dead trees.

A few Orchids have acquired the habit of growing head downwards and of these the best known among cultivated species are Cattleya citrina, Scuticaria Steelii, Masdevallia deorsa and Oncidium Jonesianum. Why these species, from different genera, depart from the orthodox habit of their fellows is one of the mysteries connected with Orchids and adds to their interest and fascination.

In methods of flower production Orchids are as versatile as in their style of growth. Cattleyas of the C. labiata group form an inflorescence at the apex of the growth and during the early stages of development the incipient spike is protected by a prominent sheath. Calanthes and Pleiones produce their spikes or flowers from the base of the previously made and leafless pseudo-bulb. Cymbidiums develop their spikes from the base of the last made and leafy pseudo-bulb. Cypripediums proceed in a different manner, as their flowers arise from the centre of the matured growth, and many other Orchids adopt a similar method.

Yet another extreme, indeed extraordinary, habit on the part of certain Orchids is the quaint one of producing descending flower spikes. These are not merely severely pendulous, but proceed in a downward direction from the pseudo-bulb. Stanhopeas provide a striking example of this unusual method, consequently the plants must be grown in wooden baskets, with the bars spaced rather widely so as to permit the descending inflorescence to emerge uninjured.

The foregoing descriptions do not by any means cover the infinite variety of growth and habit to be found among Orchids, indeed a whole book, and an entertaining one, could be devoted to this interesting subject. One other example must suffice, in conclusion, to demonstrate

this amazing versatility. It is a far cry from the gigantic Grammato-
phyllums, the tall Vandas and Renantheras, or even the lowlier Coelogynes and Cypripediums, to an Australian species which Dr. R. S. Roberts
named Rhizanthella Gardneri; and Cryptanthemis Slateri, named by
the Rev. N. M. R. Rupp—an authority on Australian Orchids.

C. Slateri was discovered accidentally by Mr. C. W. Slater in 1931.
Like the Rhizanthella, it is a subterranean Orchid, leafless, with rhizo-
matous growths that spread horizontally just below the surface of the
soil. At the flowering period the extremity of the growth turns upwards,
thickening into a very downy or flannelly head of minute flowers. The
latter have erect, fleshy sepals and petals and a dark column densely
covered with minute globular glands: the column also has two glandular
appendages.

This remarkable Orchid gave point to the opinion so frequently ex-
pressed that when Orchids first appeared in the world's flora, they were
geophytic (terrestrial), and that the epiphytic habit was a later development designed to meet the conditions arising in jungles—an effort to
reach the light.

What was the first—original Orchid? Who can tell? Among a few
races of plants it is possible to trace origins back through the aeons of
time by means of Nature prints in certain geological formations. Not so
with Orchids, for they are among the very latest of Nature's developments in floral evolution.

MIMICRY

IT is quite possible to meet people who regard Orchids with disfavour and, usually, the objections is to the likeness of the flower to reptiles or insects. Of course, allowance must be made for personal tastes, but Orchids may be opulent, expensive to purchase and expensive to keep (but not more so than many other plants), yet, for the most part, they are extremely beautiful. It must be admitted, however, that a few species mimic members of the animal world. Several of our native Orchids are mimics, notably the Green Man Orchid (Aceras anthropophorum)—a miniature caricature of a man ; and the Bee Orchid (Ophrys apifera), in which the inflated, velvety lip simulates a bee ; while Coeloglossum viride, *syn.* Habenaria viridis, the Frog Orchis, suggests a minute frog.

Among popular cultivated Orchids a Brassia spike suggests a small collection of large, colourful spiders. The Phalaenopses are known as Moth Orchids and not much imagination is needed to find a likeness to moths in the species with large white or pink flowers. Lady's Slipper is the popular title given to Cypripediums, indeed the generic title, being interpreted, means Venus's Foot; the pouched lip is the toe of the shoe, the dorsal sepal the back of it, and the ventral sepal the heel; with the petals as straps to fasten the shoe.

The Butterfly Orchids, Oncidium Papilio and O. Kramerianum, are certainly very like gorgeous, tropical butterflies. The Pleiones (Coelogynes) have earned their title of Indian Crocuses by their single, short-stemmed flowers that appear while the plants are leafless.

Certain species of Pleurothallis have tiny, greenish flowers that are easily mistaken for large insects of the greenfly persuasion.

The formation of the large and weird flowers of Stanhopea, Coryanthes and Catasetum do suggest that Flora has conducted a mésalliance with Fauna.

Bulbophyllum barbigerum has such a sensitive, mobile lip that its movement under the action of a soft breath suggests something alive—an insect of sorts; while the rocking lip of B. Lobbii invariably arrests attention, as does the much larger, fleshy lip of Anguloa Clowesii, which rocks so readily at the slightest provocation that this species is known as the Cradle Orchid. These brief notes may very well conclude with a

30

reference to Peristeria elata, once very popular, and known as the Dove Orchid because of the likeness of the combination of column, lip and petals to the bird from which the popular name is derived.

These references to mimicry could be continued extensively but limits of space forbid, so they may be concluded with the Golden Chain, demonstrated by the charming Platyclinis filiformis; Bulbophyllum pur-pureorhachis, which closely simulates a Lizard; certain species of Aer-ides, Saccolabium and Rhyncostylis, which have such dense and more or less pendulous spikes of modest-sized flowers, that they are known as Fox Brush Orchids.

INTERGENERIC HYBRIDS

ONE of the most remarkable things about Orchids is that in no other family, whether of plants, animals, insects or fishes, has there been such combinations of genera to produce hybrids. Hybrids between species belonging to the same genus are plentiful enough in several genera of Orchids and other plants, but hybrids between two or more genera are rare, except in the Natural Order Orchidaceae. The following table gives a list of the various known combinations and the names given to them. A bigeneric hybrid is the combination of two genera. Lowiara was produced by crossing a Brassolaelia with Sophronitis, thus giving a trigeneric hybrid. Further, Brassolaeliocattleya crossed with Sophrolaeliocattleya produced the artificial genus named Potinara, but Brassolaeliocattleya crossed with Sophronitis would give the same quadrigeneric hybrid, as also would Sophrolaelia × Brassocattleya.

BIGENERIC

ADAGLOSSUM = Ada × Odontoglossum.
ADIODA = Ada × Cochlioda.
AERIDOPSIS = Aerides × Phalaenopsis.
AERIDOVANDA = Aerides × Vanda.
ANGULOCASTE = Anguloa × Lycaste.
ANOECTOMARIA = Anoectochilus × Haemaria.
ARACHNOPSIS = Arachis × Phalaenopsis.
ARANDA = Arachis × Vanda.
ARANTHERA = Arachis × Renanthera.
ATHERTONARA = Vandopsis × Renanthera.
BRASSOCATTLEYA = Brassavola × Cattleya.
BRASSODIACRIUM = Brassavola × Diacrium.
BRASSOEPIDENDRUM = Brassavola × Epidendrum.
BRASSOLAELIA = Brassavola × Laelia.
CHONDROBOLLEA = Chondrorhyncha × Bollea.
CHONDROPETALUM = Chondrorhyncha × Zygopetalum.

ODONTIODA SEBASTIA

DIACATTLEYA = Diacrium × Cattleya.
DIALAELIA = Diacrium × Laelia.
DOSSINIMARIA = Dossinia × Haemaria.
EPICATTLEYA = Epidendrum × Cattleya.
EPIDIACRIUM = Epidendrum × Diacrium.
EPILAELIA = Epidendrum × Laelia.
EPIPHRONITIS = Epidendrum × Sophronitis.
LAELIOCATTLEYA = Laelia × Cattleya.
LEPTOLAELIA = Leptotes (Tetramicra) × Laelia.
MACOMARIA = Haemaria × Macodes.
MILTONIDIUM = Miltonia × Oncidium.
MILTONIODA = Miltonia × Cochlioda.
ODONTIODA = Odontoglossum × Cochlioda.
ODONTOCIDIUM = Odontoglossum × Oncidium.
ODONTONIA = Odontoglossum × Miltonia.
ONCIDIODA = Oncidium × Cochlioda.
PHAIOCALANTHE = Phaius × Calanthe.
PHAIOCYMBIDIUM = Phaius × Cymbidium.
RENANTANDA = Renanthera × Vanda.
RENANTHOPSIS = Renanthera × Phalaenopsis.
SCHOMBOCATTLEYA = Schomburgkia × Cattleya.
SCHOMBOLAELIA = Schomburgkia × Laelia.
SOPHROCATTLEYA = Sophronitis × Cattleya.
SOPHROLAELIA = Sophronitis × Laelia.
VANDAENOPSIS = Vanda × Phalaenopsis.
VANDANTHE = Vanda × Euanthe (Vanda Sanderiana).
ZYGOBATEMANNIA = Zygopetalum × Batemannia.
ZYGOCOLAX = Zygopetalum × Colax.
ZYGONISIA = Zygopetalum × Aganisia.

TRIGENERIC

BRASSOLAELIOCATTLEYA = Brassavola × Laeliocattleya;
                       Brassocattleya × Laelia;
                       Brassocattleya × Laeliocattleya;
                       Brassolaelia × Cattleya; and
                       Brassolaelia × Laeliocattleya.

CHARLESWORTHEARA = Cochlioda × Miltonia × Oncidium.

DIACATLAELIA = Diacrium × Cattleya × Laelia.

LOWIARA = Brassavola × Laelia × Sophronitis.

POTINARA = Sophronitis × Laelia × Cattleya.

ROLFEARA = Brassavola × Cattleya × Sophronitis.

SANDERARA = Odontoglossum × Brassia × Cochlioda.

SOPHROLAELIOCATTLEYA = Sophronitis × Laelia × Cattleya.

VUYLSTEKEARA = Cochlioda × Miltonia × Odontoglossum.

WILSONARA = Oncidium × Cochlioda × Odontoglossum.

QUADRIGENERIC

BURRAGEARA = Cochlioda × Miltonia × Odontoglossum × Oncidium.

POTINARA = Brassavola × Laelia × Cattleya × Sophronitis.

POLLINATION AND FERTILIZATION

"TO give any idea of the enormous varieties of floral structure met with among the Orchids would require a whole volume. In this family of all others do we find adaptations to insect visits carried out on a gigantic scale, and in not a few cases mechanism of singular beauty and delicacy." Thus wrote Anton Kerner von Marilaun in his monumental *Natural History of Plants*, which was translated into English by Dr. Frank W. Oliver. But a whole volume had already been written about this fascinating subject by Charles Darwin, and his *Fertilization of Orchids* (1862) still remains the great book of reference for all who are keen and interested.

Very simply, Kerner points out that Orchids have "flowers with petaloid perianth and inferior ovary. The stamens reduced to one, two or three, and generally united with the gynaeceum to form a column." The column usually rises from the centre of the flower and carries the pollen masses and stigmatic surface (although there are a very few Orchids which develop pollen and stigmatic surface in different flowers). There are no obvious stamens, with filaments and anthers, but microscopic examination will show that the pollen masses have a minute attachment to the column, generally at the apex, sheltered by a cap, and above the stigmatic surface. The pollen is not free, as in most kinds of plants, and, according to the genus, may be produced in from one to four, more or less rounded, processes, known as masses, though quite small, and composed of coherent grains of pollen.

How, then, does the pollen reach the stigmatic surface, which is on the side of the column facing the labellum? There are many methods of ensuring pollination and fertilization, but, in general, an insect alights on the labellum (lip), seeks for nectar, releases the cap and departs with pollinia (pollen masses) on its head. When visiting another flower the pollinia are pressed against the sticky stigmatic surface, the grains germinate, the pollen tubes penetrate to the ovary and fertilize the ovules. It will be gathered that Orchids are economical in the matter of pollen production, but they are extremely prodigal with regard to seeds, as will be seen when a ripened capsule opens, or is opened; and, for the most part, the seeds are minute. The adhesiveness of the pollinia is remarkable

35

and the insect that has dislodged them does not get rid of the burden easily, unless it rubs its head against a very rough or sticky surface.

When Darwin saw a flower of Angraecum sesquipedale he wondered why it had such an unusually long spur, extending perhaps eighteen inches from the back of the flower; he came to the conclusion that only a large and powerful moth with a proboscis long enough to probe to the extremity of the spur, in search of nectar, could secure fertilization; long years afterwards his conclusion was proved to be correct.

The weird and wonderful construction of the flowers of Coryanthes macrantha suggests a Heath Robinson imagination and extravagance. They are described elsewhere in these pages but fertilization only is under consideration here and Dr. Crüger's description, as presented to the Linnean Society of London in 1865, is such a classic that no apologies are needed for quoting it:—

"Large humble bees, noisy and quarrelsome, are attracted at first by the smell of the flower; but the smell probably only gives notice to the insects; the substance they really come for is the interior brim of the labellum which they gnaw off with great industry. They may be seen in great numbers disputing with each other for a place on the edge of the hypochile. Partly by the contest, partly perhaps intoxicated by the matter they are indulging in, they tumble down into the 'bucket' (epichile) half-full of the fluid secreted by the horn-like organs at the base of the column. They then crawl along the interior inner side of the bucket where there is a passage for them. If one is early on the look-out, as these Hymenopters are early risers, one can see on every flower how fecundation is performed. The humble-bee in forcing its way out of its involuntary bath has to exert itself considerably, as the mouth of the epichile and the face of the column fit together exactly, and are very stiff and elastic. The first bee that is immersed will have the gland of the pollen masses glued to its back. The insect then generally gets through the passage and comes out with this peculiar appendage, and returns immediately to its feast, when it is generally precipitated a second time, passing out through the same aperture, and so inserting the pollen masses into the stigma while it forces its way out, and thereby impregnating either the same or some other flower. I have often seen this, and sometimes there are so many of these humble-bees assembled, that there is a continual procession of

MILTONIA VEXILLARIA VAR. MEMORIA G. D. OWEN

ONCIDIUM CORYNEPHORUM

them through the passage specified."

Dr. Crüger was Director of the Botanic Garden at Trinidad and had ample opportunities to make observations of a remarkable species which, when flowers were seen at Chatsworth in 1887 was, according to Paxton "The wonder and surprise of all who were favoured with an opportunity of seeing them." Unfortunately very few modern Orchid growers have had Paxton's opportunity, as Coryanthes macrantha is only rarely seen in cultivation, but Stanhopea flowers are somewhat akin to those of Coryanthes.

Mechanism is used to eject the pollen masses of Catasetum. The rostellum (column) is prolonged into the curved, horn-like processes which extend over that part of the lip on which an insect would alight; if these antennae are touched more or less firmly, they transmit the pressure in such a way that the glutinous disc at the base of the pollinia is not only released, but disc and pollinia are shot out forcibly and cannot fail to adhere to the inquisitive insect that "touched the spring." Darwin stated that, on artificial disturbance, the pollinia were shot out to a distance of two or three feet.

Masdevallia muscosa, a small and not particularly showy species, is nevertheless extremely interesting as its labellum is sensitive to some purpose. This sensitiveness appears to be confined to the yellow ridge on the lip, which, when touched, causes the lip to rise and close up, consequently an insect would be trapped and pressed against the column, there, presumably, to effect fertilization; it is recorded that the trap remains closed for about twenty minutes before it reopens. This curious action is reminiscent of the mechanical arrangement of the bi-lobed leaves of the Venus Fly Trap (Dionaea muscipula), which closes over and grips a fly that alights on the central, sensitive bristles, but in this case the unfortunate captive is held, killed, and all its meaty parts are absorbed by this lowly carnivorous plant.

Darwin wrote: "Considering how precious the pollen of Orchids evidently is and what care has been bestowed on its organization and on the accessory parts; considering that the anther always stands close behind or above the stigma, self-fertilization would have been an incomparably safer process than the transportal of the pollen from flower to flower. It is an astonishing fact that self-fertilization should not have been an habitual occurrence. It apparently demonstrates to us that there

D

must be something injurious in the process. Nature thus tells us in the most emphatic manner that she abhors perpetual self-fertilization."

From pollination to fertilization may take about four months in Dendrobium nobile; two months in Phaius grandifolius; four months in Cypripedium insigne; nine months in Laelia purpurata; twelve months or so in Cattleya; a year in Odontoglossum maculatum; four months in Masdevallia; three or four months in Calanthe; and six months in Phalaenopsis Schilleriana.

GERMINATION

SEVERAL different methods of securing the germination of Orchid seeds have been used, but amateurs have no need to be frightened by the laboratory methods now adopted by all the leading commercial raisers and growers of Orchids.

In an old and successful method all that was needed were pots, crocks, Sphagnum moss, a piece of wood and a strip of canvas. All were sterilized in boiling water, except the Sphagnum. The pot was half filled with crocks, upon which a good layer of Sphagnum was laid. The piece of wood, of suitable size—usually one of the lighter, Coniferous woods was chosen—was covered with a piece of canvas, tightly stretched across the top, the ends being pinned or tacked to the underside to keep the canvas taut. The wood was then pressed firmly into the pot and in such a way that the canvas surface was well below the rim; Sphagnum was pressed around the wood as a further security against movement, and also to assist in keeping the canvas continuously moist. The seeds were sown on the moist canvas surface, the pot covered with glass and placed in a propagating frame, over bottom heat, in a warm house. The pot was occasionally dipped to about half its depth in warm water and the water conveyed to the canvas via the moss. Although the word "was" is used it is quite possible that this primitive method is still adopted by a few raisers.

The method that has found most favour—apart from the asymbiotic method—during recent years differs greatly from the former. A young and vigorous Orchid, newly potted, is chosen and the surface of the compost, closely clipped, provides the seed bed. The plant should be watered a few hours before the seeds are sown and moisture supplied afterwards by partially immersing the pot. It is desirable always to choose a plant belonging to the same genus as the seeds, or closely allied to it. Shade is necessary and, of course, a small label should be inserted on which is written the parentage of the hybrid seeds or a number corresponding with a record in the pocket book.

The first sign of germination is the appearance of a minute, almost transparent, green globule, and some time elapses before incipient roots and leaves appear. While still very tiny, these minute blobs of new life must be transferred to small pots or pans containing Sphagnum moss and Osmunda fibre, cut to an extreme fineness, to which some sand is added. A match-stick, sharpened to a chisel-like tip, with a wee central notch, may be used to lift and transfer the seedlings from the seed bed to their new quarters. Several dozen of these tiny seedlings may be accommodated in a small, amply-drained pot, which should be placed in a moist frame, or under a bell glass in a warm house. If all goes well, a further transplanting will be necessary, for as the seedlings develop they will need more space, until two or three plantlets occupy one tiny pot, from which they may be potted singly in very small pots, and thus make a real start in life as individuals. Until they have made pseudo-bulbs and sturdy leaves, all seedling Orchids need more warmth and atmospheric moisture than older, established plants of a similar genus.

The raising of hybrid Orchids is a fascinating business, for when the parents are hybrids—often with a complicated line of descent—there is always a possibility of flowering something of outstanding quality, *but* fine results are not likely to follow unless the parents are wisely chosen. First-class hybrid Orchids command a good price and are also valuable for stud purposes, but in a batch of seedlings, from the same cross, there will almost always be a larger proportion of sparrows than geese or swans.

Laboratory methods of raising Orchid seedlings are expensive and demand the most meticulous attention to every detail; they are only for the big commercial raisers and wealthy amateurs. If an amateur feels that germination holds too many pitfalls for him, he should take his seeds to a raiser who has the necessary modern outfit and let him do the raising up to the point where the seedlings can be dealt with at home; this is not a very costly proceeding, indeed, if the cross is a promising one, it is possible to make a bargain with the commercial raiser—perhaps a proportion of the seedlings in return for the service rendered in producing them.

CULTIVATION

STRUCTURES

THERE is, unfortunately, a widespread belief that specially constructed glass-houses are needed for the cultivation of Orchids. Orchids of some kind can be grown in any house where the heating apparatus will maintain a temperature of 45° on the coldest winter night. A collier in the Newcastle district grew the best specimens I have seen of Cypripedium Curtisii, and did so in a home-made greenhouse, with home-made heating apparatus. Very large pans of Coelogyne cristata have been grown in a vinery during the greater part of the year; fine Calanthes on a shelf in a house which accommodated a Banana; Odontoglossum citrosmum on a shelf high up in a temperate house; Dendrobium fimbriatum on the floor at the end of a stove; Dendrobium nobile and Maxillaria picta in a collection of sub-tropical plants; and Cypripedium insigne in practically every kind of house, except an unheated one.

Other examples will occur to growers of long experience; nevertheless those who desire to manage them successfully should grow Orchids by themselves in one or more houses, the sizes of the houses being governed by the extent of the collection. There is no need to bother too much about the type of house when houses are already in being, as these can be adapted to meet the conditions desirable for the Orchids it is proposed to cultivate. A lean-to house, facing east, was fitted with tiered staging at the back, and flat staging in the front; herein were grown, with reasonable success, such a mixed collection as Odontiodas, coloured Odontoglossums, Epidendrum vitellinum var. majus, numerous Cypripediums, Coelogynes, Sophronitis, Zygopetalums, and two or three Cymbidiums. Shading was something of a problem, but heating offered no difficulties although the hot-water pipes in the front of the house were enclosed by a brick wall, with openings through which water could be poured to fill evaporating troughs. Close observation led to adjustments as certain plants were found to grow best in particular positions.

By and large, a span-roofed house provides the best accommodation. It should be constructed substantially, and rest on walls of brick or concrete, rather than on walls of wood, as these last are apt to collapse after several years endurance of heat and moisture. Inner walls, along each side of the path, to carry the staging, are neither necessary nor desirable: iron, or concrete uprights fitted with angle-iron, will safely carry the staging on the inside of the house, while the inner margin of the outer walls will support the back edge of the staging.

Although double staging is not necessary it is most desirable and should be installed when a house is being built for the cultivation of Orchids. The lower and more permanent staging may consist of slate slabs, corrugated iron, or sheet iron, supported here and there by cross pieces of angle-iron; but there should be an upturned lip back and front, as this is the moisture-staging, to be covered with washed gravel, washed cinders, granite chips or other suitable material, kept continuously moist for the purpose of securing a steady evaporation of water and, consequently, a moist atmosphere.

The upper staging, several inches above the lower one, is to carry the plants and may consist of wooden slats, with small spaces between them, through which the moisture will rise from the lower or moisture-staging. Whether or not the plants should be placed on inverted pots depends upon the height of the roof and also upon the need of raising certain plants nearer the glass than would otherwise be the case. The advantage of the use of inverted pots is that it is possible to syringe or hose between them without unduly wetting the plants.

Ventilators must be provided on each side of the house, near the ridge, more in a cool house than in a warm one, as it is frequently an advantage to open several ventilators just a little instead of opening one or two widely. Front ventilators, low down in the outside walls, fitted with a hinged shutter, are very desirable, especially in houses where cool Orchids are grown, as these plants love the air that can be admitted on warm, moist evenings.

Where Cymbidiums, Cattleyas and other tall-growing Orchids are to be grown, much more head room must be provided than would be necessary for Odontoglossums and Cypripediums, therefore the roof should rest on glazed sides instead of on the wall itself.

When installing the heating system, always remember that it pays to provide ample piping and a boiler that is easily capable of providing more heat than is absolutely necessary, as the dry heat evolved from super-heated pipes when the fires are continuously forced in cold

CYMBIDIUM QUEEN ELIZABETH

weather, is distinctly detrimental to Orchids.

If the Orchid house is built of sound materials, it should last for very many years provided all wood-work is painted thoroughly to begin with, and painted inside and out about every third or fourth year. An annual and thorough cleaning of the house will prove advantageous to the plants and to the structure, as it will be the means of revealing weak places and give an opportunity of making the necessary repairs.

SHADE

All kinds of Orchids cultivated under glass need shade from bright sunshine at some period in their yearly life cycle, and particularly so when the new growth and leafage are tender. The amount of shade necessary varies considerably after the new growths have passed the extremely youthful stage. In general terms, the thin-leafed species need more shade than those with stout, coriaceous or leathery leaves, and all Orchids will withstand more sunshine when growth is completed. The amount of shade—its density—will depend upon the fierceness of the sun's rays and also the position of the Orchid house with regard to near-by buildings or trees. Obviously, denser shading will be needed in sunny than in dull districts. If a tall, deciduous tree throws no direct shade on a house—an Odontoglossum house for instance—but breaks up or masks the sunshine during the brightest hours of the day, the grower should be thankful for its assistance. The length of the season during which shade is needed will be determined by the position of the house as well as by the part of the country wherein it is placed. In the eastern and southern counties shading must be denser, and also maintained from an earlier to a later period than in districts where the atmosphere is moister and less clear.

War conditions have reduced the supply of blinds; old ones have outlived their usefulness and, for the present, new ones are by no means easy to obtain. As a consequence the use of a "permanent" shading material has become far more general. Summer Cloud is a popular material, but whiting, with the addition of size or soap to make it adhesive, is not infrequently used. Local experience must decide how early in the year such shading material should be painted on the roof glass, but, of course, the initial coating should be a comparatively light one; one, or even two heavier applications may be needed in sunny localities as the season progresses, but the material must be thinned in some way, and progressively, as Summer passes into Autumn. In a wet season the rain will usually suffice to reduce the shading late in the season, but every trace of this form of shading must be washed off as early in the Autumn as conditions permit, so long as the plants are not likely to be harmed— scorched—by sunshine.

Undoubtedly the best method of shading Orchid houses is by the use of blinds and the best blinds are those made of narrow laths, loosely but firmly attached to each other so that they may be easily raised and lowered by means of ropes running through pulleys placed conveniently. Lath blinds afford ample shade from sunshine and yet admit a moderate amount of light and, moreover, they are useful during the Winter as, if lowered for the night, they assist in maintaining the temperature within the house while frosts are keen, and thus assist in the conservation of fuel.

Blinds of Hessian or similar material will serve, but when they become damp some parts will lie closely on the glass and may adhere thereto if sharp frosts occur. Such blinds have a shorter life than those made of laths.

Blinds should not be allowed to touch the glass; they should roll over narrow runners of wood or metal, so that they are kept an inch or two above the glass from the eaves almost to the ridge of the house, thus permitting a current of air to pass between glass and blind.

The disadvantages of permanent shading are several. It is continuous and remains whether the sun is shining or not, whereas blinds can be lowered or raised as circumstances demand and light admitted freely during the absence of bright sunshine. Again, the houses warm up more slowly in the morning where, perforce, permanent shading is used. And, further, later in the day, during Summer, the roof glass becomes undesirably hot and this makes it necessary to damp the house more freely and frequently for the purpose of maintaining the desirable moist atmosphere around the plants. Finally, permanent shading demands closer attention to ventilation during the Summer days, and excessive ventilation to keep the temperature within reasonable limits again demands ample damping of floors and staging to prevent an arid atmosphere and the attraction of the thrips that it encourages.

TEMPERATURES

Orchids are like human beings in two respects, at least; they need fresh air to keep them in good health, and they object to draughts, and these matters must be borne in mind when temperatures are considered. The advantages of ample piping outweigh the initial cost of installation as it is far easier to maintain desirable temperatures when there is abundant surface for the radiation of heat than when the boiler has to work at its fullest capacity to provide such temperatures with fewer pipes and less radiation surface. Excessively hot pipes are dangerous, as they create a dry atmosphere that is difficult to counteract by damping floors and staging; moreover, they invite attacks from thrips and red spider by creating the conditions favourable to these pests.

Severe limitations of fuel during the war years have taught growers that the majority of Orchids can be managed successfully in lower temperatures than those so frequently recommended; nevertheless every grower strives to keep well above the danger point. A good general principle is that low temperatures should be accompanied by drier conditions at the roots and in the atmosphere.

The figures given must not be taken too literally, and are offered as a guide to the inexperienced. Orchids are found at considerable altitudes in tropical countries, where the temperature often drops to within a very few degrees of freezing point at night; others are found in very hot, humid conditions; while others grow in comfortable circumstances between these extremes.

In the cool house, where most of the Odontoglossums are grown, the night temperature during the severest weather should not be less than 40°, and 45° would be better, while the day temperature may rise to 60° with the help of sunshine, and accompanied by modest ventilation. In Summer, and especially during periods of hot sunshine, the chief difficulty will be that of keeping the temperature down by ventilating, damping, and an absence of fire heat. Full advantage should be taken of calm, moist, climatic conditions to ventilate freely at night.

In the intermediate house, where the principal occupants will be Cattleyas, many Oncidiums, and some of the Selenipediums and Vandas, the Winter temperatures may be 45° to 50° at night, and up to 70° by day, while the figures for Summer may be 60° at night and 75° by day. In the hottest, or stove, house, desirable temperatures for tropical Vandas and Angraecums will be 65° by night and 75° by day in Winter, while the range in Summer may be up to 90° or more when the sun is bright, with appropriate shading and ventilation.

Always prevent wide variations between the day and night temperatures in Winter, especially for cool Orchids, such as Odontoglossums and Cymbidiums. Conserve fire heat by trapping all the sun heat available during Spring, late Autumn, and Winter, by closing the houses early in the afternoon, before the sunshine passes from them.

VENTILATION

Ventilation and temperatures must always receive consideration in combination. Ventilation used solely as a means of reducing temperature is bad practice. Ventilation is primarily for the purpose of providing fresh air for the plants, and, whenever the outdoor conditions permit, night ventilation must receive due consideration. Those who permit the temperature to rise excessively and then open the ventilators widely until the thermometer registers a more reasonable figure, will never grow Orchids successfully. The clever grower will begin to admit fresh air quite early in the day in warm weather, and gradually increase the amount of ventilation until the sun declines, and then reduce the ventilation gradually until closing time, but permitting a little ventilation at night when the weather is warm.

Ventilation should always be given on the side of the house away from, and not towards, the wind. Due consideration must be given to the condition and position of a house in regard to ventilation. Shelter and natural shade must be taken into account, as also must the glass itself, for overlapping panes that do not fit closely may allow the admission of much air, and the ventilators must be manipulated accordingly. However, such structural deficiencies should be remedied as speedily as possible, to prevent the undue escape of heat and the admission of cold air on the side of the house facing the wind.

Successful ventilation implies keen observation, quick thinking, rapid manipulation of ventilators, experience of the local conditions, and knowledge of the needs of the plants grown. A good grower will "sense" the state of the atmosphere when entering an Orchid house, and if there is the slightest "stuffiness" or inertia, he will at once take steps to secure "brighter" conditions. (See " Structures.")

WATERING AND DAMPING

An amateur who commences the cultivation of a modest collection of Orchids quickly discovers that watering is something of a problem. He may have had plenty of experience in the cultivation in pots of both soft-wooded and hard-wooded plants, but Orchids, generally, are potted in a wholly different rooting medium, over ampler drainage. Moreover, the atmospheric conditions for Orchids are moister than those suitable for the great majority of plants grown under glass, with the exception of tropical stove plants. All these considerations give rise to a certain amount of perplexity, and the inexperienced amateur usually errs in giving too much, rather than too little, water, with the result that plants die and he is disappointed.

There are, however, a few fairly simple rules with regard to watering. The water should be stored in the Orchid house if this is at all possible so that it softens somewhat and attains a temperature approximating to that of the house itself before it is used. Clean rain-water is better than tap-water, but gutters and tank must be kept scrupulously clean.

Newly-potted Orchids require far less water than those well established. If the potting material is used in a slightly moist—not wet—condition, the plant will not need an application of water for several days after it has been potted, but atmospheric moisture must be supplied by damping the moisture-staging, spraying between the pots, and dewing overhead, the amount of damping and spraying being governed by the amount of sunshine experienced or artificial heat provided. All newly-potted Orchids should be placed at the moistest end of the house, so they may receive greater consideration and be under closer observation than established plants. As the roots permeate the compost, more direct and larger supplies of water will be needed, although these must be governed by the weather, as the amount of evaporation varies with the external conditions; it is less during dull, wet or cold weather than during the bright days of Summer.

The practice of handling every plant at regular intervals will save much trouble and time. The weight of the plant and pot, in addition to the condition of the surface of the compost, will soon prove an excellent guide with regard to watering, for if each plant that needs it is given an ample supply of water, it, and all the rest, may be left unwatered until the next time of handling, but the intervening period must be governed by the weather and amount of roots the plants have produced. Pottering about with the water pot every day is neither desirable nor necessary. Never be tempted to give water for the purpose of saving time on the morrow and never—never—dribble a little water over the compost "in case it should dry" before the next handling. Water thoroughly when water is needed and let alone until the need arises again; damping and spraying will, meantime, keep the plants growing healthily.

Established Orchids, in fairly large pots, may be treated in the same way, but the soaking these require may often be afforded best by dipping the pot, almost to the rim, in a large bucket of water, than by supplying the moisture through the spout of a water-can. If the plants do not receive the individual handling and attention suggested, one apparently small yet very important matter must not be overlooked; it is that when watering is done from the front of the staging it is quite possible to moisten the compost facing the grower and leave the back portion dry, and this applies particularly to plants in large pots. Commercial cultivators and experienced growers in charge of large private collections of Orchids "know" their plants and may often appear to take liberties which the inexperienced amateur dare not adopt. For instance, the writer has seen Miltonias, in full growth, watered from a hose-pipe—on the Continent.

Fully established and well-rooted Orchids need more water when in full growth than when growth is completed. All Orchids require less water in Winter than in Summer—but that applies to all plants grown under glass. Cymbidiums and Cypripediums require ample moisture at their roots when producing their spikes or flowers, otherwise the inflorescences will be short-stemmed, but if these Orchids, and Cattleyas and many others, are not producing flowers in due season, they need less water. Certain Orchids have a very distinct resting period after they have completed their seasonal growth, and if these are deciduous, like Calanthes, Pleiones and Thunias, they need no water after leaf-fall until there are signs of new growth or flowers.

CYMBIDIUM CREMONA

These are general observations; particular needs are described for each genus. If any "old timer" considers the subject of watering has been given undue prominence, the obvious retort is " 'Tis better to be safe than sorry."

Some day, perhaps, a hygrometer may be as much a part of the installation in an Orchid house as a thermometer, and may-be it will have a thermostatic—or would it be hygrostatic—attachment to control the amount of atomised water needed to keep the atmosphere moist. Until such a mechanical apparatus is possible, and cheap, manual labour must be employed in "damping down." Shingle, washed gravel, cinders, or whatever material is spread over the moisture-staging can be kept continuously wet by means of the water-can or the use of a small-gauge hose, and thus promote a steady ascent of moist air between the bars of the upper staging and around the plants upon it.

The frequency of damping between the pots must be governed by the weather. Damping the wall behind the hot-water pipes, and the soil below the pipes, must not be omitted, indeed liberal hosings are desirable in hot weather. When fire-heat is necessary to maintain the requisite minimum temperature during the Winter, hosing under the pipes is necessary almost every day to counteract the dry heat. Houses vary considerably in their capacity to retain moisture, but the observant grower will appreciate this fact and damp down more or less freely accordingly. The last damping operation of the day should be timed so that the atmosphere is not unduly charged with moisture at night in cold weather, or becomes unpleasantly dry before morning in warm and bright weather. Excessive condensation of water on the underside of the roof glass should be guarded against, for if drips of cold water fall on any plant trouble may arise quickly and a valuable specimen may be doomed.

Spraying the plants overhead is desirable once or twice daily in hot weather as this refreshes the leaves and aids the maintenance of a moist "growing" atmosphere. Caution is needed, however, and an atomizer is required so that spraying becomes dewing, but such dewing should be discontinued during the Winter months. Syringing may take the place of spraying and dewing for Cymbidiums that are growing freely; it encourages the development of leaves and roots and helps to keep the former free from such pests as thrips and red spider.

TOOLS AND ACCESSORIES

Comparatively few tools are needed in the cultivation of Orchids. The chief are a sharp knife; a blunt-pointed pair of scissors—sharp-pointed ones may puncture a pseudo-bulb or rhizome and the wound thus caused may become a centre from which rot may spread; a pair of first-rate secateurs; a medium-sized and rather small-meshed sieve; a hammer and a short, stout iron rod for breaking crocks; and several bluntly-pointed potting sticks, made from the hardest wood available.

Copper wire will be needed for suspending pots or baskets; screw-in eyes, for baskets or rafts; twine, of the green-twist persuasion, for tying up Cattleyas and other tall and weighty subjects; several grades of slender Bamboo rods, for supporting heavy Orchids and all flower spikes that cannot easily carry the weight of their flowers; labels of several sizes, celluloid for preference as they last a very long time; an indelible pencil or a Biro pen wherewith to write the names or numbers on the labels; a stock book in which every plant is listed, its cost, when it was bought, from whom, and any other particulars likely to be of use or interest; if the labels carry numbers only, then use a stock book in which the name of the plant, and also the corresponding number, are entered; a bottle of the best Nicotine and a two-inch measuring glass; a bottle or can of Fir-tree Oil, if available, as there is nothing quite as good as this material for making a sponging solution; a small, folding pocket-lens for the purpose of detecting the advance guards of pests, and also for the purpose of inspecting those finer parts of small flowers which are extremely beautiful as seen under magnification; a syringe is essential; an automatic sprayer is desirable for spraying Orchids with clean water, and also for spraying plants with insecticides; a small-gauge hose with adjustable nozzle, for hosing the moisture-staging, under the staging, and between the pots; a tank of reasonable proportions for holding the water needed for watering, and placed low down so that the water-can may be dipped readily and easily lifted out; a water-can of the Hawes type, with a spreader attachment; Meta and bran for use as traps for slugs; clean pots of various sizes and, possibly, teak baskets and rafts; a scrubbing brush, and a white-wash brush if the house has to be shaded permanently during the Summer.

Keep all tools clean and handy and all accessories placed where they will not interfere with work, but where they are readily get-at-able when needed. A small, portable potting bench is extremely useful where the collection is not large enough to warrant a separate but warm, and closely associated, potting shed. Potting materials are referred to in the notes which follow.

POTTING MATERIALS AND RECEPTACLES

The composition of composts for potting Orchids is a very simple business as the materials used are singularly few and simple, especially when compared with the extravagant combinations used for the cultivation of Auriculas, Primulas, Vines, etc., in the days of yore.

Clean Sphagnum moss is used extensively by Orchid growers, together with Osmunda, Polypodium, or similar Fern-root fibre; the fibre from Heather-peat; fibre from turfy loam; semi-decayed Oak and Beech leaves; crocks of various sizes; porous brick, crushed finely; and clean, gritty sand. Some growers still use small pieces of charcoal, either mixed with the compost or in the drainage system. Old, flaky cow-manure is sometimes used in the more substantial compost provided for Calanthes, Cyrtopodiums, Phaius, and even the especially vigorous Cymbidiums.

Long experience has proved that the porous earthenware pots so largely used for very many kinds of plants are the best receptacles for the great majority of Orchids. Teak-wood baskets, however, provide a more comfortable home for many decumbent or pendulous Orchids and are a necessity for Stanhopeas, which produce spikes that dive down into the compost and would rot were it not for the spacing between the bottom bars of a basket, which permits their escape and development.

Rafts—elongated adaptations of the teak basket—are suitable for Orchids that advance somewhat rapidly by means of extended rhizomes; Coelogyne pandurata is an instance.

Baskets and rafts are easily suspended from the roof by means of copper wire, and should always be considered in the case of those Orchids which enjoy more light than the majority of species.

A few, very few, Orchids succeed admirably if fixed to a block of wood, with a small amount of Sphagnum and fibre tucked around the roots. Such "receptacles" are well-nigh essential for such head-down growers as Cattleya citrina, Oncidium Jonesianum and Scuticaria Steelii —all of which do best when treated in this way and suspended from the roof, or against a wooden upright roof-support, or at the end of a house.

Vigorous Cattleyas and Laelias will often produce "leads" that extend beyond the rim of the parental home; but the compost may not need renewal, so what is to be done to provide rooting material for the new growths? Long practice will enable a grower to break pots in such a way that certain portions may be used clipped to the pots and filled with compost, to accommodate the extending growth for a year and thus permit the postponement of potting for a similar period.

All receptacles should be scrupulously clean prior to use. Scald baskets, rafts and blocks before Orchids are placed in or on them, and never use new earthenware pots until they have been soaked in water and allowed to drain.

PEST CONTROL

Sturdy growth, resulting from timely potting, suitable composts, careful ventilation and heating, and the provision of a moist atmosphere, together with general cleanliness of all parts of the house, will do more than anything else to keep Orchids free from pests.

It is not easy, however, for an amateur with severely limited time to provide for the needs of his plants, or for the grower working with very little assistance, experienced or otherwise, to give meticulous attention to those details which are summed up in "good cultivation."

Fortunately, Orchids are not so liable to pests and diseases as are many other indoor plants and it is also fortunate that means are readily available to deal with the former. Preventive measures pay good dividends on the investment in labour and materials, indeed, spraying with a Nicotine insecticide, once a fortnight, will prevent or adequately control most insect pests. Use the purest Nicotine; about as much as an average egg-cup will hold to each gallon of soft water, and apply the solution to all parts of the plant in the form of a mist-like spray. Scale insects, however, may need different treatment as these pests are usually found

AERIDES ODORATUM

around the bases of stems and pseudo-bulbs and must be removed by means of a small, moderately stiff brush, afterwards using a Nicotine preparation for sponging the affected part. Handling the plants individually at regular intervals will reveal signs of scale infestation, therefore prompt attention will prevent its spread. Frequent spraying with clear water, and syringing in the case of free-growing Cymbidiums, Vandas and Sobralias, will reduce the possibilities of insect attack.

"Damping off" of new growths and the rotting of roots are generally due to cultural errors and structural disabilities. Drips of cold water from faulty glass and woodwork are responsible for many disasters. But whether the growth or the roots rot or die, a surgical operation becomes necessary for, unless the affected parts are cut away cleanly, the trouble is likely to spread. The cut surface of a growth should be dusted with powdered charcoal or other material which will dry it quickly.

The blotches that appear on the leaves of Masdevallias, and sometimes on Odontoglossums, are the outward and visible signs of inward trouble caused by faulty watering in combination with a low temperature.

Yellowing, or loss of green colour, in leaves, stems and pseudo-bulbs, may be due to old age, or to the imminence of leaf-fall in the case of deciduous subjects, but the possibility of starvation must not be overlooked. Orchids, like other pot-grown plants, cannot continue to grow and flower successfully unless the roots are provided with new compost at reasonable intervals. Excessive dryness at the roots for a considerable period will most certainly cause yellowing of pseudo-bulbs and leaf-fall in all Orchids that have no definite and prolonged resting period.

Sponging the foliage and stems twice a year is a great aid to freedom from pests. Soft water, with a small amount of Lemon Oil added, is particularly valuable for this purpose as it cleanses and leaves the foliage in a bright and attractive condition. Use a soft sponge and only sufficient pressure to remove the dirt; severe pressure will produce a sharp sound, like a cry of pain, from an unfortunate leaf, and, sooner or later, a streak or stain will show that the epidermal cells have been damaged. Sponging in late Autumn will enable the leaves of Orchids to take full advantage of the subdued light of wintry days, while another sponging in early Spring will clear away the film of dirt deposited during the dull season and give the plants a clean start.

If circumstances limit sponging to one operation it should be done dur-

E

ing the Winter and preferably when the days commence to lengthen in the New Year. The job should be done thoroughly, the house, staging, moisture-holding material, walls, and pots being cleansed at the same time. Cleanliness is of the greatest importance in the cultivation of Orchids.

POTTING

The proper time to pot an Orchid is when new roots are being formed and the plant needs more root-room. Choose a pot or pan that will comfortably accommodate the root-system but allow room for new compost. Orchids seldom thrive if the roots are surrounded and covered by a large amount of rooting material. The receptacles must be clean, as should the crocks used for drainage. Place one large crock over the drainage hole, then add smaller pieces and, over these, place still smaller pieces. The drainage may occupy a quarter of the depth of the pot, or thereabouts; free drainage is important, as all Orchids delight in freely-percolating moisture and do not succeed if the roots are in materials that are constantly sodden. A small amount of the fibre and Sphagnum should cover the crocks.

Hold the plant so that when potting is finished, the bases of stems or pseudo-bulbs are about level with the rim of the pot. If the plant is heavy and likely to topple over, insert a supporting stick before commencing to insert the compost. Use a potting stick (see "Materials") and press the well-mixed compost firmly and evenly around and among the roots; also, press the surfacing materials quite firmly up to the bases of roots, pseudo-bulbs and growths. Add a small amount of sand as the work proceeds. When preparing the compost take care to sift out all the dust from the various fibres. Cut the latter into shorter or longer lengths, according to the size of the receptacle.

During the process of potting, never use thumbs and fingers to press the materials into position. It is by no means difficult to pot or re-pot Orchids, but patience must be exercised and when the job is finished, clip off the rough ends of the fibres so that the surface presents a pleasing surface that slopes down slightly from centre to circumference. A few heads of living Sphagnum may be inserted in the surface in the case of Odontoglossums, Odontiodas, Miltonias and Cypripediums.

GENERA, SPECIES AND HYBRIDS

IN this section of the book the principal genera, species and numerous hybrids of horticultural importance are described briefly, with equally brief cultural hints. However, in some genera several species are cited under "Other Species", as these do not make a particularly strong floricultural appeal but are left in this section because it would complicate matters if the genera were repeated under the section devoted to "Botanical" Orchids and those of lesser horticultural interest.

ADA, *Lindley*

Tribe, Vandeae; sub-tribe, Oncideae

The craving for size in Orchid flowers is apt to cause many beautiful species to be overlooked, and the genus ADA, founded by Lindley, is an unfortunate omission in many collections. Probably not more than two species are in cultivation, but one of these is so distinct in habit and has such brilliant, although small, flowers, that everyone starting a collection should obtain it. The plants succeed if grown in the cool house, with Odontoglossums, as they require similar treatment.

A. AURANTIACA, *Lindl.*—This native of Colombia is very like an Odontoglossum in leafage, but it has erect spikes, arched by the weight of the flowers at the top. The sepals and petals point forward, and do not spread out or expend except at the tips, but they are numerous, placed rather closely, almost as though strung together, and they are of a very rich shade of orange. A well-grown example may be fifteen inches high, and if it bears several spikes it cannot fail to attract. Quite easily managed; flowers in Winter or early Spring. Introduced by Schlim, 1851–1853; *Bot. Mag.*, t. 5435.

A. LEHMANNI, *Rolfe*—An interesting species, but rarely seen in collections. It is not so attractive as A. *aurantiaca*, as the flowers are cinnabar-orange and the lip is white. Introduced by Lehmann and first described in 1891. Flowers in Summer.

AERIDES, *Loureiro*

Tribe, Vandeae; sub-tribe, Sarcantheae

A moderately large genus of Vandaceous Orchids, founded by a Portuguese missionary and botanist, who discovered Aerides odoratum in Cochin China, prior to 1790, in which year he published his *Flora Cochinchinensis*. Most of the species are of tropical origin, and found in Indo-Malaya; under cultivation they succeed in a temperature that rarely falls below 60° in Winter, and seldom rises much above 85° in Summer. Ample drainage, a rooting medium composed chiefly of Sphagnum moss, and a moist atmosphere, are needed. The flowers are usually fleshy, and the lip has a curved spur.

A. CRASSIFOLIUM, *Rchb. f. et Parish*—Found in Moulmein by the Rev. C. G. Parish in 1864. A sturdy grower, with leathery leaves about six inches long, in two ranks. The roundish flowers, borne in semi-pendulous racemes, have a vertical measurement of over an inch; sepals and petals bright rose-purple; lip of similar colour. *Sel. Orch.*, III, t. 12.

A. CRISPUM, *Lindl.*—A handsome, rather variable, species from Southern India, where it was first discovered by Dr. Wallich, probably about 1835. Growth of the usual type, but with moderately tall stems. Flowers large for the genus, fragrant, borne in racemes that are occasionally branched. The sepals and petals are white, faintly flushed at the tips with rose-purple; lip bright amethyst-purple, with a white base. *Bot. Reg.*, 1842, t. 55; *Bot. Mag.*, t. 4427.

The variety LINDLEYANUM has rather larger flowers than those of the type, while WARNERI has shorter, more upright leaves and longer racemes of smaller flowers, with white sepals and petals that are lightly flushed with pale rose-purple, while the rose-purple lip has a white margin.

A. FALCATUM, *Lindl.*—First exhibited as *A. Larpentiae* at the R.H.S. Gardens, Chiswick, in 1847, but subsequently described as A. FALCATUM, this species is found in Arracan and Upper Burma. It is somewhat variable in colour, but the stout leaves are upwards of six inches long and the racemes of similar length. The flowers are of fair size, loosely arranged, with white sepals and petals, tipped with bright purple, while the lip is soft amethyst-purple. *Paxt. Fl. Gard.*, II, p. 142.

HOULLETIANUM is a variety with shorter and denser racemes, and

CYMBIDIUM GOLD MOHUR VAR. CATHAY

tawny-yellow, rather than white, flowers; var. LEONIE has larger flowers but is otherwise much like the type. *Orch. Alb.*, VII, t. 328.

A. FIELDINGII, *Hook. f.*—Probably the most popular member of the genus, and one that was known under its present title for forty years before being described and published as A. FIELDINGII by Sir J. D. Hooker. Discovered by Thomas Lobb in North-East India in 1850, while collecting for Messrs. Veitch, this species has stout, broad leaves from seven to ten inches long, and fairly large flowers that are crowded along the eighteen-inch racemes, which are occasionally branched at the base. The regularity of the dense inflorescence, and its cylindrical form, have given rise to the popular name of the Fox Brush Orchid. The petals and dorsal sepal are amethyst-purple, with a suffusion of white, and sometimes dotted with purple where the basal areas are white; lateral sepals white, with a purple mark at the tip. Lip purple and white. *Orch. Alb.*, VIII, t. 309.

A. HUTTONII, *Hook. f.*—Described by Sir J. D. Hooker as *Saccolabium Huttonii*, this is indeed very much like a *Saccolabium*. Collected by H. Hutton in the Malay Archipelago in 1866. The flowers are rose-purple, with a lip of deeper hue. *Bot. Mag.*, t. 5681.

A. JAPONICUM, *Rchb. f.*—A dwarf species from Japan, introduced by M. Linden, Brussels, in 1862. The leaves and racemes are short, and the latter are comparatively few, greenish-white, marked with red, and with bright purple marks on the lip. Needs less heat than the majority of species. *Bot. Mag.*, t. 5798.

A. LAWRENCEAE, *Rchb. f.*—This species has long leaves, and large, handsome flowers that are very fleshy, fragrant, white with deep purple tips to the sepals and petals, and a purple band down the centre of the lip. Found by Roebelin in the Philippines while collecting for Messrs. Sanders, *Orch. Alb.*, t. 270.

SANDER'S VARIETY has more evenly rounded flowers that are pale tawny-yellow, with purple tips to the sepals and petals, and a deeper yellow lip, spotted with purple on the central area.

A. MACULOSUM, *Lindl.*—Flowers large, white, with markings of bright purple on the apical halves of the sepals and petals; lip purple. *Bot. Reg.*, 1845, t. 58.

SCHRÖDERI is a taller and more robust form, with branched inflorescences and richer purple markings than the type.

A. MULTIFLORUM, *Roxburgh*—A sturdy, variable species with numerous medium-sized flowers on a raceme of moderate length. The sepals and petals are white, with purple spots and tips; lip pale purple. Widely distributed in Assam, Lower Burma and Cochin China. *Bot. Mag.*, t. 4049.

In earlier years the varieties GODEFROYANUM, LOBBII and VEITCHII were popular; these have differing colour combinations, but the two last are shorter, and the leaves are more closely placed.

A. ODORATUM, *Loureiro*—Found in Cochin-China and Nepal, A. ODORATUM was the first species of Aerides to be cultivated in Europe; introduced to Kew in 1880, it flowered at the R.H.S. Gardens, Chiswick, in 1881. The fragrant flowers are white, with a purple blotch at the tips of the sepals and petals, and light purple marks on the white lip. *Bot. Mag.*, t. 4139; *Bot. Reg.*, t. 1485.

A. QUINQUEVULNERA, *Lindl.*—Cuming found this fine species in the Philippines, while collecting for the firm of Loddiges, in whose nursery, at Hackney, it first flowered in 1837. Apical purple marks on the sepals and petals, five in all, suggested the specific name—"five wounds". The flowers are medium-sized and carried in long racemes.

A. SUAVISSIMUM, *Lindl.*—The sweetly-scented flowers are crowded on long racemes. The sepals and petals are white, flushed with lilac and have a darker lilac apical mark; lip yellowish, spotted with purple. *Fl. Gard.*, II, t. 66; *Sel. Orch.*, I, t. 11.

A. VANDARUM, *Rchb. f.*—A very distinct species, with slender, terete stems, rather like those of Vanda teres. It is found in the Sikkim Himalayas at a considerable elevation, and therefore needs comparatively cool conditions. The wide-spread flowers are usually solitary, two inches broad, undulated, white, with the lateral sepals narrower than the petals and dorsal sepal. The side lobes of the lip are curved upwards, displaying the exserted, lightly fringed central lobe. A charming Orchid. *Orch. Alb.*, III, t. 116; *Bot. Mag.*, t. 4982, as *A. cylindricum*.

A. VIRENS, *Lindl.*—A Javanese species introduced in 1843; very closely allied to A. ODORATUM. The fragrant flowers are crowded in a pendulous raceme and have the usual white and purple colouring, but the spur has a green tip. *Orch. Alb.*, IV, t. 160.

OTHER SPECIES

Other species, of less horticultural value, are A. AUGUSTINIANUM,

Rolfe ; A. EMERICI, *Rchb. f., Bot. Mag.*, t. 6728 ; A. LEEANUM *Rchb. f.;* A. MITRATUM, *Rchb. f., Bot. Mag.*, t. 5728 ; A. RADICOSUM, *A. Richard ;* and A. SAVAGEANUM *Hort. Sander.*

HYBRIDS

Messrs. Jas. Veitch & Sons raised a hybrid, A. DOMINIANUM, by crossing A. AFFINE with A. FIELDINGI, but it has not been seen for a very long time.

ANGRAECUM, *Bory*

Tribe, Vandeae; sub-tribe, Sarcantheae

A remarkable and fascinating genus of tropical Orchids, chiefly natives of Madagascar, but others are found in Tropical Africa, particularly in West Africa, in islands of the Comoro and Mascarene groups, and at least one, A. FALCATUM, comes from far-away Japan. The species are variable in habit, some being small, lowly plants and others of large growth, but in all of them the most notable floral distinction is in the tail-like spur that extends from the base of the lip and finds its most wonderful development in A. SESQUIPEDALE. With rare exceptions, the Angraecums should be grown in the warmest house and treated in the same way as Aerides and tropical Vandas. Even those species which do not possess the nobility of A. SESQUIPEDALE and A. EBURNEUM are charming Orchids and anyone who has grown and flowered the lovely A. CITRATUM would never willingly be without it. Unfortunately, perhaps, the colour range is brief, as most of the flowers are white, ivory-white or green and white, although in several instances the pedicels or spurs are red or brown, therefore there appears to be no opportunity for hybrids to produce other colours. The foliage is green and fleshy.

A. ARTICULATUM, *Rchb. f.*—One of the dwarfs, rarely exceeding six inches in height, with leaves three to five inches long ; spikes about a foot long, bearing small, pure white flowers on orange-red pedicels ; spur from three to four inches long. *Reichenbachia*, II, t. 55.

A. BILOBUM, *Lindl.*—Another dwarf, from West Africa, introduced about 1840. From six to ten, inch-wide, white flowers are borne in a graceful raceme ; pedicels red-brown ; spur pale orange. The variety KIRKII is smaller than the type. *Bot. Mag.*, t. 4159 ; *Orch. Alb.*, IV, t. 162.

A. CAUDATUM, *Lindl.*—About a foot tall, with two rows of long, strap-shaped, recurved leaves, and axillary, eighteen-inch, horizontal spikes of six or more three-inch flowers. Sepals and petals narrow, pale green, shaded with brown; lip obcordate, pointed, white; spur pale brown, eight or nine inches long, twisted towards the end. Introduced from Sierra Leone in 1834. *Bot. Mag.*, t. 4370; *Orch. Alb.*, VIII, t. 358.

A. CHAILLUANUM, *Hook. f.*—Introduced by du Chaillu in 1865. Stems slender, ten inches tall; leaves about six inches long. Spikes racemose, a foot long, carrying six to ten flowers that are milk-white, with a four-inch, greenish spur. *Bot. Mag.*, t. 5589.

A. CITRATUM, *Thouars*—An almost stemless species, from Madagascar, with tufts of six or more ovate leaves; the whole plant is about four inches high, but the arching racemes are about fifteen inches long and carry numerous straw-coloured flowers, barely an inch broad, rounded, with a whitish, club-ended spur. A free-flowering and very beautiful Orchid. *Bot. Mag.*, t. 5624; *Orch. Alb.*, VIII, t. 300.

A. EBURNEUM, *Thouars*—Introduced from Bourbon, this robust species flowered in the Hort. Soc. Gardens, Chiswick, in 1831. Stems two feet or more in height; leaves recurved, eighteen to twenty-four inches long. Spikes erect, up to two feet long; many-flowered. Flowers three to four inches broad; sepals and petals narrow, light-green; lip broad, heart-shaped, pointed, ivory-white; spur green, three inches long. A specimen with several stems occupies a large amount of space. *Bot. Mag.*, t. 4761; *Orch. Alb.*, I, t. 41; *Bot. Reg.*, t. 1522.

A. ELLISII, *Rchb. f.*—A dainty Orchid, about a foot tall, with leaves six to eight inches long, and arching or semi-pendulous spikes of a dozen or more three-inch, pure white flowers ; spur six inches long, pale red. Discovered by the Rev. W. Ellis, who brought home three plants from Madagascar in 1854; one died and the other two were purchased by Mr. B. S. Williams of Holloway, who sold one to Mr. John Day, in whose collection, at Tottenham, it flowered a few years later. Collected by Curtis in 1879, it was introduced in some quantity by Messrs. Veitch. This very distinct Angraecum has fragrant flowers. *Fl. Mag.*, N.S., t. 191; *Sel. Orch.*, III, t. 26.

A. FALCATUM, *Lindl.*—A modest little species, discovered near Nagasaki by Thunberg, in 1773–78. Introduced to British Gardens in 1873 and probably the first Angraecum cultivated in Europe. Needs cooler treatment than other species. Spikes few-flowered; flowers less than an inch wide, pure white and fragrant; spur very slender, curved, about two inches long. *Bot. Mag.*, t. 2097; *Bot. Reg.*, t. 283.

A. FASTUOSUM, *Rchb. f.*—A rare species, introduced in 1881. A very small plant, about two inches tall. Flowers white and fragrant, an inch and a half broad, borne on a few-flowered spike.

A. FRAGRANS, *Thouars*—A neat plant; about eight inches tall, with broadly-ovate, thick leaves. Flowers solitary, on short stems, white, fragrant and two inches in diameter; spur slender, green. Leaves fragrant when crushed, and at one period imported from Mauritius for their Vanilla scent. Known to cultivation for more than a hundred years. *Bot. Mag.*, t. 7161.

A. HYALOIDES, *Rchb. f.*—One of the tiniest species, collected in Madagascar by Curtis and introduced in 1879. Barely an inch high, it has six-inch racemes that carry a dozen or so of small, white, transparent flowers; spur short and slender.

A. KOTSCHYI, *Rchb. f.*—A dwarf, tufted species, discovered near the junction of the Shire and Zambesi rivers, in 1838. A beautiful little Orchid, with pendulous, ten-inch racemes, carrying eight or ten pure white flowers that are a little less than two inches wide. The pale red-brown spur is eight or nine inches long, and twisted. *Orch. Alb.*, IV, t. 179.

A. HUMBLOTII, *Rchb. f.*—Originally described as *Aeranthus Leonis*, and probably identical with *Angraecum Leonis*. A small plant, only about three inches high, but with ten-inch, leathery leaves. Spikes short and erect, few-flowered. Flowers three inches broad, large for the size of the plant, white; lip broad and rounded ; spur six inches long, white, shading to pale green. Introduced from the Comoro Islands in 1885. *Orch. Alb.*, V, t. 213 as *Aeranthus Leonis*.

A. PELLUCIDUM, *Lindl.*—In this dwarf West African species the small, semi-transparent, yellowish-white flowers are borne on a pendulous raceme. *Bot. Reg.*, t. 1844, t. 2.

A. SANDERIANUM, *Rchb. f.*—Of dwarf habit, with numerous small, pure white flowers in drooping racemes.

A. SCOTTIANUM, *Rchb. f.*—About a foot tall, with terete leaves, this distinct species was introduced from the Comoro Islands in 1878. It grows about eighteen inches tall and has short spikes of two-inch, yellowish-white flowers, with a five-inch, reddish-brown spur. *Bot. Mag.* t. 6723.

A. SESQUIPEDALE, *Thouars*—The finest of all the Angraecums. Introduced to cultivation from Madagascar in 1857 and still a popular Orchid where accommodation can be found for it. Curtis collected it in some quantity for the Messrs. Veitch. Stems stout, two to three feet tall, with broad, foot-long leaves. Spikes about twelve inches long, with two to five flowers, each about six inches in diameter, fleshy, and ivory-white; the broad-based sepals and petals end in a sharp point; lip wide, flattish, pointed at the apex, spur greenish-white, a foot or more in length. From the tip of the dorsal sepal to the end of the spur, a flower may measure a "foot and a half" and for that reason Du Petit Thouars named it sesquipedale. *Bot. Mag.*, t. 5113; *Sel. Orch.*, I, t. 31; *Reichenbachia*, I, t. 14, as *Aeranthus sesquipedalis*.

OTHER SPECIES

Several other species that will appeal to lovers of botanically interesting Orchids include A. ARCUATUM, A. DISTICHUM, A. METALLICUM, A. MOOREANUM, and A. VESICATUM. Practically all the species formerly included in Aeranthus are now included in Angraecum.

ANGULOA, *Ruiz et Pavon*
Tribe, Vandeae; sub-tribe, Cyrtopodieae

Comparatively few Orchids have received popular names but these few include the Anguloas, which hold a prominent place with the descriptive title of Cradle Orchids, which refers to the rather large, fleshy lip which rocks when the stem is knocked or shaken. Yet another title, not so frequently heard, is that of Tulip Orchids, and here again it does not require much imagination to find a likeness between Tulipa and Anguloa. The flowers are carried singly on a stiff, erect, foot-long stem, and face upwards; they are more or less cup or goblet shaped. All are sweetly scented.

The stout pseudo-bulbs are about six or eight inches long, each surmounted by a pair of broad, plicate leaves that may be so much as eighteen inches tall. Ample drainage must be provided and a compost consisting of Osmunda fibre and Sphagnum, with a small amount of peat or loam fibre and rough sand. During the growing period Anguloas

CYMBIDIUM ICARUS, EXBURY VARIETY

find a suitable home in the Odontoglossum house, but while the plants are at rest, and needing much less moisture at the roots, the kindlier accommodation of an Intermediate House should be provided. All the known species come from Colombia. The genus was founded by Ruiz and Pavon.

A. BREVILABRIS, *Rolfe*—A handsome Colombian plant and probably a natural hybrid. It is very like A. RUCKERI, but has a shorter lip. *Bot. Mag.*, t. 9381.

A. CLIFTONII, *Rolfe*—A very handsome, free-flowering species, that has been popular with lovers of the genus since Messrs. Charlesworth & Co. gained a F.C.C. for it in 1910. The colour is lemon-yellow, with dull red bases to the petals; lip tinged with cinnamon. A native of Colombia. *Bot. Mag.*, t. 8700.

A. CLOWESII, *Lindl.*—A very handsome species with large, fleshy, golden-yellow flowers, and a pale, or even whitish, lip. At the Temple Show of 1906 Messrs. Charlesworth & Co. exhibited a noble specimen, with thirty flowers. *Bot. Mag.*, t. 4313; *Bot. Reg.*, 1844, t. 63.

A. DUBIA, *Rchb. f.*—Originally imported with A. CLOWESII and was regarded as a possible natural hybrid between it and A. UNIFLORA. The sepals and petals are yellow, freely spotted on the inner surfaces with purple; lip white, with basal purple blotches.

A. EBURNEA, *Williams.*—Tastes differ, consequently certain growers prefer the quiet beauty of A. EBURNEA to the gorgeousness of A. CLOWESII and A. RUCKERI. The colour is white, with pink spottings on the lip. *Orch. Alb.*, III, t. 133; *Lindenia*, VII, t. 348.

A. RUCKERI, *Lindl.*—Commemorates a formerly well-known Orchid enthusiast. The soft yellow sepals and petals are spotted, sometimes shaded, with crimson, and the lip is crimson. A beautiful species, introduced in 1846. *Bot. Reg.*, t. 41; *Sel. Orch.*, II, t. 10.

The variety SANGUINEA has richer crimson colouring than the type. *Bot. Mag.*, t. 5384; *Orch. Alb.*, I, t. 19.

A. UNIFLORA, *Ruiz et Pavon*—The white flowers, spotted and shaded with pink, are not so large as those of the popular A. CLOWESII. *Bot. Mag.*, t. 4807; *Bot. Reg.*, 1844, t. 60.

Several distinct forms of this species have received varietal names, the chief being ALBA, pure white; and TURNERI, with much more pink colouring than the type.

HYBRIDS

The principal hybrids are A. MADOUXIANA (*A. Ruckeri* × *A. uniflora*); A. MEDIA (*A. Clowesii* × *A. Ruckeri*); and A. ROLFEI (*A. Cliftonii* × *A. brevilabris*).

ANOECTOCHILUS, *Blume*

Tribe, Neottiae; sub-tribe, Spirantheae

Blume's genus Anoectochilus used to be a large one, horticulturally, but many years ago the botanists divided it into several distinct genera, therefore growers who are fascinated by the exquisitely beautiful foliage of the Jewel Orchids must refer also to Haemaria, Dossinia, Macodes and Goodyera. All these delightful Orchids are of lowly habit and thrive best under cultivation when grown in well-drained pots in a compost consisting of Sphagnum, with a small addition of Osmunda fibre and sand. They love warmth, moisture and shade and should be covered with a bell glass. As the short spikes carry unattractive flowers, they may be pinched out so soon as seen. There are no pseudo-bulbs and growth extends by means of slender stems which should be pegged to the compost. The majority of the species in this rather large group are not easy to manage, but a pan of six to twelve growths, each furnished with short, broad leaves, invariably attracts attention and admiration. Unlike most Orchids, they are lowly foliage plants, and among the supreme tests of a grower's skill.

In the most beautiful species the ground colour of the leaves is olive-green, bronzy-green, or dark green, with a velvety and lustrous surface, but the veinings, often reticulated, may be gold or copper, silver-grey, reddish-copper, or deeper green.

For the present purpose the several genera are grouped under the general and popular heading of Anoectochilus, but the species are set out under the genus to which they belong.

ANOECTOCHILUS CONCINNUS, *Hort.*—Dark olive-green, with stripes and reticulating veins of bright reddish-copper. A native of Assam.

A. REGALIS, *Blume*—Dark velvety-green, with particularly beautiful bronze shading and netted veins of gold. Also from Assam.

HAEMARIA DAWSONIANA, *Rolfe.*—A delightful species from Malaysia. Dark green, with violet tinting, olive shading, and copper coloured veins.

H. DISCOLOR, *Lindl.*—From China. *Bot. Mag.*, t. 2055.

GOODYERA PUBESCENS, *R. Br.*—*Bot. Mag.*, t. 2540.

G. REPENS, *R. Br.*

G. ROLLISSONII, *Hort.*—A very charming golden hybrid.

ARACHNANTHE, *Blume*
Tribe, *Vandeae; sub-tribe, Sarcantheae*

Botanists differ from each other in placing certain species under Arachnanthe, Vanda or Renanthera.

The genus is a small one and consists of tropical epiphytes found in Malaysia. Under cultivation they thrive under conditions favourable to Vandas and Aerides, *i.e.*, a warm, moist atmosphere. They are not popular Orchids although very attractive when flowering freely.

A. CATHCARTII, *Benth.*—Discovered by Sir J. D. Hooker in the eastern Himalaya, in 1848, it first flowered in the Chelsea nurseries in 1870 after many failures to import it alive. The long stems, needing support, are clothed with leathery, opposite, alternate leaves. The short racemes appear along the stems and bear from three to five rounded flowers, each having a diameter of about three inches. The ground colour of the sepals and petals is dull yellow, but this is almost obliterated by the narrow bands of red-brown, which are horizontal and not longitudinal. The lip has white side lobes, striped with red, and the central lobe is yellow, marked with red. *Bot. Mag.*, t. 5845, as *Vanda Cathcartii; Xen. Orch.*, II, p. 39, as *Esmeralda Cathcartii.*

A. CLARKEI, *Rolfe*—Found in the Sikkim Himalaya by Charles Clarke, in 1875, this species was fairly popular during the period when Vandaceous plants were grown extensively. It grows like A. CATHCARTII, but the yellow sepals and petals are barred with bright chestnut-brown and the whitish, or pale yellow, lip is streaked with red. The flowers have a burnished appearance and are interesting because of the articulated lip, which oscillates at the slightest touch. *Bot. Mag.*, t. 7077.

A. LOWII, *Lindl.*—One of the most remarkable of Orchids and one which invariably attracts attention and receives admiration when seen in flower. Unfortunately, it requires a great deal of room, considerable heat, and patience, to produce a fine specimen and, apparently, it does not flower until of some considerable size. The stout stems may be three feet or more in height, furnished with two ranks of leathery, green, strap-shaped leaves eighteen or thirty inches long. When this species does flower it frequently produces a pair of spikes, axillary, and these may be from four to nine feet long, with a red-brown rachis; numerous, somewhat widely spaced flowers are borne throughout its whole length. Apart from its noble appearance, and the length of the spikes, A. LOWII is notable for its peculiar habit of producing two types of flowers, the two at the base being tawny-yellow, speckled with brown, with broader and more fleshy segments than the others. All the rest have a diameter of about three inches, with undulated sepals and petals of reddish-brown colour, barred with light yellow, while the short lip is yellow, spotted with purple, has a central light purple area and a clear yellow apex, including the incurving horn. A. LOWII succeeds best when grown with tropical Vandas. It was first described as a Vanda, and its discoverer, Sir Hugh Low, who found it in Borneo, probably in Sarawak, wished Dr. Lindley to name it *V. Lindleyana*, but the famous botanist declined the honour as he considered such a wonderful plant should commemorate its discoverer. *Veitch's Manual of Orchidaceous Plants*, Vol. II, contains an illustration and description of a specimen that flowered in Baron Alphonse de Rothschild's collection at Ferrieres, in 1885, but a subsequent note states that the same specimen flowered again in 1887 and then carried 650 flowers. *Syns. Vanda Lowii*, and *Renanthera Lowii*, *Bot. Mag.*, t. 5475; *Reichenbachia*, II, t. 71.

A MOSCHIFERA, *Blume*—An interesting species from Java, but seldom seen in cultivation; the large, creamy-white, purple-spotted flowers have a spidery appearance and a musky scent. Habit resembles that of A. CLARKEI. *Syn. Arachnis moschifera. Rumphia*, IV, tt. 190 and 199.

ARPOPHYLLUM, *Llave et Lexarza*
Tribe, Vandeae; sub-tribe, Pleurothalleae

Before the cultivation of Orchids became so specialized as it is now, a few species were included in mixed collections of stove and greenhouse plants, and one that won a great deal of popularity in such associations was ARPOPHYLLUM GIGANTEUM. To-day it is not often seen but it is easily managed in an Intermediate House. The genus Arpophyllum, native to Mexico and Guatemala, is a small one, with smallish, slender pseudobulbs, and narrow, channelled, strap-shaped leaves. The inflorescence rises from a point where the leaves are joined to the pseudo-bulbs, and carries a foot-long, cylindrical spike of small, closely-set flowers. Outward appearance is no guide to natural affinity and novices not infrequently fail to recognize Arpophyllums as Orchids.

Ample drainage is essential, as the water supply must be ample during the periods of growth and flower. Although plants may be grown at the warmest end of the Odontoglossum House, they do better in an intermediate temperature, or at the coolest end of the Cattleya House. Loam fibre, peat or Osmunda fibre, with a fairly liberal supply of finely broken crocks, or coarse sand, and some Sphagnum, provide a suitable compost.

A. CARDINALE, *Linden et Reich.*—Not seen by the author, but is recorded as very distinct, with light rose-coloured sepals and petals and a red lip. Flowers in Summer. *Pescatoria*, t. 45.

A. GIGANTEUM, *Lindl.*—Formerly very popular, this species produces a dense spike of rosy-purple flowers during late Spring or early Summer. A robust specimen may be nearly 3 ft. tall at flowering time. *Sel. Orch.*, t. 39.

A. SPICATUM, *Llave et Lex*—Very similar to the foregoing, but has bright reddish-purple flowers, and usually blooms during the late Winter months. *Bot. Mag., t.* 6022.

BIFRENARIA, *Lindley*

Tribe, Vandeae; sub-tribe, Cyrtopodieae

Although Bifrenarias are not very popular at present, a few species are to be seen occasionally at exhibitions and in private collections. Of dwarf habit, they may be cultivated with ease in the Intermediate House, in an Odontoglossum compost, with perhaps a slightly higher proportion of fibre. Although the plants like a period of semi-rest, they must not be allowed to become really dry at the roots, even in Winter.

B. HARRISONIAE, *Rchb. f.*—The best species for general cultivation, as it flowers regularly. It is a Brazilian Orchid introduced about 1821–22. The short, four-angled pseudo-bulbs are rather closely placed, and each has one broad, ten-inch, dark green leaf. The fleshy, long-lasting, three-inch flowers are borne erect on six-inch or eight-inch stems, and usually there is only one flower on a stem, but two stems and two flowers may be produced from the base of the most recently developed pseudo-bulb. The sepals and petals are about equal, the dorsal sepal slightly hooded, white or pale buff; lip three-lobed and shapely, rich purple, with darker veins, faintly hairy; the central lobe has notched margins. Flowers fragrant. ALBA, EBURNEA, and PURPURACEA are varieties distinguished by the colours indicated by the varietal names. *Bot. Mag.*, t. 2927, as *Maxillaria Harrisoniae; Orch. Alb.*, III, t. 100 as *Lycaste.*

Growers especially interested in this genus may try B. ATROPURPUREA, B. AURANTIACA, B. INODORA, and B. VITELLINA.

BLETIA, *Ruiz et Pavon*

Tribe, Epidendreae; sub-tribe, Bletieae

The Bletias are deciduous Orchids that need a decided season of rest. They need cool-house treatment, and indeed may be regarded as half-hardy. Potting is best done when new growth commences, after the resting period, and a suitable rooting medium is composed of fibrous loam, some Osmunda fibre and leaf-soil, with a reasonable amount of sand, and ample drainage.

B. HYACINTHINA, *R. Br.*—A Chinese species introduced so long ago as 1803. The slender growths are less than one foot tall, clothed with lanceolate, plaited leaves. The terminal spike is erect, and carries six or more blue-purple flowers of modest size. Quite commonly cultivated fifty years ago. *Bot. Mag.*, t. 1492, as *Cymbidium hyacinthinum.*

B. SHEPHERDII, *Hook.*—A taller grower than the previous species, with large flowers of a deep bluish-purple hue; the white lamellae on the lip provide a pleasing contrast. *Bot. Mag.*, t. 3319; *Mag. Bot.*, II, p. 146.

B. VERECUNDA, *R. Br.*—A very tall grower, with spikes that may be over four feet long and carry numerous rose-coloured flowers, in which the lip is deeper rose and has yellow lamellae on the central lobe. So far as can be ascertained this was the first exotic Orchid grown in Great Britain. Found in the West Indies and Mexico, and requires warmer treatment than the other species. *Bot. Mag.*, t. 3217, as *B. acutipetala.*

BRASSIA, *R. Brown*

Tribe, Vandeae; sub-tribe, Oncidieae

All who love flowers for their elegance and decorative value rather than for their conformity with modern ideals of size and form will find great satisfaction in the cultivation of the several species of the genus Brassia.

BRASSIA BRACHIATA

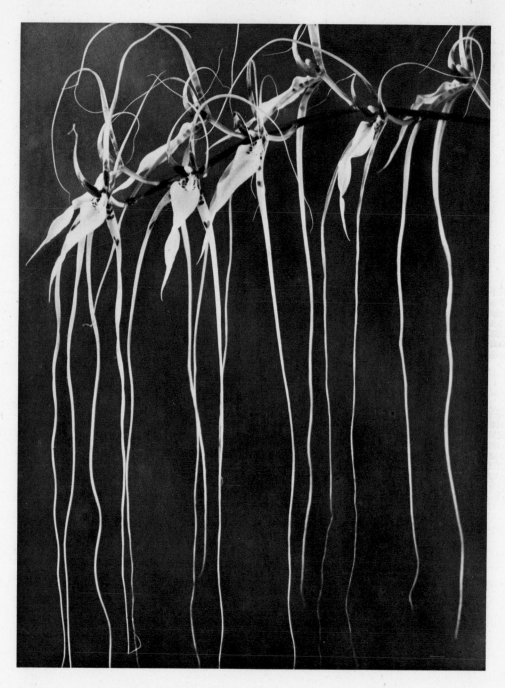

BRASSIA LAWRENCEANA VAR. LONGISSIMA

All are found in tropical America, at considerable altitudes, and may therefore be grown successfully under the same treatment as Odontoglossums, provided they are placed at the warmest end of the house. In general habit, pseudo-bulbs and leafage, they are very like Odontoglossums.

The spikes, produced from the base of the pseudo-bulbs, are long, usually arched gracefully, and carry the flowers in two rows. The flowers are remarkable for their attractive, although not brilliant, colouring, but still more remarkable for the way the sepals and petals extend narrowly until they become almost thread-like at the tips— in short, they have what is known as a "spidery" appearance. For grouping with other Orchids, either for home or exhibition display, the Brassias are eminently desirable, and, fortunately, they are easily grown.

B. BRACHIATA, *Lindl.*—A beautiful Orchid discovered in Guatemala about 1838. The light green sepals and petals are yellowish-green, spotted with brown-purple; the sepals may be six inches long. Lip, light yellow. *Bot. Reg.*, 1847, t. 29.

B. CAUDATA, *Lindl.*—This, as its name implies, has very long "tails". The colour is light greenish-yellow, spotted with dark brown on the basal part of the sepals and petals. Lip pointed, pale yellow, with a few red-brown spots. *Bot. Mag.*, t. 3451; *Bot. Reg.* t. 832.

B. GIREOUDIANA, *Rchb. f.*—The yellow flowers of this attractive Costa Rican species are spotted with chocolate-red. *Xen. Orch.*, I, t. 32.

B. LAWRENCEANA, *Lindl.*—A popular Orchid, with large flowers that are bright yellow, greenish at the base of the sepals and petals, and spotted with reddish-brown. Petals much shorter than the very long sepals. *Bot. Reg.*, 1841, t. 18; *Bot. Mag.*, t. 5748.

B. MACULATA, *R. Br.*—The yellow ground colour of the flowers is freely spotted with brown, while the white lip has spottings of purple and purplish-brown over the central area. *Bot. Reg.*, t. 1691.

The variety GUTTATA has a yellow lip and brown spots.

B. VERRUCOSA, *Lindl.*—An Orchid which still retains much of its former popularity. It is rather taller than other species, and the spikes may be two feet in length. The sepals and petals are greenish-yellow, freely marked with dark purple, while the white lip is warted with small, dark green eruptions. *Batem. Orch.*, t. 21.

F

OTHER SPECIES

Other species recorded and occasionally seen in collections include B. ANTHEROTES *Rchb. f.*, pale yellow, with blackish-brown markings. *Orch. Alb.*, IV, t. 159 ; B. LEWISII, *Rolfe;* B. WAGENERI, *Rchb. f.;* B. PICTURATA, yellow and chocolate-brown. B. WRAYAE, *Hook.*, is synonymous with *B. maculata.*

BROUGHTONIA, *R. Brown*

Tribe, Epidendreae; sub-tribe, Laelieae

Although this is a small genus, at least one species is well worthy of cultivation by those who can grow it in a warm house, suspended from the roof in a teakwood basket, and provide the atmospheric moisture desirable for the clambering species of Epidendrum.

B. SANGUINEA, *B. Br.*—Introduced to Kew in 1793, from Jamaica, this elegant species has roundish pseudo-bulbs and smallish, pale green leaves. The raceme is slender, terminal, borne aloft, and may bear from six to nine flowers that are rich purplish-crimson, about an inch and a half broad, with an orange blotch at the base of the lip. One of the oldest Orchids in cultivation. *Bot. Mag.*, t. 3076; and as *B. coccinea* in *Bot. Mag.*, t. 3536.

CALANTHE, *R. Brown*

Tribe, Epidendreae; sub-tribe, Coelogyneae

A comparatively small genus, mostly natives of India and Malaya. Many are of little horticultural interest, but the Vestitae group consists of valuable, graceful, and beautiful Orchids which flower in Autumn or early Winter; these have long, stout pseudo-bulbs and arching, many-flowered spikes, whereas most other members of the genus are without pseudo-bulbs.

C. VESTITA and its garden forms and hybrids need abundant heat and moisture when in growth ; but after the leaves have fallen very little water is required until the spikes appear from near the base of the last-made pseudo-bulb. A suitable compost consists of Osmunda and loam fibre in equal parts, sand, and a small proportion of Sphagnum moss or half-decayed Oak leaves. Potting is an annual proceeding, and should be done directly new growth is seen. The evergreen species do not require a definite period of rest. All Calanthes have spurred flowers.

C. MASUCA, *Lindl.*—Leaves a foot or more in length; spikes up to three feet tall, racemose at the end, and crowded with small, purplish-mauve flowers. *Bot. Mag.*, t. 4541.

C. ROSEA, *Bentham*—This deciduous species has conical psuedo-bulbs, and a foot-long, arching spike of six to twelve light rose-pink flowers that are sometimes shaded with white. Formerly quite popular, but had to give place to *C. vestita* and its varieties. Known to a former generation as *Limatodes rosea. Bot. Mag.*, t. 5312.

C. VERATRIFOLIA, *R. Brown*—A very robust species with a geographical distribution from Japan to New South Wales. Terrestrial and evergreen; probably the first Calanthe to be introduced to this country, and the one on which the genus was founded. Leaves up to two feet long, spikes erect, more than a yard high, carrying numerous smallish, white flowers. *Bot. Mag.*, t. 2615; *Orch. Alb.*, V, t. 218.

C. VESTITA, *Wallich*—Pseudo-bulb five to eight inches long; leaves twelve to twenty-four inches long; spikes arching, many-flowered. Flowers two to three inches in length, with a broad, prominent lip. The slightly recurved sepals and petals are white; lip three-lobed, the wide front lobe cleft at the apex, white, with a basal blotch of yellow. The colouring, however, is variable. Distinct varieties are REGNIERI, with rose-coloured, purple-veined lip; RUBRO-OCULATA, with red base; STEVENS' VAR., white, with a rosy blotch; TURNERI, very like RUBRO-OCULATA, but later in flowering; and NIVALIS, wholly white. *Bot. Mag.*, t. 4671.

HYBRIDS

Almost all of great horticultural value.

C. BELLA (*C. vestita var. Turneri* × *C. Veitchii*); C. HARRISII (*C. Veitchii* × *C. v. var. Turneri*), a very lovely and useful hybrid; C. BARON SCHRÖDER (*C. vestita var. rubra* × *C. v. var. Regnieri*); C. BRYAN (*C. vestita var. rubro-oculata* × *C. v. var. Williamsii*); C. NORMAN (*C. vestita var. gigantea* × *C. v. var. rubro-oculata*); C. OAKWOOD RUBY (*C. Sedenii* × *C. vestita var. rubro-oculata*); C. SEDENII (*C. Veitchii* × *C. vestita var. rubro-oculata*); and C. VEITCHII (*C. rosea* × *C. vestita*).

CATTLEYA, *Lindley*
Tribe, Epidendreae; sub-tribe, Laelieae

The genus Cattleya, founded by Dr. Lindley, commemorates William Cattley, of Barnet, Hertfordshire, one of the first amateurs to create a private collection of Orchids. Cattleyas are South American Orchids and for the most part are found in a wide belt of country extending from the Brazilian province of Bahia in the north, down to Rio Grande, with a few species in Venezuela and British Guiana, and others, on the far side of the continent, in Colombia and Ecuador. Indeed, it is in this Pacific coastal belt that most of the finest species of horticultural value are found. Cattleyas grow on trees, often in large masses, and when they were regularly imported in quantity very large "pieces" were frequently sent home. The majority of species are markedly pseudo-bulbous, but a few, such as C. LODDIGESII, C. INTERMEDIA, C. BICOLOR, C. BOWRING-IANA, C. GUTTATA, and others, make stem-like growths and do not form pseudo-bulbs like those found in the C. LABIATA section.

Botanists group numerous Cattleyas under C. LABIATA and make them varieties or sub-species of that handsome species, but for the present purpose the well-known forms are treated separately, for horticultural purposes, as though they were distinct species.

The majority of Cattleyas grow well together in a house where abundance of light can be admitted and a minimum temperature of 45° can be maintained at night during severe wintry weather. Ventilation is a matter of extreme importance. Cattleyas love fresh air so long as a moderately moist atmosphere can be maintained, but as the temperature decreases so should the atmospheric moisture. Probably more Cattleyas are killed by over-watering than by the other extreme, indeed, with a reasonable amount of moisture in the atmosphere they do not require large supplies of root moisture, except when growing freely, or flowering. Moreover, Cattleyas appreciate stronger light than most Orchids, therefore heavy shading is undesirable even in the Summer, but new growths must not be subjected to the direct rays of the sun, and this applies equally to hybrids and species.

In general, the potting compost should include a large proportion of peat fibre or Osmunda fibre, with a moderate amount of Sphagnum moss and sharp sand. For the robust species and hybrids the addition of a small amount of semi-decayed Oak or Beech leaves may be added, indeed, provided the drainage is ample and watering done with extreme care, this addition appears to accelerate growth and thus allows a longer period of bright weather during which these growths may become firm and be the better able to withstand the cold and dull weather of Winter.

CATTLEYA MINUCIA

Firm potting is needed and the compost should be pressed rather tightly towards the centre of the pot and around the bases of the growths. It is a good plan to put one crock over the drainage hole, lower the roots into the pot and fill smaller crocks in and around them up to about a third of the pot's depth, before beginning to insert the compost. Further, use judgment in this matter, so that when the operation has been completed, the rhizomes are on, or very close to, the surface. The time to pot is as soon as new growths emerge, as new roots are formed quickly afterwards and delay in potting may mean the breakage of the brittle roots.

C. ACLANDIAE, *Lindl.*—The furrowed stems of this Bahian species are rarely so much as six inches long, and each one has a pair of elliptic, leathery leaves at the top. The inflorescence is short and usually one-flowered. The great attraction of this species—which is best grown in a small, teak-wood basket and suspended from the roof—is the yellowish colour of the sepals and petals, heavily barred and blotched with dark blackish-purple. The lip is large for the size of the flower, and the spreading apical portion is rose-purple, veined with deeper purple. The white, rose-tinted side lobes do not incurve, consequently the exposed, bright purple column adds greatly to the colourful effect. *Bot. Mag.*, t. 5039; *Bot. Reg.*, XXVI, t. 48.

C. BICOLOR, *Lindl.*—Found in Minas Geraes and Rio de Janeiro, at considerable altitudes. The terete stems of this species may be two feet tall, encased in a thin, white, membraneous sheathing, and surmounted by a pair of stout leaves, each about six inches long. The terminal spike may carry several flowers of medium size, brownish-green, occasionally spotted with dark purple; the lip is reddish-purple and the column white, shaded with purple. *Bot. Mag.*, t. 4909; *Orch. Alb.*, VII, t. 318.

C. BOWRINGIANA, *Veitch*—Introduced from British Honduras in 1884, this very free-flowering Cattleya was named after Mr. J. C. Bowring, of Windsor. The foot-long stems have a pair of thick, oblong, deep green leaves and the terminal spike may carry as many as ten smallish flowers of rose-purple colour, often with a bluish tint; the lip has long, rose-purple side lobes that enclose the column, but the rounded apical portion is bright reddish-purple; throat white. A very fine Orchid, specially when a large specimen has six or more spikes. *Orch. Alb.*, t. 323.

C. CITRINA, *Lindl.*—One of the several Orchids of inverted habit and only managed successfully when attached, upside down, to a small raft of hard wood, with the compost tucked in around the roots and kept in position by thin copper wire. The small, ovoid pseudo-bulb has a pair of thin, glaucous-green leaves, and the pendulous, single-flowered spike emerges from between them. The fleshy sepals and petals are yellow, often of a much deeper shade than citron; lip somewhat tubular, with a rounded apex that is lightly frilled, orange-yellow, edged with white. The flowers are very fragrant and last a long time; one flower will fill a whole house with sweet scent. *Bot. Mag.*, t. 3742; *Reichenbachia*, I, t. 20; *Sel. Orch.*, III, t. 18.

C. DOWIANA, *Bateman*—Warscewicz discovered this gorgeous labiate Cattleya in Costa Rica, about 1850, but it did not flower in England until 1865. The large flowers have light yellow sepals and petals, while the spreading lip is of rich purplish-crimson, with golden veins that radiate from the centre almost to the frilled apex. *Bot. Mag.*, t. 5618; *Sel. Orch.*, II, t. 27.

The superb variety AUREA was found by Wallis in Antioquia, in 1868, and is more brilliant than the type, the general colour being richer, while the veinings are more numerous on the lip. *Orch. Alb.*, II, t. 84; *Reichenbachia*, I, t. 5.

C. GASKELLIANA, *Hort. Sander*—A handsome, large-flowered form of the labiate group, found in Venezuela and introduced in 1883. It has scented flowers, with white or purplish sepals and petals, and a light purple lip with yellow veins in the throat. There is a pure white form.

C. GIGAS, *Linden et André.*—A remarkably large labiate Cattleya, with rosy-mauve sepals and petals and a bold lip of rich crimson-purple, with deep yellow markings in the throat.

Two fine varietal forms are IMPERIALIS and SANDERIANA, the latter with longer flowers of deeper and richer colour and a magnificent magenta-purple lip. *Syn. C. Warscewiczii.*

C. GRANULOSA, *Lindl.*—Found in Guatemala by Hartweg in 1840. The terete stems are eighteen to twenty inches long, furnished with a pair of rather large, stout leaves. The terminal spike may have half a dozen medium-sized, fleshy flowers in which the sepals and petals are yellowish-green, spotted with red; lip rather short, distinctly three lobed, yellow, with a white, crimson-spotted apex. A useful Orchid but one which has lost some of its former popularity. Several varieties have been recorded and of these SCHOFIELDIANA is probably the finest and best coloured. *Bot. Reg.*, 1842, t. 1.

C. GUTTATA, *Lindl.*—Although widely spread throughout the Brazilian provinces, this species is now rather rare in cultivation. The stout stems may be thirty inches tall, with a pair of leathery leaves upwards of six inches long. The terminal spike carries four or five fleshy flowers, with yellowish-green, purple-spotted sepals and petals, the spots being more or less marginal and apical. Lip crimson-purple, with crowded papileae and white side lobes. *Bot. Reg.*, 1831, t. 1406.

Several fine forms have been in cultivation, the most notable being var. LEOPOLDII, *Linden*, with brownish sepals and petals and a varied amethyst-purple, white-lobed lip (*Orch. Alb.*, I, t. 16), and PRINZII, *Rchb. f.*, a taller grower, with light rose-purple sepals and petals and a crimson lip. *Bot. Mag.*, t. 5685.

C. INTERMEDIA, *Graham*—A very distinct, useful and free-flowering species, with foot-long stems surmounted by a pair of thick, oblong leaves. The terminal inflorescence carries upwards of three medium-sized flowers that may be white or pale yellow, with a rose-purple apex to the white-lobed lip. A very charming Orchid, found in the southern provinces of Brazil and first flowered in Britain in 1826, in the Glasgow Botanic Garden. There is a pure white form. *Bot. Mag.*, t. 2851; *Bot. Reg.*, 1836, t. 1919.

C. LABIATA, *Lindl.*—A splendid but extremely variable species introduced in 1818. There are two types, but the type that flowers in the Autumn is the most prized, and is frequently referred to as the variety VERA or AUTUMNALIS. The pseudo-bulbs are elongated, short-stemmed and carry a single large leaf that may be so much as ten inches long. The terminal spike emerges from a double sheath, and may have from two to five large flowers of beautiful texture, with sepals and petals of rose or mauve; lip, widely open, frilled at the margins, crimson-purple, with a yellow throat. Numerous forms have received varietal names and one of these has pure white sepals and petals, with a golden throat to the lip. *Bot. Mag.*, t. 3998; *Bot. Reg.*, t. 1859.

C. LAWRENCEANA, *Rchb. f.*—A very fine species but not too easily managed and consequently somewhat rare. Originally discovered by Sir R. Schomburgk in British Guiana about 1840, it was subsequently collected by Mr. Seidl and Mr. Im Thurm. A dwarf grower, with sub-dued pseudo-bulbs, each with one six-inch leaf. The short inflorescence may have from three to seven flowers of stout texture and about four inches across. The sepals are rose-purple or whitish; petals much broader, and of similar, but usually richer, colour. Lip prominent, with a crimson apex, white lines and a purple throat. The species was named after Sir Trevor Lawrence, who had a fine collection of Orchids at Bur-ford Lodge, Dorking, and was President of the Royal Horticultural Society for a very long period. It is rather variable and the variety ROSEA-SUPERBA has stouter growth, and striations of white on a rose-purple ground. *Reichenbachia*, I, t. 12.

C. LODDIGESII, *Lindl.*—A sturdy and easily grown species that flowers in Autumn. Rather less than a foot high, the stems have a pair of stout leaves and a stout, erect, terminal spike of several shapely, medium-sized, long-lasting flowers. The petals are lilac or pale rose, with whitish side lobes and a light purple mark on the apex.

A variety that is particularly popular, with more richly coloured flowers and taller growths, is HARRISONIAE, introduced in 1836. This flowers in late Spring and Summer and was named after its introducer.

C. LUEDEMANNIANA, *Rchb. f.*—A sturdy grower, from Venezuela, but rarely seen nowadays. It has rose-purple sepals and petals, shaded with white, the petals being very much broader than the sepals; lip of similar colour, with a crimson-purple apex and yellow or white blotches in the throat. *Orch. Alb.*, VI, t. 201, as *C. speciosissima var. Buchananiana; Sel. Orch.*, I, t. 16, as *C. Dawsonii.*

C. MENDELII, *Hort. Sander*—One of the loveliest of the labiate group, introduced by Messrs. Low and Co., in 1870. The sepals and broad petals are light blush and the lip is bright magenta-purple, with a yellowish disc. Easily grown, it was formerly exhibited in large, speci-men form. *Reichenbachia* I, t. 15; *Orch. Alb.*, I, t. 3.

C. MOSSIAE, *Lindl.*—One of the most beautiful of all Cattleyas, this was introduced from Venezuela in 1836 and, under good cultivation, will flower freely. The large flowers are usually pale rose, with a frilled lip that is rose-coloured, stained with purplish-rose or crimson, and with a yellow throat and markings. It is, however, a variable species so far as colour is concerned, but probably the most distinct variety is REINECKI-ANA, which is prized for its white sepals and petals, with crimson and

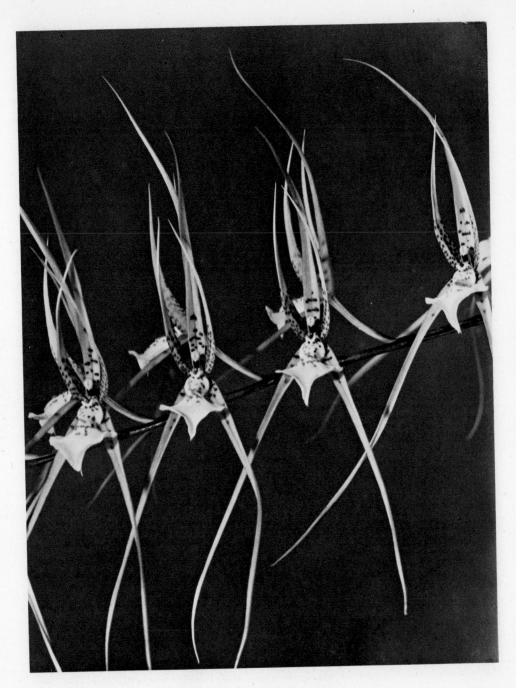

BRASSIA VERRUCOSA

p. 69

CHYSIS BRACTESCENS

CIRRHOPETALUM ORNATISSIMUM

CIRRHOPETALUM LOUIS SANDER

yellow colouring on the large, frontal portion of the lip. *Bot. Mag.*, t. 3669; *Sel. Orch.*, III, t. 16; *Bot. Reg.*, 1840, t. 58.

C. PERCIVALIANA, *Rchb. f.*—A floriferous, Winter-flowering Orchid, with medium-sized flowers, it belongs to the labiate group, is found in Venezuela and was introduced in 1882. The sepals and petals are of rich rose colour, while the lip shows a handsome combination of crimson and deep yellow, with a rose-coloured, frilled margin. *Orch. Alb.*, III, t. 144; *Reichenbachia*, I, t. 2.

C. SCHILLERIANA, *Rchb. f.*—Found in northern Brazil and introduced to Europe about 1856, this rather variable, short-stemmed species does not produce its medium-sized flowers very freely. It is somewhat like *C. Acklandiae* in habit and has purplish-brown sepals and petals, with a purple, yellow-lined lip. *Bot. Mag.*, t. 5150; *Sel. Orch.*, II, t. 25.

C. SCHRÖDERAE, *Sander*—This large-flowered, lovely Orchid comes from Colombia, and has the merit of being sweetly fragrant. It is of sturdy habit, and the light rose sepals and petals have wavy margins, the lip being of a darker shade, with an orange throat. One of the most useful of Spring-flowering Cattleyas.

C. SKINNERI, *Lindl.*—Although the flowers of this Venezuelan species, discovered by Mr. G. Ure-Skinner in 1836, are not large, they are produced freely in terminal, erect spikes, in Spring and early Summer. It is pseudo-bulbous and about fifteen inches tall when in flower. The sepals and petals are rose-purple, and the lip is of somewhat deeper hue, tubular, with a rounded, purple apex and a white throat. A fine Orchid, somewhat variable in colour, one form, ALBA, having white sepals and petals. *Bot. Mag.*, t. 4270, white form; *Orch. Alb.*, III, t. 112.

C. SUPERBA, *Schomburgk*—Introduced in 1838, this handsome species was discovered much earlier by Humboldt. A native of British Guiana, it has stems about a foot tall, each with a pair of thick leaves and a terminal spike of three or four flowers of deep rose colour, with a crimson lip that has white blotches in the throat, and a yellow disc. *Bot. Mag.*, t. 4083; *Orch. Alb.*, I, t. 33.

C. TRIANAE, *Rchb. f.*—Before hybrids became so numerous this handsome Cattleya was very popular and its extreme variability in colour, but less variation in form, led to the naming of an almost incredible number of varieties. It is pseudo-bulbous, a member of the labiate group, is found in Colombia (once New Granada), and was introduced about

1860. The large flowers may be blush, rose, or purple; the lip purple or crimson, with an orange throat that is lightly crisped or frilled at the apex. A form with pure white sepals and petals and an orange-yellow throat, named ALBA, is particularly beautiful. *Bot. Mag.*, t. 5504; *Orch. Alb.*, I, t. 45.

C. VELUTINA, *Rchb. f.*—A Brazilian species of slender, erect growth, with rather smaller flowers that have purple-spotted, coppery or orange sepals and petals, and an orange-coloured lip that has a whitish throat and violet veins. *Orch. Alb.*, t. 28.

C. WALKERIANA, *Gardner*—A handsome species, with very short stems, and shapely flowers which are large for the size of the plant and produced from short, basal, leafless growths. The sepals and very broad petals are purplish-rose or rosy-lilac, while the large, spreading, roundish apical portion of the lip is very deep rose-purple, with a white or yellowish base. Several forms have received varietal names, notably DOLOSA and SCHRÖDERIANA, but these, like the type, are now rarely seen in collections. Syn. *C. bulbosa*. *Orch. Alb.*, IV, t. 154; *Bot. Reg.*, 1847, t. 42.

OTHER SPECIES

Several other species are in cultivation although not often seen, as they have given place to hybrids, nevertheless growers who have not succumbed to the attractions of size will find interest and beauty in C. FORBESII, *Lindl.*, a dwarf, yellow-flowered species; C. FULVA, *Beer;* C. LUTEOLA, *Lindl.*, yellow; C. REX, *Linden*, a large and handsome species, with creamy-white sepals and petals and a crimson, gold-veined lip, but now rare in cultivation; and C. MAXIMA, *Lindl.*, with rosy sepals and petals and crimson-veined lip.

HYBRIDS

Very many hundreds of hybrid Cattleyas have been raised, consequently it is only possible to name a few of the most important from a horticultural point of view:—C. BALLANTINEANA (*C. Trianae* × *C. gigas); * C. BROWNIAE (*C. Bowringiana* × *C. Loddigesii); * C. CAPPEI (*C. Schröderae* × *C. Trianae); * C. CLOTHO (*C. Enid* × *C. Trianae); * C. DIETRICHIANA (*C. Hardyana* × *C. superba); * C. DUSSELDORFFII var. UNDINE (*C. intermedia var. alba* × *C. Mossiae var. Wagneri); * C. EMPRESS FREDERICK (*C. Dowiana* × *C. Mossiae); * C. FABIA (*C. Dowiana* × *C. labiata); * C. FLAVESCENS (*C. luteola* × *C. Trianae); * C. HARDYANA (*C. Dowiana* × *C. gigas);*

CATTLEYA OMAR VAR. SPLENDIDUM

C. IRIS (*C. bicolor* × *C. Dowiana*); C. LORD ROTHSCHILD (*C. Dowiana* × *C. Gaskelliana*); C. MAGGIE RAPHAEL (*C. Dowiana* × *C. Trianae*); C. MANTINII (*C. Bowringiana* × *C. Dowiana*); C. MARONAE (*C. Eldorado* × *C. labiata*); C. MINUCIA (*C. Loddigesii* × *C. gigas*); C. OCTAVE DOIN (*C. Dowiana* × *C. Mendelii*); C. OMAR (*C. Enid* × *C. Leda*); C. PORTIA (*C. Bowringiana* × *C. labiata*), very free-flowering; C. SNOWDON (*C. labiata var. alba* × *C. Suzanne Hye de Crom*); C. SUZANNE HYE DE CROM (*C. Gaskelliana var. alba* × *C. Mossiae var. Wagneri*); C. TITUS (*C. granulosa* × *C. Leopoldii*); C. TITYUS (*C. Enid* × *C. Octave Doin*); and C. WHITEI (*C. Warneri* × *C. Schilleriana*).

Certain hybrid Cattleyas may be grown into large specimens and are then magnificent when in flower. C. Portia is a particularly good example and one which can be confidently commended to amateurs who have sufficient accommodation. Mr. Humphris cultivates it successfully at Aynho Park near Banbury and one specimen produced thirty-six spikes and an aggregate of 214 flowers in the late Autumn of 1948. Most of the blooms from this and two other plants were sent to Covent Garden and realized £60. C. Mantinii and C. Fabia are also robust and free-flowering.

CHYSIS, *Lindley*

Tribe, Vandeae; sub-tribe, Bletieae

A small genus, founded by Lindley. The several species are deciduous and found in Mexico, Colombia, Venezuela and Peru. The fusiform, fleshy pseudo-bulbs are surmounted by a pair of curved leaves. Wide pans or baskets are the most desirable receptacles and the plants thrive best when suspended from the roof in an Intermediate House during the growing and flowering periods, but they find suitable accommodation at the coolest end of the Cattleya House while at rest, as they then need much less moisture than at other seasons.

The handsome, fleshy flowers are borne on rather short, somewhat pendulous racemes which emerge from the young growth in late Spring or early Summer. Although consisting of very attractive Orchids, the genus Chysis has never become particularly popular, probably because the racemes are short and the flowers are closely placed, in fact it just fails to be first-class. The compost generally used for warmth-loving epiphytes will suffice as a rooting medium, provided ample drainage is afforded.

C. BRACTESCENS, *Lindl.*—Probably the most popular species; it has white sepals and petals and a yellow and white lip. *Bot. Mag.,* t. 5186.

C. LIMMINGHII, *Lindl. et Rchb. f.*—One of the lesser species. The flowers are two inches broad, white, with a purple mark at the tips of the sepals and petals ; lip bright purple, with yellowish side lobes. *Bot. Mag.,* t. 5265 ; *Sel. Orch.,* I, t. 34.

HYBRIDS

C. CHELSONII.—A pretty hybrid raised at Messrs. Jas. Veitch & Sons' Nurseries, Chelsea. The parentage is *C. bractescens* × *C. laevis;* the lower halves of the sepals and petals are yellow, the upper halves reddish-brown; lip white, blotched with purple.

C. LANGLEYENSIS (*C. bractescens* × *C. Chelsonii*)*;* and C. SEDENII (*C. bractescens* × *C. Limminghii*), are hybrids raised in the Veitchian establishment.

CIRRHOPETALUM, *Lindley*

Tribe, Epidendreae; sub-tribe, Dendrobieae

This genus consists of lowly epiphytes, chiefly natives of Malaya and the East Indies. They have small, monophyllous pseudo-bulbs, and the inflorescence is umbellate, but frequently one-sided. The lateral sepals are prolonged into tails, and brought so closely together as to appear like one segment. They are delightful little Orchids, often brilliantly coloured, and well worth cultivation in an Intermediate House, in an Odontoglossum compost.

C. CUMINGII, *Lindl.*—Three or four inches tall, with a regular umbel of six to twelve purple flowers, the dorsal sepal having a fringe of long, dark hairs. *Bot. Mag.,* t. 4996.

C. FASCINATOR, *Rolfe*—A species from Annam, with long, green tails that are striped with purple; the petals are fringed with amethyst-purple appendages.

C. MEDUSAE, *Lindl.*—Flowers cream-coloured, spotted with yellow, the lateral sepals tapering to slender tails about four inches long. *Bot. Mag.,* t. 4977.

C. ORNATISSIMUM, *Rchb. f.*—A most attractive species, with rather large, long-tailed flowers, light yellow, striped and shaded with purple, in a few-flowered umbel. *Bot. Mag.,* t. 7229.

C. PICTURATUM, *Lindl.*—Umbels with eight or more green, red-spotted flowers; the dorsal sepal is thread-like; lateral sepals dull green. A pretty species. *Bot. Mag.*, t. 6802.

C. ROBUSTUM, *Rolfe*—A strong grower, often eighteen inches tall, with large flowers; sepals yellow, shaded with green and brown; petals long, tawny-brown.

C. THOUARSII, *Lindl.*—This has an umbel of eight to fifteen flowers that are not so "tailed" as in other species; tawny-yellow, with purple warts and wine-red stains; petals small and thread-like. *Bot. Mag.*, t. 4237; *Bot. Mag.* t. 7204 (*var. concolor*).

OTHER SPECIES

Among species of equal interest but of botanical rather than horticultural value, some of the most distinct are C. COLLETII (a specimen with nineteen inflorescences was exhibited in 1936); C. LONGISSIMUM, C. FARRERI, C. FIMBRIATUM, C. ROTHSCHILDEANUM, C. MINIATUM, a true miniature; C. REFRACTUM, with nodding flowers on a pendulous spike; and C. PULCHRUM, with a pendant inflorescence.

HYBRIDS

Several remarkably beautiful hybrids have been raised by Messrs. Sander; these have large umbels of large, long-tailed flowers, in which the colours are green, cream and crimson.

C. FASCINATION (*C. Fascinator* × *C. longissimum*); and C. LOUIS SANDER (*C. longissimum* × *C. ornatissimum*).

COCHLIODA, *Lindley*
Tribe, Vandeae; sub-tribe, Oncidieae

The few species of cool-house Orchids that make up Lindley's genus Cochlioda are all charming little plants, but C. NOEZLIANA is particularly beautiful, and famous as a partner in the production of the lovely bigeneric race of Odontiodas, the other genus concerned being Odontoglossum. All thrive under the conditions found successful for the latter genus. All are low-growing, evergreen, and hail from the uplands of Peru and Ecuador.

C. NOEZLIANA, *Rolfe*—An exquisitely lovely Orchid that produces arching spikes of small but brilliant orange-scarlet flowers, with a yellow disc on the neat lip. Introduced by the Messrs. Linden in 1891, from

Northern Peru. Frequently and erroneously listed as *C. Noetzliana. Bot. Mag.*, t. 7474.

C. ROSEA, *Benth.*—The rosy-carmine flowers, each with a very distinct white column, are smaller than those of *C. Noezliana.* Discovered by Hartweg and introduced in 1865. *Bot. Mag.*, t. 6084.

C. SANGUINEA, *Benth.*—Somewhat like the foregoing, but the flowers are rosy-pink, with a pale lip and a white column. Branched spikes are occasionally seen. Discovered about 1851, but not introduced until 1866. *Bot. Mag.*, t. 5627.

C. VULCANICA, *Benth.*—Spikes more erect than in the previous species; has dark rose-coloured flowers and a paler disc on the lip. Introduced from Ecuador in 1872. *Bot. Mag.*, t. 6001. The variety GRANDIFLORA has somewhat larger flowers and richer colouring.

COELOGYNE, *Lindley*

Tribe, Vandeae; sub-tribe, Coelogyneae

When Lindley founded the genus Coelogyne, so long ago as 1825, he was fortunate in having C. CRISTATA as his type. This lovely species is still one of the most popular of Orchids, but was even more popular years ago, when amateurs with only modest facilities had not the distractions created by hosts of hybrids in other genera. All species of Coelogyne are evergreen, and the majority are fascinating plants, varying considerably in size, the largest being C. PANDURATA, with its remarkably distinct green and black flowers.

The time for potting is when new roots are being produced; deep receptacles are undesirable, but plenty of drainage material is essential. Equal parts of Osmunda or peat fibre, and Sphagnum, with a modicum of coarse clean sand or finely broken crocks, combine to form a suitable rooting compost. As a general rule the species may be divided into those that require a moist atmosphere, and, as nearly as possible, tropical heat, and those that thrive best under quite temperate conditions.

Although evergreen, all Coelogynes need far less moisture during the dull months, and when they have completed their growth for the season. Moreover, if the compost is moderately moist when potting is done, very little root moisture will be needed until new roots have extended considerably, but light overhead sprayings are desirable during fine weather until the re-established plants need larger supplies of moisture.

C. ASPERATA, *Lindl.*—A floriferous species. The flowers are three inches broad, light yellow, with red-brown and orange markings on the lip. The drooping racemes may carry so many as a dozen flowers, and make a goodly display. C. ASPERATA is a native of Malaya, and is best grown in the warmest house, except during the Winter, when an intermediate temperature will suffice. *Orch. Alb.*, t. 311.

C. BARBATA, *Griff.*—This native of Assam, introduced in 1878–79, thrives with *C. cristata*, and is particularly useful as it blooms during the Winter, producing elegant flowers that are white, with a marginal fringe and crests of deep brown hairs. Seldom grows more than fifteen inches high. *Orch. Alb.*, t. 143.

C. CORRUGATA, *Lindl.*—About nine inches tall, this native of Southern India is one of the few species that has erect spikes. The flowers are fairly large, white, with a central yellow, orange-shaded area on the lip. The pseudo-bulbs are distinctly ribbed or corrugated, hence its name. *Bot. Mag.*, t. 5601.

C. CRISTATA, *Lindl.*—One of the easiest of Orchids to manage and flower successfully in late Winter or Spring. The pendulous racemes may carry so many as six or eight flowers, each three or four inches broad, and of the purest white, save for a crest and central area of yellow on the lip. The variety ALBA is wholly white, while C. C. VAR. LEMONIANA has pale yellow colouring on the lip. Small plants are charming, but large specimens, with a dozen or more racemes, are splendid. Unfortunately, the flowers bruise rather easily, and every bruise leaves a dark, disfiguring mark. Remember, also, not to cut the spikes too close to the base, as new growth arises from the sheathing base of the flower stem and is easily damaged. *Bot. Reg.*, 1841, t. 57; *Orch. Alb.*, t. 54 (*alba*).

C. DAYANA, *Rchb. f.*—One of the most remarkable and graceful of Orchids, as those who have seen a large specimen with a dozen or more pendulous racemes, each from two to three feet long, will admit. It does best in a pan or basket suspended from the roof in the warmest house. It has been called the Necklace Orchid, and this popular title is appropriate. The individual flowers, two inches or so in diameter, would not attract, but the dangling strings of two dozen or more produce a quietly beautiful effect. The colour is rather dull yellow, with lines of chocolate-brown, and a blotch of similar colour on the yellowish or

whitish lip. A grand specimen of this Bornean species exhibited by
Baron Sir Henry Schröder at one of the last of the Temple Shows remains
as a very happy memory in the minds of all who saw it. *Orch. Alb.*, t. 247.

C. MASSANGEANA, *Rchb. f.*—If *C. Dayana* were non-existent then C.
MASSANGEANA would be regarded as remarkable. It has a similar habit of
growth and long, pendulous racemes of medium-sized, light yellow
flowers, in which the brown lip has a white edging and veinings and crests
of bright yellow. Unfortunately, C. MASSANGEANA is not so robust as its
near relative, and not so frequently seen in first-rate condition; it may be
grown in an intermediate temperature. *Bot. Mag.*, t. 6979.

C. OCELLATA, *Lindl.*—A very pretty and altogether charming species
from the Khasia Hills. It succeeds if grown with the Odontoglossums
during Spring, Summer and Autumn, but should be wintered where the
conditions approximate to those of the Cattleya house. Of modest size,
the flowers are notable for the two yellow, orange-circled spots, and a
brown throat on the lip; otherwise the colour is clear white. The spikes
are semi-erect. The variety MAXIMA differs from the type in having
larger flowers—three inches across—that are sweetly scented. *Bot.
Mag.*, t. 3767.

C. PANDURATA, *Lindl.*—As this very striking Orchid is found in the
hot and moist districts of Borneo, it must be grown in the warmest house
throughout the year. The oval, compressed pseudo-bulbs are set widely
apart on a stout rhizome, consequently it should be placed in an
elongated basket or raft, where the atmosphere is continuously moist,
but a trifle less moist during the dull months of the year. The rooting
medium should consist very largely of Sphagnum and crocks, to which
a little Osmunda fibre may be added, all so arranged that water supplied
to the roots may pass through freely. Moreover, the broad, petiolate
leaves may be two feet tall, therefore, C. PANDURATA is certainly not a
plant for a small, low-roofed house. The long, almost horizontal spikes
are semi-pendant at their ends. On these, the large flowers are un-
crowded, and there may be half a dozen or more on each spike. The
combination of colouring is very unusual, even among Orchids; each
flower may be four or five inches broad, with green sepals and petals
and a yellowish-green lip that is heavily veined and blotched with black.
The best specimen known to the author was grown suspended over a
tank of warm water; the raft was extended to accommodate the new

COELOGYNE INTERMEDIA

COELOGYNE MASSANGEANA

growth, one or two old bulbs being cut out and the raft shortened at the back. C. PANDURATA does not take kindly to root disturbance. *Bot. Mag.*, t. 5084.

C. MOOREANA, *Rolfe*—Certainly one of the easiest of Coelogynes to manage under cultivation; while in flower it may be used to adorn the drawing room, and will not resent such conditions provided the roots are kept reasonably moist. Free of growth, and particularly free in the production of flowers, a plant in a forty-eight-sized pot will send up several erect spikes of fair-sized blooms that are white, except for the bright yellow throat and centre of the lip. C. MOOREANA is one of the best of Orchids wherewith to start a modest collection. The warmest end of the Cool House will suit it, with slightly warmer conditions in the Winter. This useful Orchid was discovered by Micholitz in Annam, about 1905, and has become very popular.

C. SPECIOSA, *Lindl.*—This neat Orchid may be grown with *C. cristata*, and is a desirable species for amateurs who have small Orchid houses. Seldom above nine inches tall, it produces short, erect spikes that carry a pair of large flowers which have narrow, buff-green, rather translucent sepals and petals, and a big, yellowish lip that is freely marked and crested with bright crimson-brown, but has a white apex. *Bot. Mag.*, t. 4889.

OTHER SPECIES

All the foregoing species are worthy of cultivation, but plant lovers may also find interest and beauty in C. CUMINGII, C. ELATA, C. FULIGINOSA, C. FUSCESCENS, C. FLACCIDA, C. OCHRACEA, C. SANDERAE, C. TOMENTOSA and C. VEITCHII.

HYBRIDS

About half a dozen or more hybrids have been raised by crossing some of the best species, and one of the earliest to appear was C. COLMANII (*C. cristata var. alba* × *C. speciosa var. major*), raised by Sir Jeremiah Colman and flowered in 1907. In this, as in the bolder C. INTERMEDIA (*C. cristata* × *C. Massangeana*) that appeared in 1913, the influence of *C. cristata* is very marked. C. ALBANENSE (*C. pandurata* × *C. Sanderiana*) was raised by Messrs. Sander and flowered in 1913. C. SANDERIANA (*C. pandurata* × *C. albanense*), was also raised at St. Albans. C. BRYMERIANA (*C. asperata* × *C. Dayana*), and C. BURFORDIENSE

G

(*C. asperata* × *C. pandurata*) have had their admirers and the latter is frequently seen.

CYMBIDIUM, *Swartz*
Tribe, *Vandeae; sub-tribe, Cymbidieae*

The present popularity of Cymbidiums has been created by the hybridist, for, with the exception of Cypripedium, no genus includes so many Orchids of horticultural merit. There are comparatively few species, and these are all Cool House Orchids, although C. ERYTHROSTYLUM and C. GRANDIFLORUM need rather more warmth when making their growths and during the Winter. The size and long-lasting qualities of the flowers made the species popular long before Mr. H. G. Alexander began to raise hybrids. He had charge of Sir George Holford's collection at Westonbirt, Tetbury, Gloucestershire, and received every encouragement from his employer, with the result that C. ALEXANDERI appeared in 1911; this was the progeny of *C. eburneo-Lowianum* × *C. insigne*, and it opened the way to a multitude of crosses and combinations and bewildering colour variations, all beautiful. C. INSIGNE was the key with which Mr. Alexander opened the treasure house and by far the greater number of the hybrids that give so much pleasure during the early months of the year claim descent from C. INSIGNE, C. LOWIANUM and C. EBURNEUM.

Cymbidiums will withstand a lower Winter temperature than most Orchids; they may not appreciate so low a figure, but if they are grown where the thermometer registers not less than 40° in the severest weather, they will receive no harm, provided they are kept rather dry at the roots, with a moderately dry atmosphere, during such cold conditions.

The potting materials for these robust Orchids must be of a somewhat more substantial character than for most other kinds—more Osmunda fibre and loam fibre and less Sphagnum. Free drainage is essential, as an abundance of water is needed when growth and root activity are at their peak. A free use of the syringe is desirable while growth is vigorous but when the pseudo-bulbs have completed their development, rather drier conditions are suitable. So soon as flower spikes begin to appear more water, in reason, will be needed to meet the increasing demands upon the roots. There may be anything from four to twenty flowers on a spike, therefore it is a mistake to allow the spikes to remain on the plant until the flowers fade; fortunately, Cymbidium flowers last a very long time when cut and placed in water. Moreover, carefully packed, they travel well and are of substantial texture, hence their great popularity with florists. After the removal of the spikes, a brief period of rest, with less water at the roots, seems necessary, but the plants must be watched for the first signs of renewed activity, so that potting may be done as early as possible to ensure a long season of growth during the best climatic conditions. Some hybrids are less robust than others and must be treated accordingly, but, on the whole, these modern Cymbidiums are easy to manage and among the very best of Orchids for an inexperienced amateur to cultivate.

C. CANALICULATUM, *R. Brown*—A rather low-growing species with a pendulous raceme of small flowers, brown and green colouring on the sepals and petals, and a white, pink-marked lip. Somewhat rare in cultivation. Discovered by Robert Brown in north-east Australia between 1802 and 1804. Introduced by J. Veitch about 1865.*Bot. Mag.*, t. 5851.

C. CHLORANTHUM, *Lindl.*—Seldom seen in cultivation, this species is closely allied to *C. canaliculatum*, but grows taller. It has more or less erect spikes, and yellowish-green flowers, with a red, pale yellow, red-spotted lip. *Bot. Mag.*, t. 4907.

C. DEVONIANUM, *Lindl.*—This species, discovered by Gibson on the Khasia Hills about 1836, is "obscurely pseudo-bulbous", with leaves seldom a foot tall, and has a pendulous raceme of flowers that are rather more than an inch broad. The colour is variable, but usually buff or olive-green, with purplish markings, while the prominent lip is reddish-purple or rose-purple. Paxton's *Mag. Bot.*, X. 97; *Bot. Mag.*, t. 9327.

C. EBURNEUM, *Lindl.*—A beautiful Orchid from the Khasia Hills, found by W. Griffith in 1837. Growth erect, pseudo-bulbs seldom prominent, may produce so many as a dozen leaves on one growth. The sturdy spike rarely produces more than two flowers, but these are large, widely expanded, ivory-white, except for a few spots of purple on the lip, and sweetly fragrant. *Bot. Man.*, t. 5126.

The variety DAYI, *Jennings*, has large flowers, while the variety PARISHII, *Hook.*, has an orange-yellow central area on the purple-spotted lip.

C. FINLAYSONIANUM, *Lindl.*—Discovered by Finlayson in Cochin China. The pendulous raceme may carry many smallish, tawny-yellow flowers, with a reddish lip that has a white, purple-marked central lobe. *Bot. Reg.*, 1846, t. 25 (as *C. pendulum*).

The variety ATROPURPUREUM, *Lindl.*, from Borneo, has larger flowers of rich maroon-purple colour, with a white, purple-spotted lip. Introduced about 1852. *Bot. Mag.*, t. 5710.

C. GIGANTEUM, *Lindl.*—A handsome species discovered by Wallich, in 1821, on the Khasia Hills. The prominent pseudo-bulbs are compressed and the leaves may be fully thirty inches long. The robust, arched racemes carry large flowers in which the light yellow-green sepals and petals are striped with red, while the lip is of similar colour, and has a yellow, red-spotted central lobe. A most effective Orchid when grown well. *Bot. Mag.*, t. 4844.

C. INSIGNE, *Rolfe*—A beautiful and robust species, with tall, erect spikes, up to four feet tall, which may have so many as a dozen flowers, each four inches across. The colour is variable and may be white, pink, or soft rose, but the sepals and petals have red spots at their bases; the broad lip is of similar, or darker, colour, with bright crimson markings. A superb Orchid that likes slightly more warmth than the majority of hybrids derived from it in association with *C. Lowianum* and *C. eburneum*. C. INSIGNE was found in Annam in 1901 and its introduction by Messrs. Sanders caused great excitement among Orchid lovers, while its use as a parent produced hybrids of great beauty and usefulness. *Bot. Mag. t.*, 8312.

C. LOWIANUM, *Rchb. f.*—Few Orchids have gained such swift popularity, and maintained it, as C. LOWIANUM, collected by Boxall in 1877, in Burma; it flowered at Messrs. Low's Nursery at Clapton in 1879 and was probably Boxall's most important discovery. A fine, easily grown Orchid, C. LOWIANUM has been cultivated in many mixed collections of plants for upwards of half a century. It is a robust species, with large flowers in which the sepals and petals are yellowish-green, with reddish veins, while the lip has light yellow side lobes, and a very prominent, rich brownish-red, or crimson, apex that is margined narrowly with soft yellow; the white area behind the deep colour provides a striking contrast. The pendulous racemes may be a yard long and bear so many as two dozen flowers that are nicely spaced. Two spikes that had been exhibited throughout one of the earlier Chelsea Shows were cut, taken home, and placed in water, in weighted vessels, so that they hung down

CYPRIPEDIUM CLARE DE LUNE

from the mantelpiece, where their flowers lasted in good condition for a month. A grand exhibition plant, that may be grown into a large specimen carrying several spikes. *Reichenbachia*, 2nd Ser., II, t. 53; *Orch. Alb.* X, t. 471.

C. PARISHII, *Rchb. f.*—This handsome species, from Moulmein, is somewhat like *C. eburneum* and has erect spikes of two or three sweetly-scented flowers, in which the sepals and petals are cream-white, with a white lip that has an orange centre and some purplish spots, and an orange apex. It flowers in late Summer and early Autumn. *Orch. Alb.,* I, t. 25.

C. TIGRINUM, *Parish*—Discovered in Tenasserim in 1863, by the Rev. C. S. Parish, this distinct species is now rarely seen in cultivation. The semi-erect, slender spikes carry few flowers and these have olive-green sepals and petals, spotted with red at their bases; the lip has yellow side lobes, striped with reddish-brown, while the central lobe is marked with purple-brown on a white ground. *Bot. Mag.*, t. 5457.

C. TRACYANUM, *Hort.*—An interesting and showy Orchid closely allied to *C. giganteum*, but the original plant was purchased at a sale of *C. Lowianum*, about 1888, by Mr. A. H. Tracy, of Twickenham, in whose nursery it flowered in 1890. The long, arching racemes bear from a dozen to twenty flowers of large size, greenish-yellow, with numerous broken longitudinal lines of deep crimson; lip creamy-white, with crimson spots and a broadly fringed margin. A very attractive but rather rare Orchid. *Lindenia*, t. 514.

OTHER SPECIES

Species of less horticultural value include C. MADIDUM, *Lindl* (*Bot. Reg.*, 1840); C. PENDULUM, *Swartz* (*Bot. Mag.*, t. 337, as *C. aloifolium*); C. AFFINE, *Griffith* (*Orch. Alb.*, III, t. 140); C. (CYPERORCHIS) ELEGANS, *Lindl.* (*Bot. Mag.*, t. 7007); C. HUMBLOTII, *Rolfe;* C. (CYPERORCHIS) MASTERSII, *Griffith* (*Bot. Reg.*), 1845, t. 50; C. HOOKERIANUM, *Rchb. fil.* (*Bot Mag.*, t. 5574) is now regarded as synonymous with *C. giganteum*.

HYBRIDS

Growers with little knowledge of hybrid Cymbidiums should find those listed eminently useful in assisting them in making a selection or creating a collection.

White.—C. Alexanderi (*C. eburneo-Lowianum* × *C. insigne*); C. Balkis (*C. Alexanderi* × *C. Rosanna*); C. Dorchester (*C. Alexanderi* × *C. Tityus*); C. Gabriel (*C. Olympus* × *C. Flamenco*); C. Jungfrau (*C. Alexanderi* × *C. Eagle*); and C. Queen Elizabeth (*C. Olympus* × *C. Flamingo*).

Blush or Pale Rose.—C. Cassandra (*C. Alexanderi* × *C. Goosander*); C. Corisande (*C. Rosanna* × *C. insigne*); C. Cornelia (*C. Charmian* × *C. Nancy Harte*), C. Gloriana (*C. Ceres* × *C. Flamingo*); C. Janette (*C. Alexanderi* × *C. Joy Sander*); and C. Rosalita (*C. insigne* × *C. Delysia*).

Deep Rose.—C. Babylon (*C. Olympus* × *C. Pauwelsii*); C. Ceres (*C. insigne* × *C. l'Ansonii*); C. delysia (*C. Petrel* × *C. Ceres*); C. rosa-mundi (*C. Flamingo* × *C. Delysia*); C. sunrise (*C. Ceres* × *C. Swallow*); and C. Susette (*C. insigne* × *C. Majali Sander*).

Green.—C. Adelma (*C. Lowio-grandiflorum* × *C. Letty*); C. irina (*C. Adastra* × *C. Adelma*); C. Jacqueline (*C. Curlew* × *C. Erica Sander*); C. Lowio-grandiflorum (*C. Lowianum* × *C. grandiflorum*); C. Melisande (*C. Curlew* × *C. Erica Sander*); and C. Miretta (*C. Claudette* × *C. Mirabel*).

Yellow and Golden-Green.—C. Aton (*C. Baldur* × *C. Pearl*); C. Esmeralda (*C. Lowianum* × *C. Venus*); C. Hawfinch (*C. Alexanderi* × *C. Bustard*); C. Pharos (*C. Flamingo* × *C. Warbler*); C. Swallow (*C. Pauwelsii* × *C. Alexanderi*); and C. Syrinx (*C. Goldfinch* × *C. Ophir*).

Red and Bronze.—C. Beau Brummel (*C. Althea* × *C. Ceres*); C. Candace (*C. Pocahontas* × *C. Carisbrook*); C. Carisbrook (*C. Ceres* × *C. Ralph Sander*); C. Joyful (*C. Joy Sander* × *C. Ceres*); C. Perseus (*C. Toucan* × *C. Pearl*); and C. Pocahontas (*C. Toucan* × *C. Pearl*).

A few other hybrids of high quality are C. Bodmin Moor (*C. Alexanderi, Westonbirt var.* × *Erica Sander*); C. Pearl (*C. Alexanderi* × *C. grandiflorum*) and its variety magnifieum; C. Rio-Rita (*C. Pearl var. magnificum* × *C. Ruby*); C. Erica Sander (*C. grandiflorum* × *C. Pauwelsii*); C. Baldur (*C. Alexanderi* × *C. Castor*); C. Joy Sander (*C. Pauwelsii* × *C. Ceres*); C. Icarus (*C. Apollo* × *C. Pauwelsii*); C. Swallow (*C. Alexanderi* × *C. Pauwelsii*); C. Pauwelsii (*C. insigne* × *C. Lowianum*); C. Gottianum (*C. eburneum* × *C. insigne*); C. Golden Oriole (*C. Plover* × *C. Woodhamsianum*); C. Carisbrook (*C. Ceres* × *C. Ralph Sander*); C. Gold Mohur (*C. Beryl* × *C. Martin*), and its variety

CATHAY ; the very handsome C. GENERAL MONTGOMERY (*C. Dorchester* × *C. Olympus*); and C. CREMONA (*C. Cooperi* × *C. Elfin*).

CYPRIPEDIUM, *Linnaeus*.

Tribe Cypripedieae

Over a very long period Cypripediums have been among the most popular of Orchids and this popularity is due to the winter-flowering habit of the majority and to the long-lasting quality of all the flowers. Even when hybrids were few in number and the big-flowered, rounded flowers of so many modern and fashionable hybrids were entirely unknown, it was quite the usual thing to find good batches of CYPRIPEDIUM INSIGNE and C. LEEANUM in every garden where glasshouse accommodation could be found. With a few exceptions, Cypripediums need a moist, warm atmosphere, for, although C. INSIGNE can be grown as a Cool House subject, it produces more and better flowers under somewhat warmer conditions.

The C. Maudiae group, and others with mottled leaves, are distinctly Warm House subjects, although not needing the high temperature of a Tropical House. The few species of the C. BELLATULUM group like more sunshine than the others, but, on the whole, Cypripediums are a shade-loving race.

The potting compost may consist of fibrous loam, with a little Osmunda fibre—especially for the weaker growers—a modest amount of Sphagnum moss and sharp, not fine, sand. Firm potting is desirable and the base of a plant should be so placed that it is raised as high, or a trifle higher, than the rim of the pot or pan, but the surface compost should be so arranged that it slopes down to just below the rim, thus making for ease in watering. Good drainage is essential, as established plants in full growth need plenty of water. When growth is completed for the season somewhat less water is desirable until the flower buds appear in the centre of the season's growth, and then more water must be given, otherwise the flower stems will be short and the flowers of big hybrids will not develop properly.

When the plants have been relieved of their flowers a reduced water supply will ensure a brief season of rest until new growths appear, root activity recommences, and it is time to re-pot—Cypripediums must never be allowed to become dry at the roots but, obviously the supply of water must accord with the season and the condition of the plants. If the compost is moist, but not sticky, at potting time, no water will be needed for a week or two, provided there is abundance of atmospheric moisture and an overhead spraying is given on favourable days. There is no doubt that Winter-flowering Cypripediums should have as long a season of growth as possible, hence early re-potting is essential to secure a good display of flowers.

Cypripediums, so generally recognised by the inflated, pouched, slipper-like lip, are probably the most primitive of Orchids, and, with the exception of one or two hardy species from Canada and the northern United States, are distributed throughout the eastern parts of the Old World. With the exceptions cited, there are no Cypripediums in America, but the family is represented in South America by the closely allied Selenipediums.

Species of Cypripedium may be intercrossed fairly readily, while germination and the raising of seedlings offer no difficulties to a careful grower, consequently hybrids are numerous. Moreover, the intercrossing of hybrids and their progeny has resulted in the production of well-nigh innumerable forms, the majority adding considerably to the flowers available during Winter, and in a great variety of colours, but chiefly green, white, yellow, brown, purple and red-purple. It is a pity that modern raisers concentrate so much on the production of large and rounded flowers, and much less on that elongation of stem which is so desirable in a cut flower.

One of the latest and most successful groups consists of hybrids with C. INSIGNE and C. NIVEUM in their parentage; these are long-stemmed and the flowers are white, or creamy-white. Most of these have been raised at Lord Aberconway's gardens at Bodnant, by Mr. F. C. Puddle, his gardener. Messrs. Black & Flory, Messrs. H. G. Alexander, Ltd., Messrs. Armstrong and Brown and the late Mr. George Moore, have all taken a large part in raising and popularizing hybrid Cypripediums.

C. ARGUS, *Rchb. f.*—Found by Gustav Wallis in 1872, in the Philippines, this species is not popular with present-day growers. The broad, short leaves are spotted with dark green ; the dorsal sepal is white, with vertical lines of green, and ciliate margins; petals white, with green veins, but purple towards the tips, and bearing numerous blackish

CYMBIDIUM BALDUR

CYMBIDIUM GENERAL MONTGOMERY

CYPRIPEDIUM GIGAS CORNDEAN HALL

CYPRIPEDIUM JOYCE RUCK

warts; lip brownish-purple, shaded with brown and spotted with rich purple. *Bot. Mag.*, t. 6175.

C. BARBATUM, *Lindl.*—A species found in the Malay Peninsula by Cuming, in 1840. The flowers are finely poised on tall stems. The dorsal sepal is white, shaded with green at the base, and marked vertically with branching or feathered lines of deep-purple; petals green, brown and purple, with tiny warts and hairs along the margins, especially on the upper edges; lip shapely, brownish-purple. *Bot. Mag.*, t. 4234; *Bot. Reg.*, 1842, t. 17.

Several varieties have been recorded, notably CROSSII, GRANDE, LATESEPALUM, NIGRUM and SUPERBUM.

C. BELLATULUM, *Rchb. f.*—A particularly striking species, of squat habit, with large, roundish flowers borne on short stems. A native of Malacca and introduced by Messrs. Low & Co. in 1888. The dorsal sepal and petals are fleshy, slightly cupped, white, or cream-white, more or less heavily spotted with blackish-purple. Lip, comparatively small, rather egg-shaped, and with a smaller aperture than in most other species; white or cream-white, lightly spotted with blackish-purple. *Lindenia*, IV, t. 149.

The variety ALBUM created quite a sensation when exhibited by Sir Frederick Wigan in 1895. The flowers are pure, unspotted white. Discovered by Mr. R. Moore, but the plant shown by Sir Frederick was one among a small consignment of the type sent home by C. Curtis.

The finest form of the type is EXHIM'S VAR.; HARDY'S VAR. and ROSEUM have been recorded.

C. CALLOSUM, *Rchb. f.*—A species that still retains its popularity, as the large flowers are borne on tall stems and the bold dorsal sepal is white, with vertical veins that are green at the base and gradually merge into bright wine-red as they ascend. The out-spread petals are slightly deflexed, green, shading to rose-purple at the tips; lip brown-purple on a greenish base, with dark purple spots on the infolding side lobes. Discovered in Cochin China by Regnier, about 1885. A handsome Cypripedium. VAR. SANDERAE is a very beautiful form, mostly green and white. *Orchidophile*, VIII, p. 145.

C. CHARLESWORTHII, *Rolfe*—In the Autumn of 1893 Messrs. Charlesworth, Shuttleworth & Co., Heaton, Bradford, created a sensation in the Orchid world when they exhibited an entirely new Burmese species which Mr. Rolfe named in compliment to Mr. Charlesworth. The new-comer was not only recognized as a very fine Cypripedium but raisers regarded it as the potential parent of a new race of hybrids. The leaves and general habit are not unlike those of *C. insigne*, but the flower stem is shorter. The flower has a broad, orbicular dorsal sepal that is slightly hooded at the tip, of deep rose colour, finely veined with a deeper shade. The slightly deflexed petals have blunt tips and are brownish-yellow, veined with brown; lip broad, dull yellow, shaded with brown and some-times with a rosy tint. Not long after this Charlesworthian introduction two other firms received importations and Messrs. Low & Co. offered five hundred plants for sale by auction, therefore C. CHARLESWORTHII soon became distributed throughout private and commercial collections. At present, unfortunately, the species is not frequently seen. *The Orchid Review* gave a coloured illustration as a frontispiece to its first volume (1893). *Bot. Mag.*, t. 7416.

C. CILIOLARE, *Rchb. f.*—Discovered in the Philippines, in 1882, this is a distinctly handsome species that raises its large flowers, on foot-long stems, above leaves that are tessellated with two shades of green. The broad dorsal sepal is white, with a purple base and closely-placed green veins; there are hairs on the margins. Petals green, with purple apices, black hairs on the margins, and black warts on the basal portions. Lip bold, purple-brown, with black spots on the yellowish side lobes. Not often seen, but well worthy of attention. *Illus. Hort.*, 1884, t. 530.

C. CONCOLOR, *Parish*—A variable and small-flowered species dis-covered by Rev. C. Parish, in 1859, in the Moulmein district. It belongs to the *niveum-bellatulum* group and, like its kin, seems to thrive best when the drainage consists chiefly of limestone, with small pieces worked into the compost. The short leaves are green, mottled with grey-green, and have purple-shaded undersides. The short-stemmed, yellowish flowers are speckled with purple; the small lip is of similar colouring and has a small orifice. Somewhat rare in cultivation. Several varieties have been recorded: CHLOROPHYLLUM, pale in colour; REGNIERI, rather deep-er in colour and often with two or three flowers on a stem; and TON-QUINENSE, with broader sepal and petals and a closer aggregation of spots. *Bot. Mag.*, t. 5513; *Orch. Alb.*, VII, t. 302.

C. CURTISII, *Rchb. f.*—A species with large, well-proportioned flowers, on tall stems. Found in Sumatra, in 1882, by C. Curtis and introduced by the Messrs. Veitch. The dorsal sepal has a green centre, surrounded by a wide white band, and veined with green and purple brown; petals deflexed, purplish, spotted with purple, veined with green and narrowly edged with dull white; lip large, brownish-purple. An easily grown Orchid that needs Warm House treatment. *Orch. Alb.*, III, t. 122.

The very fine albino variety SANDERAE is a pretty companion for the type.

C. DAYANUM, *Rchb. f.*—Never abundant, this native of north-east Borneo is now rare in cultivation. The white, green-veined dorsal sepal is attractive; petals dark green on the inner halves and dull purple on the outer; lip purple-brown, veined with green and spotted with purple on the side lobes. *Xen. Orch.*, III, t. 201.

C. DRURII, *Beddome*—A very distinct species, found in Travancore in 1865. The dorsal sepal and the petals are curved inwards and each segment has a central and conspicuous band of blackish purple. The ground colour of the dorsal sepal is greenish-yellow, but the petals are of a brighter, more golden shade. Lip rounded, bright yellow. *Illus. Hort.*, 1877, t. 265; *Fl. Mag.*, t. 425.

C. FAIRIEANUM, *Lindl.*—A real gem and although the flowers are small, they invariably attract attention by their ballet-girl grace. A native of Assam, some mystery surrounded its first introduction, but a flowering plant was exhibited in London in 1857 by Mr. Fairie, of Aigburth, Liverpool, after whom it was named by Dr. Lindley. It has green foliage and the slender stem carries an elegant flower of modest size. The dorsal sepal is oval, with subdued undulations along the margins; the ground colour is white, but there is a basal stain of green, the whole veined and pencilled with purple. The petals curve upwards at the tips, like an old-time moustache, or suggesting an elegant ballet-girl daintily lifting her skirt; the undulate margins are purple, fringed with hairs, and the colour scheme is pale yellow, with thin veins of purple. Lip rather elongated and displaying the infolded side lobes; dull green with subdued purple reticulations. In the early years of its introduction, and while still rare, many plants succumbed to the hot conditions of a Stove House, but later generations of growers have found it succeeds in an intermediate temperature. This beautiful species is often labelled C. FAIRREAEANUM, but Veitch, Lindley, Hooker and Van Houtte all spelt the name as cited at the head of this note. *Bot. Mag.*, t. 5024; *Orch. Alb.*, II, t. 70.

C. GODEFROYAE, *Godefroy*—This interesting and beautiful species has an interesting history. It appears to have been discovered by Murton, who was previously employed at Kew, and the plants he collected were purchased by M. Godefroy of Argenteuil, France. Unfortunately, Murton died before his plants could be despatched, so another Englishman, Mr. Alabaster, then superintendent of the public gardens at Bangkok, took charge of them; but he was taken ill and the plants died. Later, Alabaster obtained more plants, most of which were sent to M. Godefroy and a few to Kew. A lime-lover, C. GODEFROYAE has mottled green leaves that are spotted with purple on the reverse surface. The stems are rarely more than three inches long and usually bear one flower which is from two to three inches in breadth, with dull white or yellowish sepal and petals, freely spotted with reddish-purple. The lip is similarly coloured but the markings are minutely speckled. The sepals and petals are spreading and not cupped, as in C. *bellatulum*. C. GODEFROYAE is rare in cultivation. The variety LEUCOCHILUM has a white, unspotted lip. *Orch. Alb.*, IV, t. 177; *Bot. Mag.*, t. 6876.

C. HIRSUTISSIMUM, *Lindl.*—Found on the Assam side of the Khasia Hills and introduced about 1857. The flowers do not conform to modern standards, but they are attractive, four inches wide, carried on tall, purple-haired stems. The dorsal sepal is distinctly keeled, pale-green, with a darker green centre and base, and veins of purple. The outspread petals have undulate margins and are twisted towards the ends, green, spotted with purple and furnished with blackish hairs. This species always commands attention when in flower. *Bot. Mag.*, t. 4990; *Sel. Orch.*, I, t. 15.

C. INSIGNE, *Wallich*—Few Orchids have maintained their popularity so long as this native of north-east India, where it was discovered by Dr. Wallich, who sent it to England in 1819, where it first flowered the following year in the Liverpool Botanic Garden. It is variable in colour but always easily recognized; in good forms the ten-inch stems carry one flower (occasionally two), that is three or four inches broad. The bold dorsal sepal has a light-green central and basal area, and a white apical portion, the whole more or less prominently spotted with purple-brown, although in some forms the spots are pale violet on the white portion. Petals light Apple-green, with brownish or purplish veins. Lip light green, often yellowish-green, shaded with brown. Probably no species is grown

CYPRIPEDIUM HARMACHIS VAR. GOLDEN RADIANCE

so extensively for the special purpose of providing cut flowers for the market during the early Winter. Easily grown under fairly cool conditions, it is cultivated in almost every collection of indoor plants, even where Orchids are not a speciality. *Orch. Alb.*, IV, t. 155; *Bot. Mag.*, t. 3412.

Many varieties have been recorded, notably MAULEI, PUNCTATUM-VIOLACEUM, and the very large HAREFIELD HALL var., over which there was a celebrated lawsuit many years ago, but the most distinct and beautiful form is SANDERAE, which occurred as a single plant in a large importation of C. INSIGNE flowered at Messrs. Sanders' nursery, St. Albans. So far as is known, all the thousands of plants in cultivation are direct descendants of this solitary specimen. It has bright greenish-gold flowers, with a broad, white area on the upper part of the dorsal sepal. The variety SANDERIANA is somewhat similar but by no means so popular as SANDERAE.

C. LAWRENCEANUM, *Rchb. f.*—A bold and attractive Orchid discovered by F. W. Burbidge in North Borneo in 1878. The large, widespread flowers may be five inches across and the outstanding feature is the fine white dorsal sepal, with broad vertical lines of reddish-purple, alternately long and short. The green, purple-shaded petals are dotted with hairy, blackish warts along both ciliate margins. Lip fully pouched, purplish, shaded with brown. *Orch. Alb.*, I, t. 22 ; *Bot. Mag.*, t. 6432.

The variety HYEANUM, *Rchb. f.*, is an albino that is always very much admired.

C. NIVEUM, *Rchb. f.*—A delightful and dainty species with mottled leaves and roundish flowers, about three inches broad. The white dorsal sepal and petals are "dusted" with purple dots, the former slightly concave, and stained at the back with purple. Found in the Lankowi Islands, where it was collected by Curtis and Förstermann, growing on limestone hills. *Bot. Mag.*, t. 5922; *Reichenbachia*, I, t. 34.

The finest form of C. NIVEUM is the variety GOLIATH, which has larger, purer white flowers on taller stems.

C. PHILIPPINENSE, *Rchb. f.*—A distinct species found in the Philippines by J. G. VEITCH, in 1864. Not often seen in cultivation. The dorsal and ventral sepals are much alike, ovate and pointed, white, with broad, purple-brown lines. Petals narrow, pendulous, twisted, yellowish at the bases, then purplish, and green at the tips; lip buff-yellow, faintly veined with brown. *Bot. Mag.*, t. 5508.

C. PURPURATUM, *Lindl.*—A native of Hong Kong and introduced in 1836. The orbicular dorsal sepal is white, stained with green in the centre and prominently striped with purplish-brown. Petals spreading, reddish-purple, veined with green and with some black warts at the bases. Very handsome when well-grown. *Bot. Reg.*, XXIII, t. 1991; *Bot. Mag.*, t. 4901.

C. ROTHSCHILDIANUM, *Rchb. f.*—Introduced from New Guinea, this remarkable species commemorates Baron F. de Rothschild. The tall stems rise above long foliage and may carry two or three large flowers. The dorsal sepal is yellow, shaded with white and striped with blackish-purple. Petals wide-spread, greenish-yellow, with dark lines and blotches; lip scoop-shaped, pointing forward, reddish-brown, with a yellow-edged rim. *Bot. Mag.*, t. 7102; *Reichenbachia*, II, t. 61.

C. SANDERIANUM, *Rchb. f.*—Collected by Förstermann in 1885, in the Malayan islands. Remarkable for the length—sometimes two feet—of its narrow, pendulous, yellowish, purple-spotted petals. Sepals concave, pointed, greenish-yellow, striped with brown; lip distinctly shoe-shaped, purplish above, greenish-yellow beneath. *Reichenbachia*, I, t. 3.

C. SPICERIANUM, *Rchb. f.*—A very pretty and useful species, from Assam. The very broad dorsal sepal is pure white except for a greenish base and a central vertical band of reddish-purple. Petals deflexed, rather short, yellowish-green, with speckles and central line of red. Very free-flowering. *Orch. Alb.*, III, t. 119; *Bot. Mag.*, t. 6490.

C. STONEI, *Hook.*—Another remarkable species with large flowers borne on tall stems. Dorsal sepal white, softly marked with dark red; petals long, decurved, narrow, pendulous, tawny-yellow, shading to reddish-brown at the tips, and dotted sparingly with red-brown. Lip pointed forward, rose, reticulately veined with crimson. Always a rare plant. *Bot. Mag.*, t. 5349; *Orch. Alb.*, I, t. 8.

The variety PLATYTAENIUM, *Reich.*, has larger and more brightly coloured flowers. Very rare. *Sel. Orch.*, III, t. 14.

C. SUPERBIENS, *Rchb. f.*—This Malayan species has bold flowers in which the ovate, pointed dorsal sepal is white, lined and veined with green; petals deflexed, white, veined with green, spotted with black and with hairy margins. Lip deeply pouched, purplish-brown, and faintly veined with a darker shade. Was formerly confused with *C. barbatum*. *Sel. Orch.*, II, t. 12.

C. VENUSTUM, *Wallich.*—Discovered in Sylhet by Dr. Wallich. The rather small flowers have a white, green-veined dorsal sepal, and green and purple petals with black spots; lip greenish-yellow, shaded with rose and veined with green. *Bot. Mag.*, t. 788; *Bot. Reg.*, t. 788.

C. VILLOSUM, *Lindl.*—A very popular species in earlier years, easily grown and one that was a parent of numerous primary hybrids. Found by Thomas Lobb, about 1852, in Moulmein. The dorsal sepal is green, purple at the base and centre and white at the apex; the lower margins are recurved, giving the sepal a constricted appearance: petals broadly spoon-shaped, brownish-yellow, curved forward, and with ciliate margins. Lip shapely, yellowish, shaded with brown and rimmed with yellow. The flowers are beautifully burnished. *Fl. des Serres*, XIV, t. 1475.

The variety BOXALLII discovered by Boxall, has brighter and deeper colouring; AUREUM has much more yellow in its make-up.

OTHER SPECIES

Other species include C. EXUL, C. CARICINUM, C. HAYNALDIANUM, C. HOOKERAE, C. JAVANICUM, C. MASTERSIANUM and C. PARISHII.

HYBRIDS

Many of the early and primary hybrids are worthy of cultivation and some of the most attractive are C. ARTHURIANUM (*C. insigne* × *C. Faireanum*); C. HARRISIANUM (*C. villosum* × *C. barbatum*); C. LATHAMIANUM (*C. Spicerianum* × *C. villosum*); C. LEEANUM, a variable and beautiful Orchid (*C. insigne* × *Spicerianum*); C. MONS DE CURTE (*C. villosum var. Boxallii* × *C. insigne var. Chantinii*); C. MAYNARDII (*C. purpuratum* × *C. Spicerianum*); C. MORGANIAE (*C. superbiens* × *C. Stonei*); C. NITENS (*C. insigne var. Chantinii* × *C. villosum*); C. OENANTHUM (*C. Harrisianum* × *C. insigne var. Maulei*); C. TITYUS (*C. Spicerianum* × *C. oenanthum var. superbum*); C. TRIUMPHANS (*C. nitens* × *C. oenanthum*); C. VIPANI (*C. philippinense* × *C. niveum*); and C. ACTAEUS (*C. insigne* × *C. Leeanum*).

It is quite impossible to mention more than a very few of the later hybrids but the following are all good: C. ALCIBIADES (*C. Leeanum* × *C. Mons de Curte*); C. ALFRED HOLLINGTON (*C. ciliolare* × *C. philippinense*); C. AYLINGII (*C. niveum* × *C. ciliolare*); C. CALYPSO (*C. insigne var. Boxallii atratum* × *C. Spicerianum*); C. CHARLES RICHMAN (*C. bellatulum* × *C. barbatum*); C. EARL OF TANKERVILLE (*C. Exul* × *C.*

nitens); C. EURYALE (*C. Lawrenceanum* × *C. superbiens);* C. GERMAINE
OPOIX (*C. Mme. Coffinet* × *C. Fairieanum);* C. GIGAS VAR. CORNDEAN
(*C. Lawrenceanum* × *C. Harrisianum var. nigrum);* C. GOWERIANUM (*C.
villosum var. Boxallii* × *C. hirsutissunum);* C. JOYCE RUCK (*C. Ballet
Girl* × *C. Boltonii);* C. MAUDIAE (*C. Rothschildeanum* × *C. super-
ciliare*) and its fine form CLARE DE LUNE; C. SANACDERAE (*C. insigne
var. Sanderae* × *C. Sanaciaeus);* C. ROSETTI VAR. GOLIATH (*C. insigne
var. Sanderianum* × *C. Maudiae);* C. THALIA (*C. insigne var. Chantinii* ×
C. Baron Schröder); C. VEXILLARIUM (*C. barbatum* × *C. Fairieanum);*
C. WINNIFRED HOLLINGTON (*C. niveum* × *C. callosum);* C. HELLAS,
WESTONBIRT VAR. (*C. Desdemona* × *C. Tania);* C. HARMACHIS VAR.
GOLDEN RADIANCE (*C. Selene* × *C. Gwen Hannen*) and C. F. C. PUDDLE
(*C. Actaeus* × *C. Artarte).*

CYRTOPODIUM, *R. Brown*
Tribe, Vandeae; sub-tribe, Cyrtopodieae

Handsome, terrestrial Orchids, from Central America, and although
they have a horticultural value they need tropical and very moist conditions when in free growth, and flowering.

C. ANDERSONII, *R. Brown*—The thick stems are up to three feet tall,
carrying dozens of two-inch, tawny flowers with yellow lips. Flaky cow
manure may be added to the compost of fibrous loam, peat and
Sphagnum moss. The author grew this finely with the base of the pot in
the warm water of a tank containing tropical Water Lilies, including
the Victoria regia. *Bot. Mag.,* t. 1800; *Orch. Alb.* IV, 176.

C. PUNCTATUM, *Lindl.*—A gorgeous Orchid when it produces a
branched, yard-long inflorescence carrying scores of glittering, bright
yellow, red-marked, two-inch flowers. The erect side lobes of the lip are
chestnut-brown. Well worth growing where sufficient heat and space
are available. *Bot. Mag.,* t. 3507; *Orch. Alb.,* V. t. 202.

C. VIRESCENS, *Rchb. f. et Warm.* is a dwarf species and C. WOODFORDII,
Sims has greenish-yellow flowers and a purple-shaded lip.

DENDROBIUM, *Swartz*
Tribe, Epidendreae; sub-tribe, Dendrobieae

A very large genus, confined to the Old World, and containing many
species of high horticultural value. The geographical range is through

CYPRIPEDIUM PARISHII

India, Burma, Siam, Malaya, the Philippines, Sumatra and along the eastern coast of Australia, from northern Queensland to Victoria, with an outlier in Tasmania. In such a large and widely distributed genus there are, naturally, many very modest species which are not worth cultivation, except in botanical collections. Numerous species have pseudo-bulbs, but the most popular Dendrobiums have stems of varying height, but no definite pseudo-bulbs, while a few have swollen stems which taper at each end. The leaves vary in size and texture, those arranged on the long stems being usually the shorter, while those on species with pseudo-bulbs and clavate or fusiform stems are generally larger and stouter. In habit, too, there are considerable divergences, some are only a few inches tall, like D. SENILE and D. LODDIGESII; others tall, like D. LITUIFLORUM and D. SUPERBUM, although, in Nature, these stems are more or less pendant, but are kept upright under cultivation. Both in size and shape the flowers show wide differences; in good forms of D. PHALAENOPSIS they are rounded and broad; small in D. SPECIOSUM; large in D. FORMOSUM and D. MACCARTHIAE. Moreover, flowers are borne singly, or in twos and threes from the nodes, as in D. NOBILE and many others; in dense terminal pendulous clusters, as in D. DENSI-FLORUM; and in arching, graceful spikes, as in D. PHALAENOPSIS and D. SUPERBIENS. The colour range is from white, through many shades of yellow, to rose, purple and crimson.

All the more or less deciduous species, chiefly those with long stems, need abundance of heat and moisture when growing, but much drier, brighter and cooler conditions so soon as growths have finished. The thick-leafed species, such as D. SPECIOSUM, D. DENSIFLORUM and D. THYRSIFLORUM require moderately warm treatment throughout the year and plenty of moisture except in the dull months of the year. The majority of Dendrobiums require less heavy shading than most Orchids. The compost should be fairly substantial and consist of equal proportions of Osmunda fibre, peat or loam fibre, and Sphagnum moss, the moss increased and the fibres reduced for the less robust species. Dendrobiums have a comparatively small root system, therefore are best grown in rather small pans or pots, although D. WARDIANUM, D. PENDULUM, D. PIERARDII and others of similar habit look far better when grown in teak-wood baskets and suspended so that the growths hang down and display their flowers in a natural manner. These and similar species may

H

be watered occasionally with weak liquid cow manure so soon as the new basal growths develop—always provided the plants are well-established and in good health.

The species described below are among the best from a horticultural point of view, and the selection is severely limited, but there are others, less showy but beautiful and of extreme interest to "the curious gardener"—to use an old-fashioned phrase that denoted a person who loved plants as plants—and not necessarily for the great display they make.

D. AGGREGATUM, *Roxb.*—A species with small, clustered, single-leafed pseudo-bulbs, short, stout leaves and drooping, racemose spikes of from six to twelve roundish, yellow flowers, with a deep orange lip. The variety MAJUS, slightly larger and richer in colour, is the form most generally cultivated. *Bot. Mag.*, t. 2643; *Bot. Reg.*, t. 1695.

D. ATRO-VIOLACEUM, *Rolfe*—This erect species created a good deal of excitement soon after it was introduced from New Guinea in 1891, and even more in 1898, when Messrs. Sanders secured an importation of about five thousand plants, which were sold by auction by Messrs. Protheroe & Morris. Unfortunately, the species has not taken very kindly to domestication.

Stems clavate, up to two feet tall; spikes terminal, with six to ten medium-sized flowers that have creamy-white, purple-spotted sepals and petals and a violet-purple, green-tongued lip. Very distinct in form and colour; handsome and attractive.

D. AUREUM, *Lindl.*—A beautiful, slightly variable species, widely distributed in India, Burma and the Philippines. First collected by Gibson and introduced in 1837. The sturdy growths, twelve to eighteen inches tall, are furnished with oblong-lanceolate, four-inch, deciduous leaves. The fragrant, three-inch flowers, produced in twos or threes from the nodes, are bright amber-yellow; lip recurved at the apex, deep yellow, velvety, with purple and brown markings. Known also as *D. heterocarpum*, and as such is figured in *Bot. Mag.*, t. 4708.

D. BENSONIAE, *Rchb. f.*—An erect-grower, with stems up to two feet tall. Flowers rounded, produced from the nodes in twos or threes, nearly three inches broad, white, with an orange disk on the white lip. Formerly very popular. *Bot. Mag.*, t. 5679; *Fl. Mag.*, t. 353.

D. BIGIBBUM, *Lindl.*—A rather tall Australian species, known at Kew in 1824, but not introduced in any quantity until forty years later. The slender, terminal, racemose spikes carry numerous, two-inch, round, neat, magenta-purple flowers, with a lip of deeper colour and a white disk. A very useful Orchid as the flowers last in good condition for a long period. *Bot. Mag.*, t. 4898; *Orch. Alb.*, I, t. 38.

D. BRYMERIANUM, *Rchb. f.*—This very remarkable species was introduced from Burma in 1874. The stout stems are eighteen to twenty-four inches tall, slightly swollen in the middle; leaves about four inches long, persistent. Spikes short, racemose, produced from the upper portions of the stem, usually bearing one flower, occasionally two or three. The three-inch flowers have a longer vertical measurement; sepals and petals golden yellow; lip large, very slightly recurved, golden-yellow, with fringed side lobes and a central lobe extended into a spreading, lacy, much branched, finely divided fringe of great beauty and wonderful construction. *Bot. Mag.*, t. 6383; *Fl. Mag.*, n.s., t. 459.

D. CAPILLIPES, *Rchb. f.*—Very dwarf, stems stout, about four inches long; leaves few and small. Flowers solitary or in pairs. Spikes short and erect, few-flowered. Flowers large, golden-yellow, with an orange blotch on the lip. A little gem that used to be grown well in the Gatton Park Collection. *Xen. Orch.*, II, t. 169.

D. CHRYSANTHUM, *Lindl.*—Very tall, the slender stems often six feet long, furnished with small, deciduous leaves. Spike racemose, nodding, produced from the nodes of the last-made and still leafy stem, and usually carrying about half a dozen rich yellow flowers with two red-purple blotches on the pretty, fimbriated lip. Free flowering, but too big for most structures. *Bot. Reg.*, t. 1299; and in *Bot. Reg.*, 1839 as *D. Paxtoni*.

D. CHRYSOTOXUM, *Lindl.*—A somewhat variable species, found in Burma at considerable elevations. Stems about a foot tall, bearing six-inch to nine-inch racemes from near the top. The several two-inch flowers are bright golden-yellow, with an orange-yellow lip, streaked at the base with red. *Bot. Mag.*, t. 5053.

D. CREPIDATUM, *Lindl.*—Stems thick, twelve to eighteen inches long, strongly jointed; leaves short, deciduous. Flowers small, in short clusters produced freely from the nodes; white, shaded with lilac; the lip has a deep yellow disk. *Bot. Mag.*, t. 4992.

D. CRYSTALLINUM, *Rchb. f.*—Stems somewhat pendulous, twelve to eighteen inches long. Flowers about two inches broad, white, marked or shaded with light purple at the ends of the sepals and petals; lip dark yellow, white-edged. *Bot. Mag.*, 7, t. 6319.

D. DEAREI, *Rchb. f.*—A very pretty Orchid from the Philippines; somewhat after the style of *D. formosum*, but with clustered spikes of several three-inch flowers that are pure white except for a greenish-yellow blotch at the centre of the lip. *Orch. Alb.*, t. 120.

D. DENSIFLORUM, *Wallich*—This showy species was discovered by Wallich, about 1828, growing in the hot, moist valleys of Nepal. The clavate stems are four-angled, twelve to eighteen inches tall, with shortish, leathery, persistent leaves. The pendulous, cylindrical racemes, densely flowered, are from six to nine inches long. Flowers two inches wide, round, with clear yellow sepals and petals and a showy, orange lip. The variety SCHRÖDERI has white sepals and petals. *Bot. Reg.*, t. 1828; *Bot. Mag.*, 3418.

D. DEVONIANUM, *Paxton*—A remarkably beautiful and free-flowering species discovered by Gibson in the Khasia Hills, in 1836, when collecting for the Duke of Devonshire. The slender, pendulous stems, clothed with short, narrow, deciduous leaves, are about two feet long. Flowers two inches broad, borne singly, or in pairs, from the nodes; white, tipped with bright purple; lip broad, rounded, narrowly fringed, white, with an orange base and an edging of bright purple. *Bot. Mag.*, t. 4429; *Mag. Bot.*, VII, p. 169.

D. DRACONIS, *Rchb. f.*—Allied to *D. formosum*, stems hairy, somewhat above a foot tall, with short clusters of smallish, ivory-white flowers, marked with orange-red at the base of the lip.

D. FALCONERI, *Hook.*—A graceful species with slender, branching stems; introduced from Assam in 1856. The three-inch flowers are solitary, produced from the nodes; sepals and petals white, tipped with purple; lip purple, bordered with orange. Immensely popular in former years. *Bot. Mag.*, t. 4944; *Orch. Alb.*, VI, t. 257.

D. FARMERI, *Paxton.*—Closely akin to *D. densiflorum* in style and size. The pendulous, rather loose racemes carry numerous two-inch flowers, pale yellow, tinted with rose or lilac; lip roundish, pale yellow, with a deeper yellow disk. A fine Orchid. *Bot. Mag.*, t. 4659; *Mag. Bot.*, XV, t. 241; *Orch. Alb.*, III, t. 99.

D. FIMBRIATUM, *Hook.*—Somewhat like *D. chrysanthum*, with loose, pendulous racemes of about eight three-inch flowers; yellow, with an

CYPRIPEDIUM ROSETTI VAR. GOLIATH

orange-yellow blotch on the fringed lip. *Bot. Mag.*, t. 4160 (*var. oculatum*); *Mag. Bot.*, VI, p. 169, as *D. Paxtoni*.

D. FINDLAYANUM, *Parish et Rchb. f.*—Stems slender, about eighteen inches long, prominently jointed; leaves short, deciduous. The three-inch flowers are produced from the nodes in pairs; lilac, tinted with white; lip yellow. *Bot. Mag.*, t. 6438.

D. FORMOSUM, *Roxburgh*—One of the very finest Dendrobes, and best known in cultivation by its variety GIGANTEUM. Discovered by Roxburgh but introduced from the Khasia Hills by Gibson in 1837. Stems stout, erect, twelve to eighteen inches long; Leaves ovate-oblong, stiff. The beautiful four-inch flowers are pure white, with very broad, rounded petals, and borne in axillary clusters of three to five. Lip spreading, white, with a large orange central blotch. May be grown in the Intermediate House or even the warmest end of the Cool House. *Bot. Reg.*, 1839, t. 64; *Mag. Bot.*, VI, p. 49; *Orch. Alb.*, VII, t. 308.

D. HOOKERIANUM, *Lindl.*—A splendid but rare Orchid, allied to *D. fimbriatum*, bearing pendulous racemes of from eight to a dozen four-inch, golden-yellow flowers, with a purple basal blotch on the orange-yellow, fimbriated lip. Discovered by Sir Joseph Hooker in 1848, in Sikkim. *Bot. Mag.*, t. 6013.

D. INFUNDIBULUM, *Lindl.*—This Burmese species was introduced about 1858 and needs somewhat cooler treatment than most Dendrobes. It belongs to the Formosae section, and is from eighteen to twenty-four inches tall, with three to five three-inch flowers on short spikes. Pure white, except for a yellow or reddish-orange blotch on the spreading lip. The variety JAMESIANUM, still quite popular, has a somewhat stiffer habit and has a red blotch on the lip; Reichenbach gave it specific rank. *Bot. Mag.*, t. 5446; *D. Jamesianum* in *Orch. Alb.*, V, t. 221.

D. JAPONICUM, *Lindl.*—A charming little Orchid, about ten inches tall, with pairs of fragrant, white flowers; lip white, with basal purple markings. Quite a common plant in Japan and in cultivation since 1860.

D. MACCARTHIAE, *Thwaites*—A native of Ceylon, where it is known as the Wesak Orchid, and is under Government protection. The semi-pendant, slender stems have a few short leaves, and the racemes are few-flowered. The flowers, about four inches broad, are rosy-mauve, while the flattened lip is mauve-purple, with a central red-purple blotch that is surrounded by white. *Bot. Mag.*, t. 4886.

D. MacFARLANEI, *Rchb. f.*—A dwarf and beautiful New Guinean species, with white flowers about five inches broad; lip long, white, stained with purple on the side lobes and in the throat. Now referred to *D. Johnsoniae.*

D. MACROPHYLLUM, *Rchb. f.*—A sturdy species with stout, fifteen-inch stem and large creamy-white, two-inch flowers in terminal racemes. The lip is yellow, marked with purple. Also known as *D. Veitchianum. Bot. Mag.,* t. 5649.

D. MONILIFORME, *Swartz*—For those who can only grow small plants, this dwarf Japanese species will commend itself. The flowers are of moderate size, produced from the nodes of the short stems, fragrant, white, with purple markings on the lip.

D. MOSCHATUM, *Lindl.*—Were it not for the length of its stems—up to six feet—this species would be popular by reason of the musky scent of its four-inch, yellowish flowers, borne in racemes of a dozen or more. The nankeen-yellow sepals and petals are shaded with rose, while the deeper yellow lip has two reddish-purple blotches in the throat, each edged with orange. The variety CALCEOLARIA has smaller but richer yellow flowers, and has been known as *D. Calceolus. Bot. Mag.,* t. 3837; *var. calceolaria, Orch. Alb.,* IV, t. 163.

D. NOBILE, *Lindl.*—Widely distributed through north and north-eastern India and southern China, this grand old Orchid has enjoyed great popularity for more than a hundred years, as it flowers freely and regularly, provided it is given a resting period after the completion of its eighteen-inch stems. It is variable in floral colouring and the shapely flowers have a diameter of about three inches. The sepals and petals are white-tipped, and often shaded with rose-purple; lip neat and rounded, white or rose-purple, with a big red-purple or crimson area in the throat. The flowers are produced from the nodes, last well when cut, and when button-hole bouquets were fashionable, this was a popular subject. Numerous varietal forms have received names; var. NOBILIUS has larger and more richly-coloured flowers; ALBIFLORUM is white; and ANDERSON-IUM is much like NOBILIS; but the most distinct of all is COOKSONIANUM, in which the petals are heavily blotched at the base with maroon. When specimens were the vogue, D. NOBILE was frequently grown and exhibited as very big plants. *Mag. Bot.,* VIII, p. 7; *var. nobilius* in *Orch. Alb.,* V, 214.

D. PARISHII, *Rchb. f.*—A dwarf species, from Moulmein, introduced about 1863. The medium-sized, usually solitary, flowers are bright rose-purple, with maroon blotches on the lip. *Bot. Mag.*, t. 5488.

D. PHALAENOPSIS, *Fitzgerald*—This beautiful, graceful and popular species is found in New Guinea and North Queensland. The spikes are racemose, with six to a dozen shapely flowers three to four inches broad. The colour varies, but, usually, the sepals are light rosy-mauve, with slightly recurved tips; petals broader, rich mauve, veined in the centre with deeper colour; lip, maroon-purple, with incurving side lobes and a pointed apex. The variety SCHRÖDERIANUM is more robust, with larger and more richly coloured flowers. A large house at Bruges filled with flowering plants remains a pleasant mental picture. *Bot. Mag.*, t. 6817; *Orch. Alb.*, IV, t. 187.

D. PIERARDI, *Roxburgh*—The pendulous, three-feet stems of this species are crowded with pairs of two-inch semi-transparent flowers, that are pale mauve or whitish, with a yellow, purple-based lip. A fine plant when grown in a suspended basket. Also known as *D. cucullatum*. *Bot. Mag.*, t. 3584; *Bot. Reg.*, t. 1756.

D. PRIMULINUM, *Lindl.*—Stems slightly decumbent, a foot or more long, with pairs of flowers produced at the nodes; sepals and petals small, lilac-mauve; lip broad, rounded, pale primrose-yellow, with basal veinings of purple. *Orch. Alb.*, VII, t. 86; *Bot. Mag.*, t. 5003, as *D. nobile var. pallidum*.

D. PULCHELLUM, *Roxburgh*—A glorious deciduous species, but its tall stems—up to four feet—tax the available accommodation in most Orchid houses. It was formerly known as *D. Dalhousieanum*, and this name is still commonly used. The pendulous, apical racemes may have from five to ten flowers of large size, often five inches broad. The broad sepals and petals are nankeen-yellow, tinted with rose; lip fringed, with a pair of large crimson blotches in the throat. Found in Burma and India and introduced by Gibson, in 1837, who found it in the Calcutta Botanic Garden. Fine examples are seen frequently at the Chelsea Shows. *Bot. Mag.*, t. 1846; and *Sel. Orch.*, I, t. 22, as *D. Dalhousieanum*.

D. SCABRILINGUE, *Lindl.*—Discovered by Thomas Lobb in Moulmein in 1849, this dwarf species has black-haired stems and smallish, ivory-white flowers; lip yellow, with orange-yellow lines. A pretty plant. *Bot. Mag.*, t. 5515, as *D. hedyosmum*.

D. SENILE, *Rchb. f.*—Very dwarf, and notable for the long, woolly hairs on the three-inch stems. Flowers about two inches broad, in pairs, rich yellow, with orange-yellow lip. *Bot. Mag.*, t. 5520.

D. SPECIOSUM, *Smith.*—A particularly robust Orchid from the eastern coastal region of Queensland. The stems are stout, about a foot or more tall, and almost pseudo-bulbous, bearing two or three leathery, ten-inch leaves. The spikes are nearly terminal, from twelve to twenty-four inches long, with a densely racemose, semi-pendulous end. The flowers are small, cream-yellow, slightly fragrant; lip spotted with purple. The variety BANCROFTIANUM is smaller, but even more floriferous than the type; HILLII is a larger plant, with creamy-white flowers. All forms of D. SPECIOSUM are seen at their best when grown into large specimens, but they are too big for accommodation in small collections. *Bot. Mag.*, t. 3074; *Bot. Reg.*, t. 1610; *var. Hillii* in *Orch. Alb.*, V, t. 198.

D. SPECTABILE, *Miq.*—Found in New Guinea; about a foot tall, with terminal, many-flowered spikes. The twisted sepals and petals are light yellow, shading to deeper yellow, and spotted with crimson; lip yellow, with red-brown markings.

D. SUPERBIENS, *Rchb. f.*—An Australian species, very distinct and handsome. The erect stems are from one to four feet long, with numerous two-inch flowers on a nodding raceme. Crimson-purple sepals and petals, with paler, sometimes white, margins; lip short, purple, with white on the raised lines of the disk. Also known as *D. Goldei*. *Reichenbachia*, I, t. 39.

D. SUPERBUM, *Rchb. f.*—A Philippine species introduced about 1838. Stems pendant, two to four feet long. The four-inch flowers are produced in pairs from the nodes, magenta-purple, with a wine-red lip. Easily recognized by its distinct odour of Rhubarb; the variety ONOSMUM, however, is scentless. *Mag. Bot.*, XV, p. 97.

D. TERETIFOLIUM, *R. Brown*—A very dwarf Australian species, with slender, branching stems and rather long leaves. Flowers of medium size, white, borne in loose panicles. *Bot. Mag.*, t. 4711.

D. THYRSIFLORUM, *Hort.*—A magnificent Orchid and practically identical with the equally handsome *D. densiflorum*, except that the rounded sepals and petals are white and the broad lip is deep orange-yellow. A popular Dendrobe, and deservedly so. *Bot. Mag.*, t. 5780, as *D. densiflorum var. alboluteum; Fl. Mag.*, n.s., t. 449; the variety

DENDROBIUM FIMBRIATUM VAR. OCULATUM

DENDROBIUM GATTON SUNRAY

DENDROBIUM ROLFIAE VAR. ROSEUM

DENDROBIUM THYRSIFLORUM

WALKERIANUM, with larger flowers in longer racemes, is figured in *Sel. Orch.*, III, t. 21.

D. TORTILE, *Lindl.*—Discovered in Tenasserim by Thomas Lobb and introduced in 1847. A charming little Orchid, barely a foot tall, with three-inch, rosy-lilac sepals and petals and primrose-yellow, purple-blotched lip. *Bot. Mag.*, t. 4477.

D. WARDIANUM, *Warner*—There are two forms of this splendid Orchid, one, from Burma, has pendant stems, two to four feet long; the other, with shorter stems and smaller flowers, is found in Assam. The species was introduced about 1856. A few years ago plants were imported regularly and in large numbers, and it was then a very popular subject even where Orchids were not a speciality. The widespread, four-inch flowers are produced in pairs from the nodes and have purple tips to the white sepals and petals, and two maroon blotches at the base of the purple-tipped lip. *Orch. Alb.*, III, t. 113; *Reichenbachia*, I, t. 9.

D. VICTORIAE-REGINAE, *Loher*—A very distinct species from the Philippines, about a foot tall, with smallish flowers produced from the nodes. Particularly notable for the purplish-blue (or violet-purple) upper halves of the otherwise white or creamy sepals and petals. Introduced about 1896. *Bot. Mag.*, t. 9071.

OTHER SPECIES

Species of considerable beauty but of less horticultural value are numerous and of these the following is a fair selection:—D. ADUNCUM, D. AMETHYSTOGLOSSA, D. BARBATULUM, D. BOXALLII, D. CANALICULATUM, D. COELOGYNE, D. CYMBIDIOIDES, D. JOHANNIS, D. LINAWIANUM, D. LUTEOLUM, D. RHODOCENTRUM, D. SANGUINEOLENTUM, D. SUAVISSIMUM and D. TRANSPARENS.

HYBRIDS

The spate of Dendrobium hybrids has slackened during recent years, but they include many fine, free-flowering plants. It is only possible to cite a few of them here.

D. AINSWORTHII (*D. nobile* × *D. aureum*); D. CASSIOPE (*D. moniliforme* × *D. nobile var. albiflorum*); D. EURYALUS (*D. Ainsworthii* × *D. nobile*); D. GATTON SUNRAY (*D. pulchellum* × *D. illustre*); D. MELANODISCUS (*D. Findlayanum* × *D. Ainsworthii*); D. OWENIANUM (*D. Linawianum var. majus* × *D. Wardianum*); D. CHESSINGTONENSE (*D. aureum* × *D. Wiganiae*); D. AUSTINII (*D. Ainsworthii* × *D. Cybele*); D. LEEANUM

(*D. phalaenopsis* × *D. superbiens*); D. ROLFIAE (*D. nobile* × *D. primulinum*) and its var. ROSEUM ; D. THWAITESIAE (*D. Ainsworthii* × *D. Wiganiae*); and its fine Veitch's variety; D. VENUS (*D. Falconeri* × *D. nobile*); D. WIGANIAE (*D. nobile* × *D. signatum*).

DISA, *Bergius*

Tribe, Ophrydeae; sub-tribe, Satyrieae

A genus of South African Orchids that contains numerous species of little horticultural value and one that has frequently been regarded as the most superbly magnificent of all Orchids. DISA GRANDIFLORA certainly merits all the admiration it has received and all the high claims made on its behalf.

The Disas are terrestrial, of tufted habit, with rich green leaves, tuberous roots and no pseudo-bulbs. Practically all of them enjoy moisture, especially atmospheric moisture, during the season of growth and flower, with much less moisture during the resting period. They love cool conditions and plenty of fresh, moist air. Pans are the best receptacles; drainage must be ample and a suitable compost consists of very fibrous loam from which loose soil has been removed, together with some fibrous peat or Osmunda fibre, flaky leaf-soil, some Sphagnum, sand and finely broken charcoal. Potting should be done early in the year, directly new growth commences; firm potting is desirable.

D. GRANDIFLORA, *Linn.*—A magnificent Orchid when seen at its best, with tall spikes of three to seven flowers that may be so much as five inches wide. The two broad, pointed sepals are vivid scarlet, while the large dorsal sepal is hooded, contracted into a spur, whitish, or pink, flushed and veined with crimson or scarlet. The inconspicuous petals are close to the column and spotted with red; the lip is a very narrow, scarlet, tongue-like organ. There is, however, some variation in colour and some of these are more pink than scarlet. Flowers in Spring or early Summer.

DISA GRANDIFLORA provides a severe test of horticultural skill and there is no doubt that hot and arid conditions have been responsible for very many failures. That this superb Orchid can be managed successfully in this country is proved by the records of magnificent displays at Chatsworth and Waddesden Manor, where they were grown with Cape Heaths and Indian Azaleas. Fair success has been achieved by housing the plants in a low, frost-proof pit, provided with ample means of affording ventilation, and the pans plunged in a deep bed of Sphagnum. An illustration in *The Gardeners' Chronicle* of 1875 shows a well-filled pan of plants carrying a total of twelve spikes.

Table Mountain is the principal home of D. GRANDIFLORA, but as collectors appeared likely to exterminate it, it is now a protected subject. *Bot. Mag.*, 4073; *Bot. Reg.*, t. 926.

D. RACEMOSA, *Linn.*—A very pretty species, with numerous, smallish, rosy-purple flowers on a stem from fifteen to twenty-four inches tall. *Bot. Mag.*, t. 7021.

D. TRIPETALOIDES, *N.E. Br.*—Flowers small, numerous, white, flushed with rose-pink and lightly spotted with crimson. *Bot. Mag.*, t. 7206.

OTHER SPECIES

Other species known to have been in cultivation include D. COOPERI, *Reich*, carmine-rose (*Bot. Mag.*, 7256); D. CORNUTA, *Swartz*, yellow and carmine (*Bot. Mag.*, t. 4094); D. CRASSICORNIS, *Lindl.*, white and purple (*Bot. Mag.*, t. 6529); D. GRAMINIFOLIA, *Banks*, blue (*Orch. Alb.*, IX, t. 399); and D. INCARNATA, *Lindl.*, orange and yellow (*Bot. Mag.*, t. 7343).

HYBRIDS

The late Mr. W. Watson, of Kew, was keenly interested in Disas and made several crosses, but Messrs. James Veitch & Sons were much more successful and raised several hybrids of great beauty; but it is feared that some of these have fallen out of cultivation. Others were raised by Mr. H. J. Elwes and Messrs. Black & Flory.

The chief hybrids are:—D. BLACKII (*D. grandiflora* × *D. Luna*), 1915; D. DIORES (*D. grandiflora* × *D. Veitchii*), 1898; D. ELWESII (*D. kewensis* × *D. Veitchii*); D. KEWENSIS (*D. grandiflora* × *D. tripetaloides*), 1893; D. LANGLEYENSIS (*D. racemosa* × *D. tripetaloides*); D. LUNA (*D. racemosa* × *D. Veitchii*), 1902; D. PREMIER (*D. tripetaloides* × *D. Veitchii*), one of the best, rosy-magenta, 1893; D. VEITCHII (*D. grandiflora* × *D. racemosa*), rosy-purple, 1892; and D. WATSONII (*D. grandiflora* × *D. kewensis*), 1900.

EPIDENDRUM, *Linnaeus*

Tribe, Epidendreae; sub-tribe, Laelieae

This is one of the very largest of the genera into which the Natural Order Orchidaceae is divided. Confined to the American Continent, the geographical range is more or less continuous from the southern United States, through Central America—Mexico and the West Indies—down to Peru on the eastern side, and to the Brazilian Province of Minas Geraes on the western side of South America. Wide distribution always means great variation, consequently there are Epidendrums with short or long pseudo-bulbs, and some with tall, flexuous, clambering stems, while the flowers vary considerably in size, form and colour. Some are found at considerable elevations above sea level; others inhabit lower, forestal regions, but, in general, they thrive under cultivation in an Intermediate House, a few liking warmer or cooler treatment. In so vast a genus—probably five hundred species—the horticultural value of these Orchids varies very much; large numbers are hardly worth cultivation under glass, but some that find little or no favour here are useful in tropical countries, where they may be grown out of doors. Bearing in mind all these factors, it will, obviously, be no easy matter to make a selection of species with sufficient attractions to make their cultivation worth while. Moreover, any selection of this kind must be arbitrary, and will depend upon the tastes of the selector, and whether display or interest is the guide. The following selection is, admittedly, a severe one, but will serve as a guide to those newly engaged in the fascinating business of making a collection of Orchids.

Regarding nomenclature, Epidendrums have had an unhappy time. All the Tropical American epiphytal Orchids he knew were placed by Linnaeus in the genus he founded, but, later, Robert Brown and Lindley sorted out these species, and others of later introduction, and Bentham subsequently grouped the species into four sections, defined chiefly by the shape of the pseudo-bulbs and stems, and the position of the lip of the flower in relation to the column.

E. ALATUM, *Bateman*—Pseudo-bulbs pyriform, about four inches long, each with two, or three, foot-long, leathery leaves. The erect, panicled spike carries numerous, two-inch, fragrant flowers, with greenish-yellow, brown-based sepals and petals, and a yellow, orange-edged front lobe to the lip. The latter has also a few rows of purplish hairs. *Bot. Mag.*, t. 3898, as E. *calochilum*.

E. ATROPURPUREUM, *Willldenow*—A tall grower, with two or three fifteen-inch leaves on the ovoid, three-inch pseudo-bulbs. The stout, erect spike is racemose at the top and carries eight or ten flowers nearly

DENDROBIUM AUSTINII

three inches in diameter. The sepals and petals are yellowish-green and reddish-brown, the former incurving at the tips. Lip white, with a central crimson-purple blotch. A handsome Orchid when seen at its best. Several varieties are recorded; ALBUM has a pure white lip; RANDIANUM, formerly much in request, has larger and brighter flowers, with a rayed blotch of red-purple on the white lip; and ROSEUM, in which the lip is rose-coloured. *Orch. Alb.*, IV, t. 149; *Bot. Mag.*, t. 3534, as *E. macrochilum*.

E. BRASSAVOLAE, *Rchb. f.*—Although attractive and distinct, this Guatemalan species, one of Warscewicz's discoveries, is of botanical rather than horticultural interest. The pyriform pseudo-bulbs are diphyllous and the racemose spikes about eighteen inches tall. The wide-spread flowers have a diameter of about five inches. The narrow, pointed, sepals and petals are light yellow; lip trowel-shaped, pale yellow, with a white base and purple apex. *Bot. Mag.*, t. 5664.

E. CILIARE, *Linn.*—One of the commonest species and one that has been in cultivation since its introduction in 1790. The diphyllous stems are five or six inches long, and the spikes six to eight inches tall. Flowers small, with narrow, yellowish-green sepals and petals, and a white lip that has an almost thread-like central lobe. *Bot. Mag.*, t. 463; *Bot. Reg.*, t. 783.

E. CINNABARINUM, *Lindl.*—Stems terete, slender, up to four feet tall, with shortish, ovate-lanceolate leaves along the upper part. The long spikes end in a dense raceme of two-inch, cinnabar-red flowers that open in succession; lip yellow. Very attractive. *Bot. Reg.*, 1842, t. 25.

E. COCHLEATUM, *Linn.*—Pseudo-bulbs short, diphyllous; leaves six inches long. The erect spikes end in a panicle of six or seven three-inch flowers; sepals and petals yellowish-green, twisted or pointed backwards; lip roundish or fan-shaped, yellowish green, with a purple blotch on each spike. *Bot. Mag.*, t. 572.

E. COOPERIANUM, *Bateman*—Introduced from Rio de Janeiro in 1869. Stems erect, two to three feet tall, with apical, many-flowered racemes of smallish flowers. The narrow sepals and petals are yellowish-brown, the latter brighter than the former; lip bright rose, with a small central lobe. Still a rare plant. *Bot. Mag.*, t. 5654.

E. DICHROMUM, *Lindl.*—Introduced from Pernambuco in 1864. Pseudo-bulbs cylindric and diphyllous; leaves leathery, one foot long.

Spikes paniculate, many-flowered, up to two feet tall. The two-inch flowers have rose, yellow-shaded sepals, and broader, rose-coloured petals; lip, purple, with darker makings on the fairly large central lobe. *Bot. Mag.*, t. 5491.

E. ELONGATUM, *Jacq.*—Stems slender, terete, up to eighteen inches tall; leaves short and leathery. Spikes tall, ending in a dense raceme of rose-coloured flowers, each about one inch broad. *Bot. Mag.*, t. 611.

E. ENDRESII, *Rchb. f.*—One of the prettiest of the dwarf species. Stems slender, eight inches to a foot tall; leaves, heart-shaped, short. The terminal spike carries about a dozen inch-wide, shapely, white flowers with a few violet-purple spots on the lip. *Bot. Mag.*, t. 7855.

E. FALCATUM, *Lindl.*—A particularly dwarf Mexican species, with monophyllous stems barely two inches long. Spikes axillary, one-flowered. Flowers about two inches broad, yellowish-green, with a white, yellow-tipped lip. Also known as *E. aloifolium*, *E. lactiflorum* and *Brassavola Pescatorei. Bot. Mag.*, t. 3778, as *E. Parkinsonianum.*

E. FRAGRANS, *Swartz*—A widely distributed species that first flowered in this country at Kew, in 1778. Stems fusiform, five to nine inches tall, with one or two foot-long leaves. Spikes short and few flowered. The two-inch, fragrant flowers have creamy-white sepals and petals and a white, purple-marked lip. One of the oldest of cultivated Orchids. *Bot. Mag.*, t. 152, as *E. cochleatum.*

E. FREDERICI-GUILIELMI, *Warsc. et Rchb. f.*—A robust, Peruvian species, with stout stems up to five feet tall; leaves about eight inches long. Spikes paniculate, with numerous two-inch flowers that are reddish-purple. *Xen. Orch.* I, t. 51.

E. IONOSMUM, *Lindl.*—Pseudo-bulbs rounded, short, triphyllous; leaves about four inches long. The small, sweetly-scented flowers, on foot-long spikes, are greenish-brown, edged with pale yellow; lip yellow, and with red streaks.

E. LINDLEYANUM, *Rchb. f.*—A pretty Mexican Orchid with thick, terete, foot-long stems. Spikes up to two feet long, racemose, carrying many two-inch flowers, rose-purple, with a white base to the lip. Also known as *Barkeria Lindleyana. Bot. Mag.*, t. 6098; *Mag. Bot.*, XIII, p. 193.

E. NEMORALE, *Lindl.*—More interesting than beautiful. Pseudo-bulbs short and rounded. Spikes two feet tall, branched, flowers about four inches across; sepals and petals narrow, pale rosy-mauve;

lip rosy-mauve, with a white centre. *Bot. Mag.*, t. 4606, as *E. verrucosum.*

E. PRISMATOCARPUM, *Rchb. f.*—A fine and easily-grown species, with ovoid, four-inch pseudo-bulbs, each with a pair of long leaves. Spikes erect, many-flowered. Flowers rather less than two inches broad, of neat form, with sulphur-yellow, purple-spotted sepals and petals and a narrow, pointed, trowel-shaped, rose-purple, yellow-tipped lip. *Bot. Mag.* t. 5336; *Sel. Orch.*, I, t. 9.

E. RADIATUM, *Lindl.*—Very like *E. fragrans*, but with stouter pseudo-bulbs and larger flowers.

E. RADICANS, *Pavon*—A very beautiful Guatemalan species, introduced in 1839. The scandent stems may be four or five feet tall, with short, ovate leaves. Spikes rather short, racemose, many-flowered. Flowers less than two inches wide, brilliant cinnabar-red, shaded with orange; lip fringed, with an orange-yellow central lobe. Needs a lot of room in a Warm House, but the flexuous stems may be trained round slender stakes. *Orch. Alb.*, IV, t. 161; *Mag. Bot.*, XII, p. 145.

E. STAMFORDIANUM, *Bateman*—A fine Orchid introduced from Guatemala in 1837. The foot-long, fusiform stems carry two or three stout leaves. Spikes produced from the base of the stem, a foot or more long, often branched, densely flowered. Flowers fragrant, less than two inches broad, with yellow, red-spotted sepals and petals and a boldly three-lobed, white or pale yellow lip. Not too easily managed but always attracts attention when in flower. *Bot. Mag.*, t. 4759.

E. VARIEGATUM, *Hook.*—This widely distributed species has been in cultivation since 1832; needs plenty of clear light. Stems fusiform, eight inches tall; leaves leathery; spikes erect; flowers greenish-yellow, freely spotted with red; lip white, tipped with red-purple. *Bot. Mag.*, t. 3151.

E. VITELLINUM, *Lindl.*—A grand Mexican Orchid. Pseudo-bulbs short; leaves erect, glaucous green; spikes erect, or slightly nodding, many-flowered. Flowers rounded, about an inch and a half broad, vivid cinnabar-red, with a small yellow lip and orange-yellow column. A most useful and attractive species of which there are Summer and Autumn-flowering forms. The variety MAJUS is finer than the type, with more numerous and more brightly coloured flowers, and is the form usually grown. The plants need a decided rest after the completion of growth.

An intermediate temperature suits it, with plenty of light and less moisture during the resting period. *Bot. Mag.*, t. 4107.

E. WALLISII, *Rchb. f.*—Stems slender, up to five feet tall; leaves short. The short terminal or axillary spikes bear three or four neat flowers with a diameter of two inches. The sepals and petals are yellow, lightly spotted with dark purple; lip, broadly fan-shaped, notched at the margins, white, flecked with red-purple and lined with yellow at the base. *Orch. Alb.*, II, t. 74.

E. XANTHINUM, *Lindl.*—A graceful species, with slender stems two feet tall; leaves short, alternate. The terminal inflorescence is a rounded cluster of numerous, small, bright yellow, orange-tinted flowers. Each of the three lobes of the lip are deeply fringed. *Bot. Mag.*, t. 7586.

HYBRIDS

Comparatively few hybrids have been raised, but all the following are good:—E. ENDRESIO-WALLISII (*E. Endresii* × *E. Wallisii*); one of the older hybrids, dwarf, with purplish flowers; E. ARMSTRONGII, a form of this hybrid; E. O'BRIENIANUM (*E. erectum* × *E. radicans*) has terminal clusters of small, bright carmine flowers, with orange crest, habit of *E. radicans;* E. BOUNDII (*E. Burtoni* × *E. radicans*); E. BURTONI (*E. ibaguense* × *E. O'Brienianum*); E. CHARLESWORTHII (*E. Frederico-Guilielmi* × *E. radicans*); E. DELLENSE (*E. radicans* × *E. xanthinum*); E. PHOEBUS (*E. O'Brienianum* × *E. vitellinum*); and E. RADICO-VITEL-LINUM (*E. radicans* × *E. vitellinum var. majus*).

GRAMMATOPHYLLUM, *Blume*
Tribe, Vandeae; sub-tribe, Cymbidieae

The few species of this genus of Malayan Orchids are handsome plants, but, unfortunately, they are too large for all but the largest houses, for they are the giants of the race. They thrive in considerable warmth and a moist atmosphere, with a rooting compost of Osmunda, loam fibre and Sphagnum moss.

G. FENZLIANUM, *Rchb. f.*—Introduced from Amboina. The pseudobulbous stems are thick and four to six inches long, with three or more narrow, foot-long leaves. The arching spikes are three or four feet tall, produced from the base of the stem, and carry several flowers from two to three inches broad. The greenish-yellow sepals and petals are heavily blotched and spotted with brown; the lip is oblong and of similar colouring. The variety MEASURESIANUM is recorded as much superior to the type.

G. MULTIFLORUM, *Lindl.*—Smaller than the former, but otherwise very much like it, with yellow-brown streaks on the side lobes of the lip. *Mag. Bot.*, VI, p. 217.

G. SPECIOSUM, *Blume*—The giant of the giants; it has pseudo-bulbous stems from five to eight feet tall, with aerial roots near their bases. The leaves may be two feet long and the erect spike from four to eight feet tall. Numerous six-inch flowers are rather widely spaced on the upper part of the spike, yellow, marked with purple-brown. This native of Malaya was introduced in 1852, and must be a grand sight when grown and flowered successfully in the Far East, as it used to be in the Penang Botanic Gardens, where the author's uncle had a specimen over forty feet in diameter, with thirty spikes ! *Bot. Mag.*, t. 5157.

LAELIA, *Lindley*

Tribe, Epidendreae; sub-tribe, Laelieae

A genus of handsome Orchids from South America, where many species grow in association with Cattleyas, with which they are closely related, and therefore, for the most part, need similar cultural treatment. L. ANCEPS and allied species are found in Southern Mexico. The dainty L. MONOPHYLLA is a native of Jamaica, while L. PURPURATA is found in the Panama and Santa Catherina provinces of Brazil. Brazil, however, is the home of numerous species.

L. ALBIDA, *Lindl.*—The white and fragrant flowers of this pretty species are too small to suit the tastes of most modern Orchid growers. The crowded pseudo-bulbs are surmounted by a single, leathery leaf and the slender spikes, about eighteen inches tall, carry about half a dozen flowers, two inches broad, white, with yellow lines on the lip. A Mexican species, introduced in 1832. *Bot. Mag.*, t. 3957.

L. ANCEPS, *Lindl.*—A graceful, beautiful and variable, winter-flowering species, formerly very popular. First introduced by the Messrs. Loddiges, in 1835, from Mexico. The stout, ribbed pseudo-bulbs usually carry a single leaf, and occasionally two leaves, about six inches long. The semi-erect spikes are somewhat arched by the weight of from two to five flowers which are seldom less than four inches across. The comparatively narrow sepals and petals are light purplish-rose, but the elongated lip is bright crimson-purple, with yellow markings in the throat. The side lobes are infolded, except at the tips, and the apical portion is tongue-shaped. *Bot. Mag.*, t. 3804; *Orch. Alb.*, II, t. 75.

High prices were often paid for very fine or distinct forms and among the three dozen named varieties the most notable are ALBA, pure white; DAWSONIANA, with larger and rounded, white flowers; AMESIANA; KIEN-ASTIANA, white, rose lip; SANDERIANA, very like DAWSONIANA; SCHRÖ-DERAE, rose sepals and petals, maroon lip; and VEITCHII, rose-purple lip.

L. AUTUMNALIS, *Lindl.*—Closely allied to *L. anceps*, the chief difference being found in the more open side lobes, and broader, rounded apical portions of the lip; and, of course, it produces its sweetly-scented flowers in the Autumn. The tapering pseudo-bulbs are usually diphyllous and the reddish spike, generally two feet tall, bears from five to six four-inch flowers of rose-purple colour, with a white throat to the purple-tipped lip. Introduced about the year 1836, and found in the highlands of Mexico. This and *L. anceps* thrive in an intermediate temperature, with plenty of atmospheric moisture during the growing period. *Bot. Mag.*, t. 3817; *Bot. Reg.*, 1839, t. 27.

Several varieties have been recorded and the one named ATRORUBENS is the most richly coloured.

L. CINNABARINA, *Lindl.*—A slender grower, with single-leafed stems from six to ten inches tall. The slender, eighteen-inch spike is racemose and bears from six to twelve, somewhat small, bright cinnabar-red flowers. This attractive species was introduced in 1836 and is a native of Minas Geraes. The flowers open in succession in Spring, consequently the display is a long one. *Bot. Mag.*, t. 4302; *Mag. Bot.*, VII, p. 193.

L. CRISPA, *Lindl.*—This pretty, but now rather rare, species from the mountains of Rio de Janeiro was sent to the R.H.S. in 1826 and flowered in the Society's gardens at Chiswick, in 1827. It has eight-inch stems, each with a single, long leaf; the spike of four or more flowers is stout and erect. The sepals and petals are narrowed towards the bases, the latter having wavy or crisped margins; they are white, or tinted with purple. The lip has short side lobes and a long, wavy-edged apical portion that is vivid purple, with fine veins of purple in the whitish, or yellowish, throat. *Bot. Reg.*, t. 1172; *Mag. Bot.*, V, p. 5.

DENDROBIUM THWAITESIAE, VEITCH'S VAR.

L. FLAVA, *Lindl.*—A dwarf species, with stout stems and foot-long peduncle of bright orange-coloured flowers of modest size, but there are several on the spike. The lip is wavy and often of deep orange. A native of the Brazilian province of Minas Geraes, it was introduced in 1839, and has been used extensively by hybridists on account of its rich colour.

L. FURFURACEA, *Lindl.*—Of lowly habit, with ovoid pseudo-bulbs scarcely three inches long, usually monophyllous. Spikes rather short, with two or three four-inch flowers, rose-purple, with a rich purple apex to the lip. Found at high elevations in Mexico and introduced in 1832. Somewhat rare and not frequently cultivated. *Bot. Mag.*, t. 3810; *Bot. Reg.*, 839, t. 20.

L. HARPOPHYLLA, *Rchb. f.*—A plant of neat habit, with slender, mono-phyllous stems about a foot tall. The spike is scarcely so long as the leaves and carries four or more three-inch flowers of a bright orange-red shade, with a whitish, toothed edge to the recurved apex of the lip. A showy, South Brazilian Orchid, introduced about 1865. Useful to the hybridist for the production of bright-coloured hybrids. *Orch. Alb.*, III, t. 117.

L. JONGHEANA, *Rchb. f.*—Not frequently seen in cultivation, but is a very showy, dwarf species, introduced from Southern Brazil in 1834. The short spike seldom has more than one, large, flattish flower, with rose-purple sepals and petals and a yellow disc on the white-throated lip. *Bot. Mag.*, t. 6038.

L. MONOPHYLLA, *N.E. Br.*—A native of Jamaica, this beautiful little species was discovered by Dr. Bancroft, but appears to have been lost to cultivation until re-discovered by Sir Daniel Morris in 1887, on trees growing from 3,000 to 5,000 feet above sea level. Needs comparatively cool treatment. Of tufted habit, the stems are about eight inches tall, prominently sheathed, with one narrow leaf. The short, slender spike carries a solitary flower rarely more than two inches broad, with narrow sepals and petals and a tiny lip, all of vivid orange-scarlet colouring. For amateurs to whom size is no criterion of value, this is a delightful and very distinct Orchid. *Bot. Mag.*, t. 6683.

L. PERRINII, *Lindl.*—Introduced from Rio de Janeiro several years before 1838, L. PERRINII has never been very plentiful in British collec-tions. The single-leafed pseudo-bulbs are about eight inches tall, with short spikes of about two flowers, that are four or five inches broad.

The sepals and petals are rose-purple, while the prominent lip is crimson-purple, with a pale yellow disc on the white throat. Can usually be depended upon to flower in early Winter. *Bot. Mag.*, t. 1838, as *Cattleya Perrinii; Mag. Bot.*, XIII, p. 5.

L. PUMILA, *Rchb. f.*—The terete stems of this charming species are barely three inches long, and monophyllous. The short spike carries one beautifully proportioned flower, nearly four inches broad, and of a lively rose-purple shade. The petals are much broader than the sepals. The lip is somewhat tubular, as the forward ends of the infolded side lobes spread outwards and join up with the spreading, rounded apex, the whole being crimson-purple, with a central, triangular, pale purple mark and a whitish, yellow-lined throat. Should be grown in a shallow pan in an intermediate temperature. A beautiful Orchid, of which there are two distinct varieties—DAYANA, with rounder flowers of deeper colour; and PRAESTANS, which has a crimson-purple, trumpet-shaped lip. L. PUMILA was introduced from British Guiana about 1837, but was probably discovered by Dr. Gardner in 1836. *Bot. Mag.*, t. 3656, as *Cattleya pumila; Sel. Orch.*, II, t. 32.

L. PURPURATA, *Lindl.*—Half a century ago, and less, this grand old Orchid was extremely popular and large numbers of plants were imported annually. It is not difficult to manage and a grower of average ability can produce large specimens, each with half a dozen spikes of three or more large, spreading flowers. The sepals and petals are too narrow for modern tastes, but the big trumpet-shaped lip, with its rounded, spreading, deep purple apex, and purple-veined, white throat, is very conspicuous. It is variable in colour, the sepals and petals ranging from white to deep rose-purple, while the lip may be crimson-purple. The late Mr. John Cypher, of Cheltenham, used to grow this species as large specimens and exhibit them at the early Summer shows.

Very many forms have received varietal names, notably SCHRÖDERAE, with white sepals and petals; ALBA, purest white, with light-coloured lip; ATROPURPUREA, deep rose; BRYSIANA, deep rose, with darker veins; RUSSELLIANA, white, shaded with lilac; and WILLIAMSII, rosy-lilac, with rich purple veins.

We owe the introduction of this fine Orchid to François Devos, who found it in Santa Catherina province in 1847 and sent plants to Messrs. Verschaffelt, Ghent, Belgium. *Sel. Orch.*, I, t. 40; *Orch. Alb.*, VI, t. 209.

L. RUBESCENS, *Lindl.*—A very dwarf plant with a slender, ten-inch spike of four or more rather small, shapely flowers. The lilac or rose sepals and petals are heavily marked with crimson-purple on the forward parts of the side lobes and the base of the front lobe of the lip. A pure white form is seen occasionally. *Bot. Mag.*, t. 4905; *Orch. Alb.*, IV, t. 163, as *L. peduncularis.*

L. SUPERBIENS, *Lindl.*—The stout, diphyllous, pseudo-bulbs of this species are ten or twelve inches long, while the jointed spikes may be four to six feet long, and carry from six to twenty flowers in a loose, terminal cluster. Each flower is about five inches broad, and has rather narrow, rose-coloured sepals and petals, with a dark purple or crimson apex, and a yellow disc to the lip. L. SUPERBIENS provides a connecting link between Laelia and Schomburgkia. Introduced through Hartweg, in 1842, but discovered previously by Mr. G. Ure-Skinner, in Guatemala. Needs comparatively cool treatment. *Bot. Mag.*, t. 4090; *Orch. Alb.*, VI, t. 244.

L. TENEBROSA, *Rolfe.*—A handsome, large-flowered species from Bahia, with the habit of *L. purpurata*, but one that has not fulfilled the hopes raised by its introduction. The reddish-brown, almost orange, sepals and petals are most attractive and set off the bold crimson-purple, rose-edged lip. Several more brightly-coloured forms have appeared, the best of these being TRING PARK var., and WALTON GRANGE var. *Reichenbachia*, 2nd Ser., II, t. 33.

L. XANTHINA, *Lindl.*—An interesting species introduced from Brazil in 1858. The monophyllous pseudo-bulbs are about eight inches long, and the spike bears three to five smallish flowers that are prized for their clear yellow sepals and petals and the small, white-throated, yellow-based lip that is veined and shaded with crimson. *Orch. Alb.*, I, t. 23.

OTHER SPECIES

Other species, which have been in cultivation occasionally, include L. BOOTHIANA, *Rchb. f.* (*L. lobata*); L. GOULDIANA, probably a natural hybrid between *L. autumnalis* and *L. anceps;* L. GRANDIS, *Lindl.*, pale yellow (*Bot. Mag.*, t. 5553); L. MAJALIS, *Lindl.*, rosy-lilac (*Bot. Mag.*, t. 5667); and L. LUNDII, *Rchb. f.*, syn. *Bletia Lundii.*

HYBRIDS

Although pure Laelia hybrids are by no means so numerous as Cattleya hybrids there are many of them. A few of the best are L.

BRESEIS (*L. harpophylla* × *L. purpurata*); L. EDISSA (*L. anceps* × *L. purpurata*); L. EUTERPE (*L. crispa* × *L. pumila var. Dayana*); L. LATONA (*L. cinnabarina* × *L. purpurata*); L. OWENIANA (*L. pumila var. Dayana* × *L. xanthina*); L. PILCHERI (*L. crispa* × *L. Perrinii*); L. SANDERAE (*L. xanthina* × *L. Dormanniana*); L. BELLA (*L. purpurata* × *L. grandiflora* —*majalis*); and L. FIREFLY (*L. Coronet* × *L. harpophylla*), a neat and beautiful orange-coloured hybrid.

LYCASTE, *Lindley*
Tribe, Vandeae; sub-tribe, Cyrtopodieae

The geographical distribution of this useful genus is pretty much the same as that of Odontoglossum, consequently most species may be grown in the Cool House, although a few do better in the cool end of the Intermediate House, with, for the most part, a more substantial rooting compost. Ample moisture is needed during the growing period, but less during the Winter and during the resting season of each species. L. SKINNERI is the most popular member of the genus as it flowers late in the year and the flowers last for a long time. With a few exceptions, Lycaste flowers are borne singly on an erect stem.

L. AROMATICA, *Lindl.*—This has short pseudo-bulbs, and leaves six to ten inches long. The short, slender scapes extend horizontally and usually carry one very sweetly-scented, golden-yellow flower about an inch and a half broad, with a brassy sheen; lip yellow, spotted with orange. Introduced from Mexico in 1826; a very pretty Orchid for a low-roofed house. *Bot. Reg.*, t. 1871.

L. CANDIDA, *Lindl.*—Another dwarf species, about a foot tall, discovered by Warscewicz about 1849. The two-inch flowers are pale green, or whitish, with spots or shadings of rose; lip white, with rose-purple dots. Often referred to *L. brevisparha, Klotzch. Orch. Rev.*, 1902, p. 113.

L. COSTATA, *Lindl.*—A sturdy grower, with short, diphyllous pseudo-bulbs and leaves about twenty inches long. The four-inch flowers are carried on an eight-inch stem and are ivory-white. The lateral sepals are very small, An attractive Orchid. *Bot. Mag.*, t. 5706; *Orch. Alb.*, VIII, t. 384.

L. CRUENTA, *Lindl.*—A beautiful, low-growing Orchid discovered in Guatemala in 1841. The pseudo-bulbs are short, diphyllous, and the leaves are about sixteen inches long. The stems are short and the greenish-yellow flowers are rather larger than those of *L. aromatica*, but scentless. There is usually a red blotch at the base of the lip. A free-flowering Orchid. *Orch. Alb.*, VIII, t. 375; *Bot. Reg.*, 1842, t. 13.

L. DEPPEI, *Lindl.*—An attractive species, with foot-long leaves—three or more—and short pseudo-bulbs. Stems about eight-inches tall; flowers four inches wide, with pale green, red-spotted sepals, pure white petals, and a yellow, red-spotted front lobe in the lip. *Bot. Mag.*, t. 3395; *Bot. Cab.*, t. 1612.

L. FULVESCENS, *Hook.*—The large, diphyllous pseudo-bulbs are sur-mounted by eighteen-inch leaves and the stems are about ten inches tall, each bearing a large, nodding, yellowish-brown flower with a fringed, orange-brown lip. Discovered in Columbia in 1842. *Bot. Mag.*, t. 4193.

L. GIGANTEA, *Lindl.*—The tallest species, with leaves over two feet long; stems somewhat shorter than the leaves. The large, spreading flowers have olive-green sepals and petals and a purplish, yellow-edged lip. Hartmeg discovered this striking Orchid in Ecuador in 1842. *Orch. Alb.*, IX, t. 408; *Bot. Mag.*, t. 5616.

L. LANIPES, *Lindl.*—A tall grower, with four-inch flowers that have greenish-white sepals, white petals, and an ivory-white, fringed lip.

L. LEUCANTHA, *Klotzsch*—In this tall species the four-inch flowers have green, brown-shaded sepals, whitish, yellow-tipped petals, and a light yellow lip with a cream-white central lobe. Discovered in Costa Rica by Warscewicz in 1849.

L. LOCUSTA, *Rchb. f.*—Very like *L. costata* in habit, with large green flowers and a fringed lip. The white column is very conspicuous. SANDER'S var. is a very fine form.

L. MACROBULBON, *Lindl.*—Much like *L. aromatica* and *L. cruenta*, but has larger pseudo-bulbs and fragrant, three-inch flowers, yellow or green-ish-yellow, with a brighter yellow lip that is sometimes spotted with crimson. *Bot. Mag.*, t. 4228, as *Maxillaria macrobulbon*.

L. MACROPHYLLA, *Lindl.*—A tall grower. The flowers are four-inches broad, with olive-green sepals, shaded with red; white, rose-spotted petals, and a white, red-marked lip. *Orch. Alb.*, V, 230; as *L. plana;* and V. III, 306.

L. SKINNERI, *Lindl.*—No Lycaste is so popular as this attractive, sturdy, free-flowering species, that is extremely variable in floral colouring. Discovered in Guatemala by G. Ure-Skinner, who brought home numerous plants in 1841, but it flowered first in the Rev. John Clowes' collection at Manchester in 1842. The leaves may be upwards of eighteen inches long and the stems about half as long, bearing a widespread, handsome flower from four to six inches broad. The sepals and petals are soft rose, with darker rose shadings; lip, whitish, or rose, with crimson spots. A score of forms have received varietal names and the most distinct of these are ALBA, ALBA MAGNIFICA, ARMENIACA, PURPU-RATA, RUBELLA and VIRGINALIS. *Bot. Mag.*, t. 4445; *Mag. Bot.*, XI, p. 1; *Orch. Alb.*, V, t. 224 (Alba). *Reichenbachia*, Ser. II, t. 18 (*armeniaca*).

L. TETRAGONA, *Lindl.*—A distinct species, an outlier, introduced from southern Brazil in 1827, and first flowered at Kew, two years later. The four-angled pseudo-bulbs bear a single leaf, up to eighteen inches long, while the short stems carry three or four yellowish-green flowers, marked with brownish-yellow; lip whitish and maroon-violet. *Bot. Mag.*, t. 2146; *Bot. Reg.*, t. 1428, as *Maxillaria tetragona*.

HYBRIDS

Some of the most beautiful of the numerous Lycaste hybrids are L. BALLIAE (*L. macrophylla* × *L. Skinneri*); L. IMSCHOOTIANA (*L. cruenta* × *L. Skinneri*); L. HYBRIDA (*L. Deppei* × *L. Skinneri*); L. BRUGENSE (*L. gigantea* × *Skinneri*); L. GRATRIXIAE (*L. candida* × *L. macrophylla*); L. LADY COLMAN (*L. Locusta, Sander's var.* × *L. imschootiana var. alba*); and L. SIR JEREMIAH COLMAN (*L. lanipes* × *L. Skinneri var. alba magnifica*).

MASDEVALLIA, *Ruiz et Pavon*

Tribe, Epidendreae; sub-tribe, Pleurothalleae

It is regrettable that Masdevallias have lost much of the popularity they enjoyed a few years ago. They are fascinating Orchids and a few amateurs were to be found who devoted a whole house to their cultivation, while every grower cultivated a few species or hybrids as these added to the interest of the collection, and in many instances provided flowers of brilliant colour and unusual form.

The general uniformity of habit is remarkable in so large a genus; the plants are tufted and have no pseudo-bulbs, consequently they need no decided season of rest; moreover, as the majority are found at considerable elevation on the mountains of Central and Southern America, they may be grown in an Odontoglossum compost, in a Cool or Intermediate House, where abundance of atmospheric moisture is maintained. In very many Orchids the lip is the most prominent part of the flower and not infrequently the most colourful, but in Masdevallias the more or less connate sepals provide the chief attraction and as these are extended into tails—which vary greatly in length, according to the species—the flower assumes an un-Orchid-like appearance. The species and hybrids which bear a single flower on a comparatively tall and slender stem, are those of the highest horticultural value. To lovers of the curious, Masdevallias are intensely interesting, therefore, to a brief selection of the more attractive species a list of "botanical" species is added.

M. BELLA, *Rchb. f.*—Somewhat like *M. Chimaera*, but easily distinguished by its large, shell-like lip, which is white. The sepals are about equal, broad at the base and ending in a slender three-inch tail; tawny-yellow, curiously and irregularly marked with chocolate-red; tails red. Petals very small, yellow, spotted with red. The large, solitary flowers are carried on a pendulous stem and have a Puckish appearance. Leaves about six inches long. *Lindenia*, VI, t. 257.

M. CAUDATA, *Reich.*—A variable species introduced from Colombia about 1874. Leaves three inches long; stems about the same length, bearing a single flower, an inch and a half wide, with long, slender tails to the sepals. The upper sepal is concave, yellow, with red longitudinal veins; lateral sepals mauve-purple, mottled with white. Petals and lip very tiny. A very pretty, free-flowering Orchid. *Bot. Mag.*, t. 6372; *Orch. Alb.*, I, t. 5; *Reichenbachia*, Ser. I, t. 13 (var. *xanthocorys*).

M. CHIMAERA, *Rchb. f.*—The mythological name of this species suggests its variability, and its quaint, almost grotesque appearance. The narrow leaves are barely eight inches long and the slender, erect or semi-pendulous scapes may be from twelve to eighteen inches long and bear from three to five flowers that open in succession, therefore the stem should not be cut when a faded flower is removed. The flowers are among the largest found in the genus. The sepals are broadly-ovate and rather abruptly contracted into tails three or four inches in length, hairy, yellow freely spotted with reddish-purple; tails, yellowish-brown; petals tiny; lip small, saccate, white.

The principal named varieties are GORGONA, densely spotted, very hairy, with an orange lip; BACKHOUSEANA, with larger flowers, but shorter tails, yellow, spotted with red; ROEZLII, very heavily and darkly spotted; WALLISII, with lighter, almost white, ground-colour, and brownish spots; SANDERIANA, with large and very long-tailed, yellowish flowers, marked with crimson; and WINNIANA, very like ROEZLII, but with heavier markings and a yellowish, purple-dotted band across the upper sepal. *Bot. Mag.*, t. 6152 (var. *Wallisii*); *Orch. Alb.*, V, t. 203 and VI, t. 243; *Reichenbachia*, I, t. 19 (var. *Backhouseana*).

M. COCCINEA, *Lindl.*—A beautiful but extremely variable species introduced from Colombia in 1869. Leaves six to nine inches long; stems a foot or more long, each surmounted by one handsome flower in which the showy part consists of the two broad, flattish, pointed, lateral sepals, the upper sepal being reduced to a tail-like process. The colour is pinkish-rose or magenta-purple; petals and lip inconspicuous. About thirty forms have received varietal names and some of the best are ARMENIACA, apricot, flushed with crimson; ATROSANGUINEA, blood-red; FLAMBEAU, crimson-scarlet; GRANDIFLORA, large, rich magenta, flushed with crimson; HARRYANA, large, vivid crimson-red; SANGUINEA, bright-crimson, flushed with orange; VIOLACEA, violet-magenta; and WALKERIANA, very large, brilliant crimson. *Bot. Mag.*, t. 5990; *Orch. Alb.*, V, 224; III, t. 105; and III, t. 110.

M. DAVISII, *Rchb. f.*—A Peruvian species belonging to the Coccinea group. The upper sepal has a wide, triangular base and an inch-long tail; lateral sepals broad, pointed, yellow, very lightly marked with orange. Distinct, and showy. *Bot. Mag.*, t. 6190; *Orch. Alb.* II, t. 76.

M. ESTRADAE, *Rchb. f.*—Very dwarf and free flowering. Flowers solitary, on three-inch stems; upper sepal concave; lateral sepals, broad and flat, with two-inch tails; yellow and mauve-purple petals; and a small, white lip. The variety XANTHINA has honey-yellow flowers. *Bot. Mag.*, t. 6171.

M. FLORIBUNDA, *Lindl.*—Another dwarf, with solitary flowers on four-inch stems; buff-yellow, dotted with brown-purple. The dorsal sepal has a longer tail than the lateral sepals. Very floriferous; a little gem.

M. IGNEA, *Rchb. f.*—A very beautiful and somewhat variable member of the Coccinea group, and one of the most brilliantly coloured. Upper sepal narrow, with a two-inch tail that curves forward and over the centre of the flower; lateral sepals an inch broad, spreading apart towards their abruptly-pointed tips; brilliant cinnabar-red, flushed with crimson. *Bot. Mag.*, t. 5962; *Orch. Alb.*, II, t. 62.

M. MACRURA, *Rchb. f.*—A robust species, introduced from Colombia in 1876. The leaves are ten or twelve inches long and about three inches wide. Flowers large, fleshy, solitary, on foot-long stems. The bases of the sepals are contracted into a short, ribbed tube; tawny-yellow, studded with dark purple worts; tails stout, four inches long. *Bot. Mag.*, t. 7164.

M. MUSCOSA, *Rchb. f.*—Although this species is only two inches tall and therefore one of the midgets in a family of dwarfs, it is free-flowering and remarkable for the extreme sensitiveness of the small lip, which shuts up and encloses any tiny insect that alights on it. The late Mr. W. J. Bean, of Kew, discovered this sensitive mechanism. The six-inch stems carry one flower, about three-quarters of an inch broad, with slender tails ; buff-yellow; lip yellow, with an apricot-maroon blotch. *Bot. Mag.*, t. 7664.

M. RACEMOSA, *Lindl.*—A particularly distinct species, introduced from Colombia in 1883. Although the leaves are only four to six inches long, the racemose inflorescence is from nine and fifteen inches tall. The rounded flowers are borne alternately on opposite sides of the scape and there may be a dozen of them. The lateral sepals, over an inch wide, are without tails, but the tiny upper sepal is pointed; brilliant orange-red, flushed with crimson; petals and lip very tiny, white. Showy and interesting.

M. RADIOSA, *Rchb. f.*—Six to eight inches tall; spikes decumbent, bearing three or four flowers in succession. The inch-wide bases of the sepals form a rounded triangle, from which the three-inch tails are thrust out abruptly, the whole flower, with its minute petals and white, rose-lined lip, suggesting the appearance of some small, grotesque prehistoric animal, with feelers searching for prey. The tawny-yellow ground colour of the sepals is almost obliterated by an abundance of blackish-purple dots.

M. SCHLIMII, *Lindl.*—Leaves a foot long and three inches broad; spike longer than the leaves, racemose, with six or more medium-sized flowers.

The upper sepal is light yellow, concave; lateral sepals yellow, freely mottled with brown-purple. Tails three inches long. *Bot. Mag.*, t. 6740.

M. TOVARENSIS, *Rchb. f.*—A popular species, introduced from Venezuela in 1863. Leaves about six inches long; stems about the same length, stout, with several flowers at the apex, opening successively, consequently the stem should not be cut when a flower has faded and is removed, indeed two-year old stems have been known to produce flowers. The upper sepal has a triangular base and a tail nearly two inches long; the sepals are connate almost to the very short tails. The whole flower is purest white, glistening and semi-transparent. *Bot. Mag.*, t. 5505.

M. VEITCHIANA, *Rchb. f.*—The very large flowers place this species in the first rank, horticulturally. They are about three inches long, vertically; the upper sepal is unusually well-developed and has a long tail. The lateral sepals are broad, connate for less than half their length, and have short tails. The colour is brilliant orange-scarlet, flushed with crimson-purple; petals and lip tiny, white. *Bot. Mag.*, t. 5739; *Sel. Orch.*, II, t. 33.

OTHER SPECIES

Lovers of comparatively small, grotesque, or wonderful among Orchids will find abundant interest and fascination in the genus *Masdevallia*. The following, although not so showy as those described above, have their own attractions for the student of botany:—

M. AMABILIS, M. ARMINII, M. BARLAEANA, M. CARDERI, M. CALURA, M. CHESTERTONI, M. CUCULLATA, M. DEMISSA, M. ELEPHANTICEPS, M. EPHIPPIUM, M. GARGANTUA, M. GEMMATA, M. INFLATA, M. LEONTOGLOSSA, M. MELANOPUS, M. PERISTERIA, M. ROSEA, M. SIMULA, M. TRIANGULARIS, M. TRIARISTELLA, M. TROGLODYTES, M. VELIFERA, M. WAGENERIANA, M. POLYSTICTA, and M. XANTHINA.

HYBRIDS

New hybrid Masdevallias are rarely forthcoming, but several of those raised several years ago are quite handsome and these include M. BOCKING HYBRID (*M. cucullata* × *M. Veitchiana*); M. CHELSONII (*M. Veitchiana* × *M. amabilis*); M. COURTAULDIANA (*M. rosea* × *M. caudata*); M. GAIRIANA (*M. Veitchiana* × *M. Davisii*); M. HINKSIANA (*M. tovarensis* × *M. ignea*); M. HEATHII (*M. Veitchiana* × *M. ignea var. superba*); M. KIMBALLEANA (*M. Veitchiana* × *M. caudata*); M.

MEASURESIANA (*M. amabilis* × *M. tovarensis*); M. MUNDYANA (*M. ignea var. aurantiaca* × *M. Veitchiana*); and M. SHUTTRYANA (*M. caudata var. Shuttleworthii* × *M. coccinea var. Harryana*).

MAXILLARIA, *Ruiz et Pavon*
Tribe, Vandeae; sub-tribe, Maxillarieae

Rather more than a hundred and fifty years ago two Spanish botanists, Ruiz and Pavon, explored the Andes of Peru and discovered many Orchids. They founded the genus Maxillaria, but their description was so imperfect that several Orchids subsequently placed in it were eventually removed to other genera.

Species of Maxillaria are numerous, but comparatively few are horticulturally important. All are natives of South or Central America, some being found in the very warm valleys of Guiana and Brazil, some in the West Indies, and others at considerable altitudes on the Andes, therefore they are not all cool-house subjects. In general, an Odontoglossum compost is suitable, with ample drainage, a moist atmosphere and a fair amount of shade. Broad pans are the best receptacles for species that spread by means of their extending rhizomes; those with clustered pseudo-bulbs may be grown in pots, but several, like M. Sanderiana, appear to grow best when suspended near the roof glass, in teakwood baskets. Maxillarias have persistent, leathery leaves and the flowers are carried singly on erect stems.

M. FUCATA, *Rchb. f.*—A species with clustered pseudo-bulbs, leaves about fifteen inches long and stems six or seven inches long. The broadly expanded, thick-textured flowers have a diameter of about two and a half inches; the sepals are dull brownish-red, with white bases and yellow tips, the yellow portion boldly spotted with bright red-brown; petals small, reflexed at the ends, yellow, with red marks on the whitish base; lip rather small, yellow, marked with red-brown at the base. The variety HABSCHII has whitish sepals and petals and a pale yellow lip; it was given specific rank by Reichenbach. *Bot. Mag.*, t. 9376.

M. GRANDIFLORA, *Lindl.*—This handsome Peruvian Orchid has had many names—*M. eburneum, M. Lehmanni* and even *Dendrobium grandiflorum*. The pseudo-bulbs are short and carry one fifteen-inch leaf. The stems are usually less than six inches long while the flowers are large, milky-white, with small petals of similar colour; the lip has purple side lobes and a yellowish central lobe.

M. HOUTTEANA, *Rchb. f.*—Introduced from Guatemala and first flowered in Europe in 1849, this has always been a rare Orchid. Leaves, pseudo-bulbs and stems are short; flowers tawny-brown, edged with yellow; petals small; lip orange-yellow, with purple spots.

M. LONGISEPALA, *Rolfe*—Introduced in 1890, from Venezuela, and although the sepals are rather narrow, they are four inches long, making the flower quite attractive. The stems are about six inches tall. Sepals light purplish-brown, petals shorter and of similar colour; lip light yellow, marked with thin lines of red-brown. *Lindenia*, VI, t. 248.

M. LUTEO-ALBA, *Lindl.*—A tall grower, with large, fragrant, reddish-purple, narrow sepals that are white at the base. *Orch. Alb.*, III, t. 106.

M. PICTA, *Hook.*—One of the smallest, but also one of the most useful and easily-grown species. The four-inch stems carry one small, slightly fragrant flower. The narrow sepals and petals are tawny-yellow, with a few white marks. Lip white, with purple markings. A charming button-hole flower.

M. PORPHYROSTELE, *Rchb. f.*—Very like *M. picta*, but smaller, with brighter yellow colouring. *Bot. Mag.*, t. 6477.

M. SANDERIANA, *Rchb. f.*—The most handsome species, introduced from Ecuador in 1883–84. Of neat habit, its semi-erect stems are about six inches long and the flowers are about six inches broad. The dorsal sepal is hooded and the lateral sepals, broad at the base, have pointed ends; the colour, as also in the shorter petals, is white, heavily marked with brilliant red at their bases. Lip purplish-red, tipped with white. *Reichenbachia*, I, t. 25.

M. SANGUINEA, *Rolfe*—The smallish flowers of this narrow-leafed species, although carried on short stems, are very attractive. The red-brown sepals are edged and tipped with yellow, while the petals are yellow, spotted with crimson; lip red, tipped with creamy-white.

M. TENUIFOLIA, *Lindl.*—A very distinct species, with narrow leaves and widely-separated pseudo-bulbs. Flowers about two inches broad, red, speckled with soft yellow; lip red, tipped with yellow and spotted with purple. *Bot. Reg.*, t. 1986.

M. VENUSTA, *Lindl.*—Discovered in Venezuela in 1842 and introduced in 1851, this is a very pretty Orchid, with pure white sepals and

MILTONIA PRINCE OF ORANGE

petals and a buff-yellow lip with red spots. The flowers are about six inches broad and very beautiful. *Bot. Mag.*, t. 5296.

OTHER SPECIES

Other species of note are M. ACUTIFOLIA, M. CANDIDA, M. DICHROMA, M. IRRORATA, M. LEPIDOTA, M. NIGRESCENS, M. RUFESCENS and M. SCURRILIS.

MILTONIA, *Lindley*

Tribe, Vandeae; sub-tribe, Oncidieae

Although a small genus, Miltonia is wholly useful horticulturally, but it gave botanists many headaches as most of the species have at one time or another been placed in other genera, notably Oncidium, Odontoglossum, Brassia, Macrochilus, and Cyrtochilum. Moreover, there has been a good deal of shuffling with the species.

There are species from Colombia and Brazil, and all succeed under the conditions provided for Odontoglossums, except that slightly warmer conditions are needed during the Winter, while the large-flowered, brilliantly coloured modern hybrids appreciate a cool-intermediate temperature at all times as they are not quite so easily cultivated as *M. vexillaria* and its many beautiful varieties. Shallow pans or pots are suitable receptacles and the compost may contain more Sphagnum moss than usually allowed for Odontoglossums. Fairly heavy shading is necessary and at no time must the plants be allowed to become dry at the roots. Miltonias make a brave display when in flower, but, unfortunately, the flowers are of little value when cut and placed in water.

M. CANDIDA, *Lindl.*—Although by no means lacking in beauty, this Brazilian species is not so attractive as several other members of the genus. The stiff spikes, about sixteen inches long, carry three to five three-inch flowers, with greenish-brown sepals and yellowish petals that are blotched with bright red-brown. The convolute lip has a rounded, wavy apex, and is white, with a purple stain at the base. In most species the lip is large, flat, and by far the most important part of the flower. *Bot. Mag.*, t. 3793; *Orch. Alb.*, V, t. 200.

M. CLOWESII, *Lindl.*—The compressed pseudo-bulbs have a pair of long leaves and the spike may be from eighteen to twenty-four inches long, with six to ten three-inch flowers. The sepals and petals are red-brown, marked and tipped with yellow; the white lip is pointed and has a violet-purple throat. *Bot. Mag.*, t. 4109; *Mag. Bot.*, IX, p. 241.

M. CUNEATA, *Lindl.*—A Brazilian species, slightly dwarfer than *M. candida*. Several three-inch flowers are borne on the erect spike. The chestnut-brown sepals and petals are tipped with yellow, while the white lip has rose-coloured marks at the base. *Orch. Alb.*, I, t. 46.

M. ENDRESII, *Nicholson*—A very distinct and somewhat rare species, discovered by Warscewicz in 1849, but the introduction of living plants was due to Endres. The flattish flowers are of medium size and notable for their long petioles. Sepals and petals white, blotched with purple at their bases; lip broad, white or yellowish, with a large red-purple base and a bright yellow crest. *Bot. Mag.*, t. 6163.

M. FLAVESCENS, *Lindl.*—A very pretty, dwarf, Brazilian species, introduced in 1832. The spikes carry from seven to ten two-inch flowers, pale yellow, with red-purple streaks on the white, rather short, lip. *Bot. Reg.*, t. 1627, as *Cyrtochilum flavescens*.

M. PHALAENOPSIS, *Nicholson*—A Colombian species discovered by Schlim and introduced in 1850. Of slender habit, it has short spikes of smallish, flat flowers, with white, rounded sepals and petals, and a broad, bilobed lip that is white, with radiating streaks extending from the two large purple stains; the side lobes are flattened and of similar colouring, but more brightly marked. *Sel. Orch.*, I, t. 30; *Monogr. Od.*, t. 3.

M. REGNELLI, *Rchb. f.*—This Brazilian species is of similar habit to *M. vexillaria*, but has narrow leaves, and carries a few, three-inch flowers on the short spikes. The sepals and petals are white, shaded with rose at the base; lip soft rose, margined with white, and sometimes streaked with purple; crest bright yellow. PURPUREA is a form with richer colours. *Bot. Mag.*, t. 5436; *Orch. Alb.*, II, t. 72.

M. ROEZLII, *Nicholson*—A beautiful, compact, Colombian species, introduced about 1874. The large, four-inch flowers are flat, white, with a purple blotch at the base of each petal, and yellow stains at the base of the wide lip. *Bot. Mag.*, t. 6083; *Reichenbachia*, II, t. 31.

M. SCHRÖDERIANA, *Rchb. f.*—Originally described by Reichenbach as an Odontoglossum, this Costa Rican species has a very distinct floral design and a plant with several erect spikes, each with half a dozen flowers, is no mean ornament in a collection of Orchids. Unfortunately it now appears to be rather rare in cultivation. The sweetly-scented flowers are rather less than three inches by vertical measurement. The petals and dorsal sepal point upwards, the former slightly incurved at the tips, but they, like the lateral, deflexed sepals, are bright red-brown, marked and tipped with light yellow. The longish lip is gently constricted at about half its length, with a rose-purple base and a whitish apical half. Baron Schröder exhibited a specimen before the Royal Horticultural Society in January, 1885—the first record of flowering—hence the name. *Orch. Alb.*, VIII, t. 382; *Reichenbachia*, II, t. 96.

M. SPECTABILIS, *Lindl.*—A beautiful Orchid but not always easily managed. It is the Brazilian species on which the genus was founded and is one of the finest of all Miltonias. The sepals and petals are white, or creamy-white, often tinted with rose at the base. The large, obovate, flat lip is bright rose-purple, edged with a paler shade, or with white. Crest yellow. The spike is shorter than the six to eight-inch, pale green leaves, and seldom carries more than one flower. Many varietal forms have been described, but the best are MORELIANA, with bright rose-purple sepals and petals and a plum-purple, rose-coloured veining; and VIRGINALIS, white with a rosy blotch at the base of the lip.

M. VEXILLARIA, *Nichols*—A grand Orchid, especially when grown as a large specimen, with several spikes of its flattish, three-inch flowers. The sepals and petals are light rose, and the bilobed lip is of similar or deeper colour, with a whitish base, or mask, on which there are radiating yellow or orange lines. It is, however, variable in colour, consequently many varietal names have been given to the more distinct colour forms.

The eighteen-inch spikes carry from three to nine flowers and as a well-developed pseudo-bulb may produce two spikes, it must be recognised as an easily grown and floriferous species. A few of the more distinct varieties are CHELSIENSIS, of rich colour; LEOPOLDII, remarkable for the crimson blotch at the base of the lip; MEMORIA G. D. OWEN, a grand Orchid with sepals and petals of rich rose, the lower sepals marked prominently with crimson-purple, while the broad lip is rose, with a crimson-purple mask; and ALBA pure white, except for the faint basal markings of rose on the sepals and petals. Discovered in New Granada in 1866–67, and apparently flowered for the first time, in 1872, at Chelsea. *Bot. Mag.*, t. 6037; *Sel. Orch.*, II, t. 38; *Monogr. Od.*, t. 29, as *Odontoglossum vexillarium.*

K

M. Warscewiczii, *Reich.*—Somewhat like *M. Schröderiana*, but with smaller flowers and more spreading sepals and petals that are undulated, reddish-brown, with white tips; lip rose-purple, with a large red-brown basal area. A very free-flowering Orchid that might easily be mistaken for an Oncidium. A Colombian species, discovered in 1830 and introduced in 1868. *Bot. Mag.*, t. 5843; *Orch. Alb.*, V, t. 216.

HYBRIDS

Several natural hybrids were formerly prized, notably M. Bluntii (probably *M. spectabilis* × *O. Clowesii*), with yellow sepals and petals.

The wonderful development of home-raised hybrids with brilliant colouring commenced with M. bleuana (*M. vexillaria* × *M. Roezlii*), raised in 1889. This has white, rose-based sepals and petals and a white lip, red-brown mask and a golden crest. Then followed M. Hyeana (*M. Bleuana* × *M. vexillaria*); M. Lycaena (*M. Lord Lambourne* × *M. Princess Margaret*); M. Jules Hye de Crom (*M. Hyeana* × *M. vexillaria*); M. St. Andre (*M. Roezlii* × *M. Bleuana*); and a host of others, culminating in the large-lipped hybrids, gorgeous in ruby, crimson and red-purple, of which M. Bruges (*M. Lycaena* × *M. Princess Astrid*); M. Chelsea (*M. Sanderiana* × *M. Wm. Pitt*); M. Mrs. J. B. Crum (*M. Lycaena* × *M. Princess Mary*); M. Pulchra (*M. Lycaena* × *M. Wm. Pitt*); M. Reine Elisabeth (*M. Bleuana* × *M. Roezlii*); M. Southport (*M. Nadia* × *M. Wm. Pitt*); M. Vida (*M. Bleuana* × *M. Wm. Pitt*); M. Wm. Pitt (*M. Isabel Sander* × *M. Reine Elizabeth*); and M. Sanguinea (*M. Mrs. J. B. Crum var. Chelsea* × *M. Bruges*), are a few of the finest. M. Solfatari (*St. Andre* × *O. Sanderiana*); and M. Prince of Orange, are yellow, while M. Maiden's Blush, is flushed with pink.

NANODES, *Lindley*

Tribe, Epidendreae; sub-tribe, Epidendreae

A monotypic genus, as founded by Dr. Lindley, but referable to a sub-genus of Epidendrum. It is, however, so distinct horticulturally that we retain it under its old and popular name.

N. Medusae, *Rchb. f.*—Growths tufted, stout, pendulous, and six-inches to a foot in length, closely set with opposite, alternate, imbricating, fleshy, lanceolate and pointed leaves some three inches in length.

MILTONIA SANGUINEA

The flowers are terminal, usually solitary, about three inches broad; sepals and petals green, with wine-red centres; lip large, roundish-cordate, handsome, beautifully fringed, rich wine-purple. *Bot. Mag.*, t. 5723.

NEOMOOREA, *Rolfe*
Tribe, Vandeae; sub-tribe, Stanhopieae

A monotypic genus originally named *Moorea*, but as this name has been used for a genus of totally different plants, the title was altered to NEOMOOREA ; it commemorates Mr. (later Sir) Frederick Moore, who, when in charge of the Glasnevin Botanic Garden, Dublin, purchased the plant, with other Orchids imported from Peru, at a sale, and, when it flowered, discovered it was entirely new to science. Still a rare Orchid.

N. IRRORATA, *Rolfe*.—Pseudo-bulbs short, diphyllous; leaves about two feet long, plicate, lanceolate. Spikes produced basally, erect, about eighteen inches tall, with a dozen or so of two-inch, roundish, broadly-expanded flowers of stout texture. Sepals and petals reddish-brown, whitish at the base; lip with prominent, straw-yellow, purple-lined side lobes, and a narrow, pointed centre lobe of similar colour. *Bot. Mag.* t. 7362.

ODONTOGLOSSUM, *Humboldt, Bonpland et Kunth*
Tribe, Vandeae; sub-tribe, Oncidieae

By general consent it is agreed that the genus Odontoglossum includes many of the most beautiful of all Orchids. The greatest concentration of species is found in Colombia, but other members of the family extend the geographical distribution through Ecuador and down well into Peru. A few outliers are scattered in Central America, from Southern Mexico, though Guatemala, almost down to the Panama area, but in all instances the species make their homes at considerable altitudes along the Pacific Coastal area; they show no inclination to migrate eastwards, with one exception, *O. constrictum*, found near Caracas, on the Atlantic side.

The great majority of Odontoglossums grow naturally under cool conditions, notwithstanding the tropical conditions of the countries they inhabit, as their altitudinal range is from 5,000 ft. to 10,000 ft. above sea level, where the atmosphere is saturated with moisture and the trees on which they grow afford shade from the brilliant sunshine. The higher the altitude the lower the temperature, but, in general, the latter may be regarded as ranging from 40° at night to 80° or 90° on the hottest days. As a general rule, the Mexican species need more warmth than those from the southern half of the American continent. British growers often find it very difficult to provide sufficiently moist and cool conditions for Odontoglossums during the heat of Summer, when artificial heat is absolutely unnecessary and the shading heavy. A continuously saturated moisture-staging is eminently desirable for Odontoglossums. Few species have a definite resting season, but the few include O. GRANDE and its allies, and, as with all other Orchids, less water is needed at the roots after growth is completed, and during the Winter.

Comparatively small, well-drained pots will accommodate most species, while a large proportion of Sphagnum to Osmunda fibre will provide a suitable compost for the roots. A small quantity of sharp grit may be used as an aid to the free percolation of water, while the more robust species will enjoy the addition of a small quantity of semi-decayed Beech or Oak leaves.

Odontoglossums need to be potted firmly, but disturbance and the provision of new rooting materials should take place only in very early Spring or early Autumn. Spring potting permits the plants to re-establish themselves before the heat of Summer makes them uncomfortable; early Autumn potting allows the roots time to permeate the new compost before Winter sets in.

Very many growers have no choice in the matter, but wherever it is possible to do so the Odontoglossum house should be erected where a not too distant deciduous tree prevents the sun from shining directly upon it during the middle hours of the day.

Although many species retain their popularity it must be confessed that hybrids are more extensively grown, as they provide a wide range of form and colour, and, for the most part, are more easily managed. ODONTOGLOSSUM CRISPUM has an exciting history and extremely high prices have been paid for outstanding varieties which have appeared in importations, but to-day, thanks largely to Messrs. Charlesworth & Co., there is a goodly supply of beautiful seedlings, raised from the finest and purest white varieties. Pure and improved home-raised strains of other species might prove to be a valuable commercial proposition. Only the most desirable species, horticulturally, are described below, as the genus is an extensive one. With a few exceptions, Odontoglossums have ovoid, compressed (not rounded) pseudo-bulbs, crowned with a pair of shining, bright green, long-persisting, strap-shaped leaves.

O. BICTONIENSE, *Lindl.*—Probably the first Odontoglossum to reach this country alive, O. BICTONIENSE was discovered by Mr. Ure-Skinner and flowered for the first time under cultivation in 1835, at Bicton, hence its name. Fairly robust, it has stout, erect, tall spikes of numerous and attractive, but smallish, flowers. It is somewhat variable in colour, but, usually, the sepals and petals are yellowish-green, with red-brown markings, but the large, heart-shaped, rose-coloured lip is the most attractive feature. A variety, ALBUM, has a white lip. *Bot. Mag.*, t. 3812; *Bot. Reg.*, 1846, t. 66.

O. CERVANTESII, *Lexarza*—A dwarf Mexican species with single-leafed pseudo-bulbs, and six-inch spikes of from four to six rounded flowers about two inches broad. The sepals and broader petals are white, streaked with red-brown at their bases, while the broad, apical portion of the lip is white, with a purple mask in front of the crest. Introduced in 1847. *Bot. Mag.*, t. 4923; *Orch. Alb.*, IV, t. 107.

O. CIRRHOSUM, *Lindl.*—A particularly elegant Orchid, introduced from Ecuador in 1875, usually with single-leafed pseudo-bulbs. The arching spike is occasionally branched and may have from a dozen to a score of flowers, each with a spread of four inches. The sepals and petals are narrow and taper gradually to a fine, thread-like point that curves backwards; the whitish ground colour is prettily spotted with red-brown or crimson. The lip also tapers to a fine point and is of similar colouring, with a bright yellow crest and radiating reddish lines. A distinct and charming species. *Bot. Mag.*, t. 6317; *Orch. Alb.*, IV, t. 151.

O. CITROSMUM, *Lindl.*—Although not so easily managed, this Mexican species introduced in 1838, was most successfully cultivated and flowered by an earlier generation of growers. It is undeniably beautiful and its pendant spikes of rounded, fragrant flowers invariably excite admiration. The new growths and spikes are produced simultaneously and when the former have developed into pseudo-bulbs, the plants need very little root moisture until new growth commences. Needs warmer conditions than most species. A shelf suspended near the roof glass in a stove or Cattleya house provides a suitable home for a species that merits all the skill a grower can bestow upon it. The white, or blush, sepals and petals provide a suitable setting for the broad, reniform, yellow-crested, deep-rose lip. Pure white, deep rose, and purple-spotted varieties have been in cultivation. *Sel. Orch.*, I, t. 28; *Monogr. Od.*, t. 6.

O. CORDATUM, *Lindl.*—The pseudo-bulbs of this species are rather widely placed on the rhizome. The erect, branched spikes carry numerous three-inch flowers of rather starry form; the sepals are narrow and the petals somewhat broader, but all taper to a fine, recurved point; red-brown, marked and tipped with yellow. The cordate lip is white, with brown spots, and the apex extends into a fine point. A native of Mexico and Northern Guatemala, O. CORDATUM first flowered here in 1838, but remained a scarce plant until imported freely some twenty-five years later. *Bot. Mag.*, t. 4878; *Orch. Alb.*, IV, t. 186.

O. CORONARIUM, *Lindl.*—In this very distinct species the stout pseudo-bulbs are widely spaced and the leaves are thick and leathery. The foot-long, erect spikes carry numerous two-inch, roundish flowers of stout texture. The sepals and petals are bright reddish-brown, with a few yellow marks near the crimped margins; the short, spoon-shaped lip is yellow, with a white crest. The whole flower glitters in the sunshine, as if it were varnished. Requires rather warm conditions, is not too amenable to cultivation and not a plant for the inexperienced amateur, but a grand Orchid when it flowers freely; a raft is a better receptacle than a pot for this species. Discovered in New Granada in 1847, there are several varieties; MINIATUM, *Hort.*, with smaller flowers and more closely-placed pseudo-bulbs; and CHIRIQUENSE, *Reich.*, with larger, paler flowers. *Orch. Alb.*, I, t. 27; *Monogr. Od.*, t. 37.

O. CRISPUM, *Lindl.*—Hartweg discovered this very beautiful and useful Orchid in the Pacho district of Bogota, Colombia, in 1841, when collecting for the Horticultural Society of London. Lindley described it as *O. crispum* in 1852, but as excessively-heated houses killed many plants, the species remained scarce and Bateman, not knowing Lindley's description, named it *O. Alexandrae*, after the Princess of Wales (eventually Queen Alexandra), and this was the popular name among gardeners for many years. A variable species, very high prices were paid for particularly fine forms, and some idea of its variability and popularity may be gained from the R.H.S. account of certificated plants, which records nearly two hundred varietal names.

ODONTOGLOSSUM CRISPUM

The arching, sometimes branched, spikes may bear from six to over a dozen flowers that are rounded in the best Pacho type, white, with golden crest and occasional spots or blotches of rich red-brown. The XANTHOTES type has yellow markings. Some of the finest varieties are, or were, APIATUM, AUREUM, ROSEFIELDIENSE, BARONESS SCHRÖDER, COOKSONIAE, FRANZ MAZEREEL, HELIOTROPIUM, LEONARD PERFECT, LOUIS L. SANDER, PITTIAE, PITTIANUM, SANDERIANUM, SCHRÖDERIANUM, SOLUM, VEITCHIANUM, F. K. SANDER and XANTHOTES. Some of the earlier and more colourful forms were almost certainly natural hybrids and not pure O. CRISPUM. Easily grown, O. CRISPUM is beautiful in all but the poorer, starry forms and is invaluable for florists' work; home-raised seedlings now provide abundance of easily-grown plants with shapely, long-lasting flowers, and the heavily-marked varieties that created so much excitement in bygone years are no longer popular. *Reichenbachia*, t. 1; *Bot. Mag.*, t. 5691; *Orch. Alb.*, I, t. 47; *Monogr. Od.*, t. 14 and t. 19.

O. EDWARDII, *Rchb. f.*—Discovered by Klaboch in the Andes of Ecuador, this remarkable species flowered for the first time in this country in 1880. A sturdy grower and by no means difficult to manage, it produces reddish, erect, branching spikes from three to four feet tall, bearing large numbers of inch-wide, fragrant, purplish-mauve flowers, each with a dark yellow crest. An Orchid of considerable merit, admirable for association with other kinds and useful in floral decorations. *Bot. Mag.*, t. 6771.

O. GRANDE, *Lindl.*—The successful flowering of this gorgeously magnificent Orchid is the hall-mark of a grower's skill. Mr. Ure-Skinner found O. GRANDE in Guatemala in 1839, and it flowered for the first time in England at Woburn Abbey in 1841. Among the largest found in the genus, the shining flowers are five or six inches wide, bright yellow, irregularly barred with red-brown on the dorsal sepal and the decurved lateral sepals. The petals are heavily marked with brown on their basal halves and yellow towards the extremities. Lip short, rounded, light yellow, with red marks at its base; crest orange-yellow. The short spikes carry from three to seven flowers and a specimen with half a dozen spikes is wondrously handsome. The variety WILLIAMSIANUM, *Rchb. f.* has smaller flowers, with broader petals. *Bot. Mag.*, t. 3955; *Orch. Alb.*, II, t. 79; *Monogr. Od.*, t. 8.

O. HARRYANUM, *Rchb. f.*—The Messrs. Veitch received plants of this distinct species from Messrs. Horsman & Co., Colchester, in 1885, and it flowered at Chelsea in the following year. It is a Colombian species, of neat habit, with more or less erect spikes of very showy, large flowers, and commemorates Sir Harry Veitch. The sepals and petals are bright red-brown, marked with yellow, but the petals are white at the base, yellow at the tips and marked with purple. The very conspicuous lip is flattish, white or pale yellow, with a deeper yellow crest; the side lobes are white, lined with purple. Probably no species has carried its influence so markedly through several generations of hybrid descendants. A fine Orchid. *Orch. Alb.*, VIII, t. 336.

O. HASTILABIUM, *Lindl.*—Discovered by Linden in Colombia, in 1843, and flowered at Syon House, Brentford, in 1846, O. HASTILABIUM is a robust, easily grown species, with erect spikes a yard high, and three-inch, starry flowers. The greenish-yellow sepals and petals are curiously tessellated with reddish-purple, except at the tips; the lip has a distinctly constricted "waist", with a spreading, white, purple-based apex. *Bot. Mag.*, t. 4272; *Monogr. Od.*, t. 7.

O. INSLEAYI, *Barker*—An Autumn-flowering Mexican species collected by Ross and introduced by Mr. Barker, Birmingham, in 1838, and named after his gardener, this has the habit of *O. grande*, but the flowers are about three inches broad, with broader sepals and petals. These are greenish-yellow, freely barred with red-brown; lip rich yellow, with an edging of red spots. A most attractive Orchid, with a rounder-flowered variety named LEOPARDINUM, *Regel*, but not frequently seen in fine condition. *Monogr. Od.*, t. 4; *Mag. Bot.*, VIII, p. 203.

O. KEGELJANI, *E. Morr.*—Known widely under its old name of *O. polyxanthum, Rchb. f.*, this fine Spring-flowering species is renowned for the bright yellow of its sepals and petals, both blotched with cinnamon-brown, but more particularly on the sepals. The lip is cinnamon-brown, with a base and edging of lemon-yellow; the deep yellow crest has two raised white lines. Found by Klaboch, in 1877, on the Andes of Ecuador. Easily managed and well worth growing for its brightness, although the flowers are not round enough to please many modern growers. *Sel. Orch.* III, t. 37; *Orch. Alb.* VI, t. 258.

O. LINDLEYANUM, *Rchb. f.*—A pretty species from Bogota and Ocana, with a habit very like *O. crispum*, with which it is frequently found.

Several four-inch flowers are carried on a slender, arching spike, and they have narrow, yellow, brown-blotched sepals and petals and a brown, yellow-tipped central lobe to the lip. Rather variable, with CORADINEI, *Reich.*, as an outstanding variety that has larger and more brightly-coloured flowers. *Monogr. Od.*, t. 71.

O. LONDESBOROUGHIANUM, *Rchb. f.*—A rambling species, with large, deciduous leaves on widely-spaced pseudo-bulbs. A Mexican Orchid introduced in 1876, but needs warm conditions and is certainly not a plant for an amateur with a small house. Should be allowed to grow upright on a wood block or raft. The bright yellow flowers have concentric red-brown markings. The branched spike is two to three feet tall, and may bear numerous flowers. *Orch. Alb.*, II, t. 82.

O. LUTEO-PURPUREUM, *Lindl.*—An attractive species discovered by Linden, in 1842, in New Granada, formerly almost as popular as *O. crispum*. It is variable, and the late Mr. de Barri Crawshay cultivated it extensively and successfully at Sevenoaks. Easily grown, it still retains much of its popularity because of its striking colours. Six or more four-inch flowers are borne on arching, sturdy spikes and although the sepals and petals are neither broad nor sufficiently rounded to meet modern tastes they are very attractive. The sepals are bright red-brown, marked and tipped with clear yellow, the petals having more yellow colour. The lip is large, bright yellow or white, marked with rich red-brown at the base. Any good form is worthy of cultivation and numerous varieties have been recorded. *Orch. Alb.*, VI, t. 254; *Monogr. Od.*, t. 17.

O. MACULATUM, *Lexarza.*—A species of neat habit, with three-inch flowers on a rather erect spike. The sepals are brown, with pointed, yellow tips; petals broader and rounder, yellow, spotted with brown at their bases; and the spottings seem to be carried on to the broad, yellow, pointed lip. Distinct and easily grown. *Bot. Mag.*, t. 6455; *Orch. Alb.*, II, t. 52.

O. NEBULOSUM, *Lindl.*—A Mexican species of neat habit, with diphyllous, stout pseudo-bulbs, and rounded, three-inch flowers on an erect spike. The sepals, petals and lip are white, but all are plentifully spotted with red-brown so as to produce an attractive central pattern of colour. Always commands attention when in flower. Discovered by Karwinsky, it flowered in Brussels in 1856. *Monogr. Od.*, t. 1.

O. NOBILE, *Rchb. f.*—Discovered by Funck and Schlim in the Oak forests of Colombia, in 1847, O. NOBILE first flowered in Europe in 1851, but then, and for many years afterwards, it was known and illustrated as *O. Pescatorei, Linden.* It may be described as a dainty *O. crispum.* The arching, branched spikes may be over two feet long and carry a score or more of three-inch, shapely, white flowers. The colour is variable, however; it may be blush or faintly rose-tinted, and in the more important named varieties such as SCHRÖDERIANUM or VEITCHIANUM, there are pronounced spots or blotches of rose over the whole central area. Very high prices were paid for the finest forms of this graceful and beautiful species. Figured, as *O. Pescatorei*—commemorating M. Pescatore, a wealthy French banker who cultivated Orchids extensively—in *Orch. Alb.*, IV, t. 175; *Monogr. Od.*, t. 5; and *Sel. Orch.*, I, t. 25; while a treble-page, half-tone illustration of VEITCHIANUM figures as a frontispiece to the Odontoglossum section of Veitch's *Manual of Orchidaceous Plants.*

O. OERSTEDII, *Rchb. f.*—A slender, lowly plant, with erect, few-flowered spikes. The white flowers are small, pure white, except for a yellow base to the lip, and very sweetly scented, therefore a desirable species where accommodation is limited and size is not a prerequisite condition. Introduced from Costa Rica in 1872. *Bot. Mag.*, t. 6820 ; there is also a charming picture of it in Watson and Bean's *Orchids : their Culture and Management.*

O. PULCHELLUM, *Bateman*—This very pretty Orchid has rather small, pure white flowers, except for the yellow crest, and there may be five to seven of them so arranged on an erect spike that they appear to be upside down. A charming species that has the additional attraction of fragrance. *Bot. Mag.*, t. 4104; *Bot. Reg.*, 1841, t. 48.

O. ROSSII, *Lindl.*—Although one of the dwarfs of the genus this is also one of the most useful and beautiful. Even when in flower it seldom reaches a height of eight inches. There are usually two or three three-inch, shapely flowers—rarely four or five—on the spike, but a plant with several spikes is very attractive. The colour varies considerably, but a good form has white or blush sepals, heavily blotched with dark brown; the petals are of similar colour, but the markings are confined to the basal halves. The lip is large for the size of the flower, white or rose-tinted, with wavy margins and a yellow crest. Collected by Ross, in the Oaxaca district of Mexico, and introduced in 1837. The variety ASPERSUM, primrose-yellow, with red-brown marks, was described under that name as a distinct species, by Reichenbach. Several other varieties are recorded, including one—VIRESCENS—with white, green-spotted flowers, but not seen by the writer. *Reichenbachia*, I, t. 4.

O. SCHLIEPERIANUM, *Rchb. f.*—Very much like *O. grande* in habit and style of flowering, this Costa Rican species was introduced about 1856. It is intermediate between *O. Insleayi* and *O. grande* and Lindley regarded it as a variety of the latter. The flowers are smaller than those of *O. grande*, with yellow sepals and petals, the former barred throughout their length, and the latter only at their bases, with bright brown; lip lighter yellow, marked with brown at the base; crest orange-yellow, edged with red. *Fl. Mag.*, t. 461.

O. TRIPUDIANS, *Rchb. f.*—As is the case with many Orchids of wide natural distribution, this is a particularly variable species, and one that enjoyed considerable popularity in earlier years. Discovered by Warscewicz, about 1849, it was not introduced to this country until some twelve years later. Its geographical range is from Colombia to Peru. The usual type has yellow sepals and petals, lightly marked with red-brown, and a white or yellowish lip, marked with dark purple, and with a toothed or bristled crest. *Bot. Mag.*, t. 6029; *Fl. Mag.*, n.s., t. 208.

O. TRIUMPHANS, *Rchb. f.*—A showy and valuable species, and particularly attractive by reason of its large flowers and bright yellow colouring. Discovered by Linden, in Colombia, in 1842–43, it did not appear in English collections until about twenty-five years later, after it was imported by Messrs. Low & Co. In habit it resembles *O. nobile*, with which it is frequently found, but the flowers are three-inches broad. The ground colour of the sepals and petals is deep yellow, and appears at the tip and as mottlings between the heavy markings of red-brown. The cream-white lip has a large purple blotch towards the apex; crest-white, toothed.

Yet another variable Orchid, and many forms have received varietal names, the best being AUREUM, soft yellow, with orange markings; DELL variety, in which the yellow is of a deep golden shade, and LIONEL CRAWSHAY, with very large flowers and bright brown markings on a rich yellow ground. *Orch. Alb.*, t. 58; *Monogr. Od.*, t. 23.

O. UROSKINNERI, *Lindl.*—Closely allied to *O. bictonense*, the erect spikes and broad-lipped flowers invariably arrest attention. It was discovered by Mr. G. Ure-Skinner, in Guatemala, introduced in 1854, but did not flower in England until 1859. The spike is from two to three feet tall and the two-inch flowers are nicely spaced. The neat, greenish sepals and petals are heavily mottled with red-brown, but the spreading, heart-shaped lip is wavy, rose-coloured, with white marblings. *Orch. Alb.*, III, t. 17; *Monogr. Od.*, t. 2.

OTHER SPECIES

Odontoglossum is a large genus and several species are of little horticultural value, but O. ASTRANTHUM, *Rchb. f.*; O. BLANDUM, *Rchb. f.;* O. CARINIFERUM, *Rchb. f.;* O. CONSTRICTUM, *Lindl.;* O. CRISTATUM, *Lindl.;* O. CROCIDIPTERUM, *Rchb. f.* (fragrant); O. GLORIOSUM, *Linden et Rchb. f.;* O. KRAMERI, *Rchb. f.;* O. LAEVE, *Lindl.;* O. MACULATUM, *Lexarza;* O. MAXILLARE, *Lindl.;* O. NAEVIUM, *Lindl.* (rather like a dwarf form of *O. cirrhosum);* O. ODORATUM, *Lindl.* (fragrant); O. PARDINUM, *Lindl.*, and O. RAMOSISSIMUM, *Lindl.;* are all worthy of cultivation by those who prefer species to hybrids.

NATURAL HYBRIDS

With so many species found growing together, or near each other, the production of natural hybrids was to be expected, indeed the mating of species was suspected when Odontoglossums were imported in quantities, and in many instances the suspicion became a certainty in later years.

A few of the more important natural hybrids are O. ADRIANAE (*O. crispum* × *O. Hunnewellianum);* O. ANDERSONIANUM (*O. crispum* × *O. gloriosum);* O. ASPERSUM (*O. maculatum* × *O. Rossii);* O. BRANDTII (*O. luteo-purpureum* × *O. nobile);* O. COOKIANUM (*O. blandum* × *O. triumphans);* O. CRISTATELLUM (*O. Kegeljani* × *O. cristatum);* O. ELEGANS (*O. cirrhosum* × *O. Hallii);* O. EXCELLENS (*O. nobile* × *O. triumphans);* O. HALLII-XANTHUM (*O. Hallii* × *O. Kegeljani);* O. HARVENGTENSE (*O. crispum* × *O. triumphans);* O. HUMEANUM (*O. Rossii* × *O. cordatum);* O. WILCKEANUM (*O. crispum* × *O. luteo-purpureum*), and O. LOOCHRISTIENSE (*O. crispum* × *O. triumphans*).

HYBRIDS

Since the introduction of the modern method of germinating and raising Orchids under laboratory conditions, and its adoption by commercial growers, vast numbers of hybrids have been produced. Crossing and intercrossing has progressed rapidly with the result that thousands

ODONTOGLOSSUM BASSANIO, ASHCROFT VARIETY

of names have been given to the progeny. The modern hybrids are not hybrids in the strict sense of the word, but are a very mixed race. Floral size and shape have been "improved" along floricultural lines and colour has been marvellously developed.

No selection of hybrids will please all tastes, therefore the names cited must be regarded as representing home-raised Odontoglossums which have made the greatest appeal to the writer of these observations:—O. AMABILE (*O. crispo-Harryanum* × *O. crispum*); O. ARDENTISSIMUM (*O. crispum* × *O. nobile*); O. BRIMSTONE BUTTERFLY (*O crispum* × *O. Armstrongiae*); O. CITRINUM (*O. eximium* × *O. Boadicea*); O. CLONIUS (*O. Aquitania* × *O. The Czar*); O. CLOTH OF GOLD (*O. amabile* × *O. Wilckeanum*); O. CRISPO-HARRYANUM (*O. crispum* × *O. Harryanum*); O. HELLEMENSE (*O. crispum* × *O. harvengtense*); O. IMPERATOR (*O. Britannia* × *O. The Czar*); O. LAMBEAUIANUM (*O. crispum* × *O. Rolfeae*); O. MANDATUM (*O. crispum* × *O. Orobus*); O. MINATAUR (*O. Cordoba* × *O. Chloris*); O. MESSALINA (*O. Lambeauianum* × *O. Vuylstekei*); O. MIRUM (*O. Wilckeanum* × *O. crispum*); O. PETWORTH (*O. Alvara* × *O. Serapis*); O. PRIMULINUM (*O. excellens* × *O. Wilckeanum*); O. PURPLE EMPEROR (*O. Dusky Monarch* × *O. The Czar*); O. REVE D'OR (*O. Boadicea* × *O. harvengtense*); O. ROLFEAE (*O. Harryanum* × *O. nobile*); O. ROYAL PURPLE (*O. Edwardii* × *O. illustre*); O. TRIOMPHE D'OR (*O. triumphans* × *O. Reve d'Or*); O. VUYLSTEKEAE (*O. harvengtense* × *O. Wilckeanum*); O. WALTONENSE (*O. crispum* × *O. Kegeljani*); O. YOLANDUM (*O. Princess Yolande* × *O. crispum*); and O. BASSANIO (*O. Bure* × *O. Lawrenceanum*).

In the lists which follow a selection of six hybrids is given in four colour groups:—

Light or White Hybrids.—O. ALISPUM (*O. Alorcus* × *O. crispum*); O. CRISPELUS (*O. crispum* × *O. Belus*); O. KLONDIKE (*O. Toreador* × *O. Alector*); O. TOREILA (*O. Toreador* × *O. Sheila Stephenson*); O. PRINCESS ELIZABETH (*O. Faustina* × *O. crispum*); and O. ALECTOR (*O. Amabilicity* × *O. crispum*).

Yellow Hybrids.—O. ELISE (*O. triumphans* × *O. Ascania*); O. CRISPANIA (*O. crispum* × *O. Ascania*); O. CIDRA (*O. Telemachus* × *O. Orange Foam*); O. ASCA (*O. hellemense* × *O. Ascania*); O. TRIOMPHE D'OR (*O. triumphans* × *O. Rève d'Or*); and O. MOONGLOW (*O. Sunglow* × *O. Rialto*).

Reddish Hybrids.—O. EUDORA (*O. Dictune* × *O. Serapis*); O. MARONIUS (*O. Clemius* × *O. Marcella*); O. CLYDAMES (*O. Clydonia* × *O. St. James, F.C.C. var.*); O. HIMACHAL (*O. Cloamel* × *O. Eudora*); O. CLONIUS (*O. Aquitania* × *O. The Czar*); and O. HERMES (*O. Serapis* × *O. St. James*).

Rose or Purple Hybrids.—C. PALMYRATOR (*O. Palmyras Queen* × *O. Imperator*); O. OPHOON (*O. Ophelia* × *O. Neron*); O. JEROME (*O. Pheson* × *O. Pelican*); O. PERRYANUM (*O. Camilla* × *O. Toreador*); O. NISUS (*O. Regium* × *O. Toreador*); and O. TUBAN (*O. Neron* × *O. Purple Emperor*).

ONCIDIUM, *Swartz*

Tribe, Vandeae; sub-tribe, Oncidieae

Oloff Swartz, successor to Linnaeus, created the genus Oncidium with a few species previously included under the then omnibus title of Epidendrum. It is now a large genus and contains many species of great beauty and high horticultural value, but also many that, while interesting, are not very showy. In the earlier years of Orchid nomenclature certain species were placed under Odontoglossum and others under Miltonia, thus proving their close kinship with these genera. The two hundred species he knew were grouped by Dr. Lindley into no fewer than fourteen sections, but Bentham subsequently reduced the groups, or sections, to four—Microchila, Equitantia, Teretifolia and Planifolia.

The geographical distribution of Oncidium is from Mexico through Central America and down the Pacific coastal regions of South America, with several species on the Atlantic side and others in Southern Brazil. It is unfortunate that some of the finest Oncidiums do not enjoy a long life under cultivation in the British Isles; this did not matter very much when importations were frequent and growers were able to purchase new stock and scrap old. No doubt much of the decline in health was due to the great strain imposed by abundant flower production and the temptation to allow the display to remain so long as possible. To-day, growers cut the flowers when almost all have expanded, or, better still, allow plants to flower in alternate years. Oncidiums, for the most part, require warmer conditions than Odontoglossums, but with similar requirements regarding compost and atmospheric moisture.

Oncidiums show a wide range of habit and style of inflorescence. In some instances the spike is simple and arched, in others tall and branched, but yellow and brown are the chief colours. Two species depart from the usual type of growth by insisting upon growing head downwards, and have no pseudo-bulbs, so it will be gathered that the genus is not lacking in variety.

O. ALTISSIMUM, *Swartz*—Introduced to Kew in 1793, but was lost until about 1839, when it was sent to Glasgow and a little later was imported by the Messrs. Loddiges, of Hackney. The pseudo-bulbs are small and the leaves about a foot long, while the spike may rise to three or four feet and be sparingly and shortly branched. The flowers are less than two inches broad, yellow, with chestnut-brown markings on the sepals; the lip has a broad, yellow central lobe; the crest has ten teeth arranged in two series of five. *Bot. Mag.*, t. 2990; *Bot. Reg.*, t. 1851.

O. AMPLIATUM, *Lindl.*—This fine, Spring-flowering species was discovered in Costa Rica by Cuming in 1831-32, but is also found in Trinidad and New Granada. The erect, or slightly nodding spike may be three or four feet tall, and branched towards the top. The flowers are numerous, over an inch across. The tiny sepals are almost hidden, but, like the petals, are yellow, marked with red-brown. The large, bi-lobed lip is bright yellow, while the whitish crest is lightly marked with red-brown. The variety MAJUS has larger and more finely-coloured flowers than the type. *Bot. Reg.*, t. 1699; *Reichenbachia*, II, t. 70.

O. BATEMANIANUM, *Knowles et Westcott.*—Rare in cultivation, this sturdy species produces spikes up to four feet tall, much branched at the top. The numerous flowers are rather more than an inch broad, with light yellow, undulated sepals and petals, freely barred and blotched with chestnut-brown, while the lip is bright yellow, with a particularly complex crest. Has received several names—*O. ramosum*, *O. spilopterum*, *O. Penellianum* and *O. gallopavinum*.

O. BICALLOSUM, *Lindl.*—This native of Guatemala first flowered in this country in 1842. It is not one of the easiest to manage and is distinguished by its large and very leathery leaves. The thick, erect spikes are about eighteen inches long, branched at the top, and bear numerous two-inch flowers. The sepals and petals are yellow, toned with greenish-brown, while the spreading lip is bright yellow and has a white, red-dotted crest. *Bot. Mag.*, t. 4148; *Bot. Reg.*, 1843, t. 12.

O. BRACTEATUM, *Rchb. f.*—A useful, elegant and easily grown species. The flowers are quite small but there are plenty of them on the branched, spreading apical portion of the yard-long spike. The greenish-yellow sepals and petals are spotted with purple and the light yellow lip has a reddish-brown base.

O. BRUNLEESIANUM, *Rchb. f.*—A remarkably distinct Oncidium, but very beautiful when seen at its best, although it is rare in modern collections. The sturdy pseudo-bulbs have four-inch or six-inch leaves. The elegant spike may be eighteen inches or more in length, branched, with five or six inch-wide flowers on each branch. The branches are semi-pendulous and the flowers are not so widely expanded as in most of the popular species, as the pale yellow sepals and petals point forward, while the lip has yellow, incurving side lobes and a dark crimson central lobe. *Orch. Alb.*, V, t. 206.

O. CARTHAGINENSE, *Swartz.*—The tall, shortly-branched spikes of this graceful Orchid carry numerous inch-wide flowers, with wavy, cream-coloured segments, shaded and marked with rose or rose-purple. Widely distributed in Central and South America, O. CARTHAGINENSE first flowered in England at Vauxhall, London, in 1804, but the Vauxhall of those days was almost in the country. Has been known as *O. luridum* and is figured as *Epidendrum undulatum* in *Bot. Mag.*, t. 777.

O. CAVENDISHIANUM, *Bateman*—Introduced in 1835, from Guatemala, this Orchid provides a fine test of cultural skill. There are no pseudo-bulbs, but the long, broad, thick leaves rise from a stout rhizome. The spikes, two to three feet tall and branched at the top, carry numerous, fragrant flowers nearly two inches broad. The yellow sepals and petals are sometimes spotted with red; lip bright yellow. *Bot. Mag.*, t. 3807.

O. CEBOLLETA, *Swartz*—A very distinct species, with suppressed pseudo-bulbs and terete, tapered leaves about fifteen inches long. Spikes about two feet tall, branched; sepals and petals yellow, with red-brown spots; lip bright yellow. A most interesting Orchid, but not of first-rate horticultural value. First flowered at Clapton, in 1837. *Bot. Mag.*, t. 3568; *Bot. Reg.*, t. 1994.

O. CHEIROPHORUM, *Rchb. f.*—A charming, graceful species of lowly habit, rarely more than six inches high, and one that can be recommended for inclusion in an amateur's collection, where overhead space is severely limited. It produces slender, arching, spikes, rather longer than the leaves, and these carry about a score of tiny, fragrant, yellow flowers, each with a whitish crest. Easily grown, regular in flowering, and very pretty; found at considerable altitudes in Colombia, it may be grown in the Odontoglossum house. *Bot. Mag.*, t. 6278; *Lindenia*, III, t. 120.

O. CONCOLOR, *Hook.*—A Brazilian species that has retained its popularity ever since it was discovered in 1837 and flowered at Woburn three years later. The pseudo-bulbs are three inches long and the leaves six inches; spike semi-pendulous, about a foot long, carrying several two-inch flowers of bright yellow colour, with a large, spreading, clear yellow lip. *Bot. Mag.*, t. 3752; *Orch. Alb.*, I, t. 1. *Reichenbachia*, I. t. 30.

O. CRISPUM, *Loddiges*—A strong grower, with stout pseudo-bulbs and six-inch leaves. The erect spikes may be so much as four feet long, much branched at the top, forming a loose panicle of fairly large, undulated flowers. The colour is chestnut-brown, lightly marked and edged with yellow. A fine Orchid. *Bot. Mag.*, t. 3499; *Bot. Reg.*, t. 1920.

O. CUCULLATUM, *Lindl.*—A widely distributed and therefore a very variable species, of low growth, with erect spikes about eighteen inches tall. The flowers are rather small and few in number. A typical form has red-brown or olive-green sepals and petals, often marked or shaded with yellow; lip purplish-rose, freely spotted with bright red-purple. O. CUCULLATUM is now referred to *O. olivaceum*, but the old and popular name is given above. It should be noted that the lateral sepals are tiny and quite obliterated by the lip; and that in some varieties the lip is yellow, with no basal spots; it may even be white, with purple spots. *Lindenia*, II, t. 81½.

O. CURTUM, *Lindl.*—Introduced from Brazil about 1841, this has never been grown extensively, nevertheless it is well worthy of cultivation. The three-inch pseudo-bulbs carry a pair of sharply-pointed leaves, from six to ten inches long. The inflorescence is from two to three feet tall, loosely panicled at the top, branched, and bearing numerous two-inch flowers. The chestnut-brown dorsal sepal is irregularly barred with bright yellow, but the lateral sepals are hidden behind the fan-shaped, yellow lip, which is edged with red-brown. Somewhat variable in colour but always attractive. *Bot. Reg.*, 1847, t. 63.

O. DASYSTYLE, *Rchb. f.*—A dwarf grower and suitable for an amateur with only modest accommodation for Orchids. Introduced from the

L

Organ Mountains in 1872, it may be grown with the Odontoglossums for most of the year, but needs warmer conditions during the Summer. The sepals and petals are pale yellow, with red-brown markings; lip light yellow, with dark crimson marks on the crest. *Bot. Mag.*, t. 6494.

O. DIVARICATUM, *Lindl.*—A very fine Orchid when well grown. The small pseudo-bulbs carry a single leaf, about a foot long, but the flowering stem may be so much as four feet tall, freely and slenderly branched at the top and carry an abundance of inch-broad flowers. The red-brown sepals and petals are tipped with yellow and the lip has rounded, yellow side lobes, lightly spotted with red-brown, while the central lobe is yellow, with a basal mark of red-brown. *Bot. Reg.*, t. 1050; *Mag. Bot.*, III, p. 4.

O. EXCAVATUM, *Lindl.*—A robust species introduced from Northern Peru over a hundred years ago, and one that should be imported again when suitable conditions obtain. The yard-high inflorescence is panicled at the top and bears an abundance of medium-sized flowers that have more yellow colouring than many other species, as the petals and dorsal sepal are only lightly marked with soft red-brown, while the bright yellow lip has brown markings below the crest. *Bot. Mag.*, t. 5293; *Lindenia*, V, t. 221.

O. FORBESII, *Hook.*—A handsome Orchid introduced in 1837 and named after James Forbes, gardener to the Duke of Bedford, in whose collection, at Woburn, it flowered in the Autumn of 1838. The plant is of moderate size, but the spike may be two or three feet tall and sparingly branched. The rounded flowers have a diameter of about three inches and are remarkable for the gold-laced margins of the petals and lip. The ground colour is bright chestnut-brown, and the dorsal sepal is barred with yellow. *Bot. Mag.*, t. 3705; *Orch. Alb.*, III, t. 104.

O. GARDNERI, *Lindl.*—One of Gardner's discoveries; of medium habit, with yard-long inflorescences that are panicled along the upper half. The petals are rounded, bright red-brown, edged with golden-yellow; dorsal sepal yellow, barred with brown; lip yellow, with a marginal ring of red-brown spots of varying size. *Orch. Alb.*, I, t. 12; *Mag. Bot.*, XVI, p. 65.

O. INCURVUM, *Barker*—The airy grace of abundant, small flowers, on tall, panicled spikes, is very fascinating. The narrow, undulate sepals and petals are light rose-pink, tipped with white, while the lip is white,

MILTONIA SOLFATARI

with a pink base and a yellow crest. A very elegant Orchid. The variety ALBUM is wholly white except for the yellow crest. *Bot. Mag.*, t. 4824.

O. JONESIANUM, *Rchb. f.*—A Brazilian species with terete leaves and drooping spikes. Grows best in an intermediate or warm house, placed head downwards, or affixed to a block of wood. Very distinct, with three-inch flowers. The sepals and petals are cream-white, with spots of red-brown; lip white, with a few red spots below the crest. *Bot. Mag.*, t. 6982; *Orch. Alb.*, IV, t. 183.

O. KRAMERIANUM, *Rchb. f.*—A wonder Orchid in a genus of varied and handsome species. This is one of the Butterfly Orchids. The thick, oblong leaves are green, mottled with darker green. The flowering stem is slender and erect, about twenty to twenty-four inches tall, and the large, showy flowers open in slow succession from the apex as the latter extends. The narrow petals and dorsal sepal broaden at the tips and have undulated edges; the colour is bright red-brown; the much broader lateral sepals are orange-red, lightly marked transversely with golden yellow. Lip large, spreading, bright yellow, with an irregular border of red that shades into the frilled margin. *Lindenia*, VI, t. 246.

O. LANCEANUM, *Lindl.*—Pseudo-bulbs are absent from this fine species, introduced from Surinam in 1834. Not an Orchid for general cultivation as its big, oblong, leathery leaves occupy considerable space. The erect, stiff spike rises from the base of the newest leaf, and may be branched. The fleshy, fragrant, three-inch flowers have fairly equal sepals and petals, greenish-yellow, freely spotted with dark red-brown; lip purple, but white in some forms. *Lindenia*, I, t. 16; *Reichenbachia*, II, t. 73.

O. LIMMINGHII, *Morren.*—A small plant, with slender, few-flowered spikes of smallish flowers. The dusky-brown petals and dorsal sepal are paler brown at the margins. Lip yellow, with brown spots. *Lindenia*, I, t. 20.

O. LONGIPES, *Lindl.*—A dwarf, free-flowering species, but the short spikes bear only three to five-inch broad flowers, yellow, with brown areas at the base of each sepal and petal. A very suitable Orchid for cultivation in a low-roofed house. *Bot. Mag.*, t. 5193.

O. MACRANTHUM, *Lindl.*—A robust Orchid, with six-inch pseudo-bulbs, broad, ten-inch leaves, and a scandent flowering stem that may be from six to ten feet long and therefore should be twined round several slender stakes inserted inside the rim of the pot. The four-inch flowers are rounded, with broad yellow sepals shaded with olive-brown, and broad, undulate, yellow petals; lip quite small, pointed, with a purple base. A grand Orchid where there is ample room for it. *Bot. Mag.*, t. 5743; *Reichenbachia*, II, t. 64; *Lindenia*, IV, t. 152.

O. MARSHALLIANUM, *Rchb. f.*—A superbly beautiful Orchid of sturdy habit, with branching spikes, three to six feet tall, and three-inch flowers. The brown-barred sepals are rather insignificant, but the broad, bright yellow petals have red-brown markings over the centre and base; lip bi-lobed, spreading, golden-yellow, with red marks at the base and on the crest. A magnificent species, introduced from the Organ Mountains in 1865. *Bot. Mag.*, t. 5725; *Orch. Alb.*, V, t. 240.

O. ORNITHORHYNCHUM, *Humboldt et Kunth.*—The fairy beauty of this easily-grown Mexican or Guatemalan species always attracts. The tall, arching, branched spikes carry very many fragrant, small flowers that are soft rosy-lilac, with darker lip and golden crest. A deservedly popular Orchid, with a white form named ALBIFLORUM. *Bot. Mag.*, t. 3912.

O. PAPILIO, *Lindl.*—Very like *O. Kramerianum* in habit, leafage, inflorescence and shape of flowers. The dorsal sepal and petals are narrow, three to four inches long, upright, curved at the tips, reddish-crimson; the shorter, but much broader lateral sepals are decurved, bright redbrown, barred with yellow and have wavy margins. Lip rounded, bright yellow, with a broad marginal band of bright red. A fine Orchid that produces its large flowers in slow succession. *Bot. Mag.*, t. 2795; *Orch. Alb.*, VI, t. 279.

O. PUBES, *Lindl.*—A miniature species discovered by David Douglas and introduced in 1824. The foot-long, branched spikes bear numerous small flowers, with yellow spots on the red-brown sepals and petals, and a red-brown, yellow edged lip. *Bot. Mag.*, t. 3926.

O. SARCODES, *Lindl.*—A showy species with yard-long, arching spikes that are shortly branched along the upper part. The rounded, two-inch flowers have a red-brown dorsal sepal and petals, edged and marked with yellow. Lip yellow, spotted with red-brown at the base. *Lindenia*, V, t. 234; *Mag. Bot.*, XVII, p. 257.

O. SPHACELATUM, *Lindl.*—Although the yellow and brown flowers are small, they are borne freely on the yard-high, branched spike. Easily grown and flowers regularly in Spring or early Summer. The petals and lateral sepals stand out horizontally. A good amateur's Orchid. *Bot. Reg.*, 1842, t. 30.

O. SUPERBIENS, *Rchb. f.*—One of the few species with very long, flexuous, shortly-branched spikes, the others being *O. macranthum, O. serratum* and *O. monachicum*. The broad-bladed sepals are red-brown, but the rounder dorsal sepal is edged with yellow. The clawed, yellow petals have red-brown basal markings; lip small, purple, with a yellow crest. *Orch. Alb.*, VI, t. 276.

O. TIGRINUM, *Llave et Lex.*—A showy and popular Orchid, with stiff, ten-inch leaves and erect, sparingly-branched spikes about two feet tall. The sepals and petals are more or less equal in size, reflexed at the tips; bright yellow, barred and spotted with brown; lip slightly bi-lobed, spreading, clear, bright yellow and most effective. SPLENDENS is a particularly fine variety. *Orch. Alb.*, III, t. 137; *Reichenbachia*, II, t. 88.

O. VARICOSUM, *Lindl.*—Probably the most popular and most showy of all Oncidiums, and one that was formerly imported annually in considerable numbers, although the variety ROGERSII has always been more popular than the type. The spikes may be from four to five feet tall, branched along the upper half; the flowers are produced freely and in the variety ROGERSII they are about two inches broad, the sepals and petals small and undistinguished, yellow, with pale brown marks; lip very broad, four-lobed, two inches wide and golden yellow. *Sel. Orch.*, II, t. 31.

O. ZEBRINUM, *Rchb. f.*—Aptly named, as the white sepals and petals have transverse bars of red-brown; lip small, white, with red-brown spots. Introduced from Venezuela in 1847. *Bot. Mag.*, 6138.

OTHER SPECIES

From a host of other species the following are all worth considering, for it must be confessed that the selection given above is very largely a reflection of personal taste and horticultural value :—O. AUREUM, O. AURIFERUM, O. BICOLOR, O. CORYNEPHORUM, O. CHRYSORAPHIS, O. CRYPTOCOPIS (with flexuous spikes), O. DIVARICATUM, O. EXCAVATUM, O. FALCIPETALUM (flexuose), O. GRANDIFLORUM (flexuose), O. GRAVESIANUM, O. HASTATUM, O. INSCULPTUM (flexuose), O. LAMELLIGERUM (flexuose), O. LEUCOCHILUM, O. LURIDUM, O. MICROCHILUM, O. PHYMATOCHILUM, O. PULCHELLUM and O. WENTWORTHIANUM.

HYBRIDS

Considering the extent of the genus, the number of Oncidium hybrids is quite small, but even so, it is particularly interesting to note that some of the most beautiful and useful species have been used sparingly, or not at all, as parents. Nor, so far as we have records, have such glorious Orchids as O. VARICOSUM var. ROGERSII, O. MARSHALLIANUM, O. SARCODES or O. CRISPUM been raised artificially; if they were, no doubt cultivation would be easier and flowering more certain.

Several Oncidiums, formerly known as species, are now regarded as natural hybrids; these are O. HAEMATOCHILUM (*O. Lanceanum* × *O. luridum*); O. MANTINII (*O. Forbesii* × *O. Marshallianum*); O. PUNCTATUM (*O. Forbesii* × *O. Gardneri*); O. STANLEYI (*O. curtum* × *O. Marshallianum*), and O. WHEATLEYANUM (*O. crispum* × *O. Dasytyle*).

Home-raised hybrids include O. BURZEFFIANUM (*O. Marshallianum* × *O. varicosum var. Rogersii*); O. HYBRIDUM (*O. lamelligerum* × *O. tigrinum*); O. KAIULANI (*O. flexuosum* × *O. ornithorynchum*); O. McBEANIANUM (*O. macranthum* × *O. superbiens*); and O. VIZER (*O. ampliatum* × *O. Papilio*).

PERISTERIA, *Hook.*

Tribe, Vandeae; sub-tribe, Stanhopieae

Now alas! The Peristerias are despised and rejected by most growers and it is unfortunate that the most popular species—P. ELATA, the well-known Dove Orchid—occupies a good deal more space than most fanciers can provide. The warmest end of the intermediate house suits them, and as they root strongly the proportions of loam fibre and Osmunda fibre should exceed that of Sphagnum moss. The water supply should be greatly reduced when growth is completed.

P. ELATA, *Hook.*—A splendid and stately Orchid found in Panama and one that has been in cultivation for well over a hundred years. The pseudo-bulbs are stout and about six inches long; leaves from two feet to a yard long, moderately broad. The spike is erect, up to five feet tall, and produced from the base of the last-made pseudo-bulb. The upper half of the spike may carry a dozen or more rounded, fleshy, fragrant flowers, nearly three inches wide. The sepals and petals are waxy-white, the former broadest and overlapping; all incurve at the margins, and provide "shelter" for the lip and column, which, together, bear a fanciful likeness to a dove, hence the popular name. The Spanish settlers in Central America named it El Espirito Santa, or Holy Ghost plant. *Bot. Mag.*, t. 3116; *Orch. Alb.*, VII, t. 327.

OTHER SPECIES

There are other species, notably P. CERINA, with smaller, yellowish flowers; P. ASPERSA, with large, yellowish-brown flowers; and P. PENDULA, with pendulous spikes of yellowish-white, purple-spotted flowers.

PHAIUS, *Lour.*
Tribe, Epidendreae; sub-tribe, Bletieae

A genus of handsome, robust Orchids, with a wide distribution through Malaya, parts of Africa, Madagascar and Australia. Rather large, but well-drained pots are needed and a fairly substantial compost—with exceptions—containing a large proportion of Osmunda and loam fibres. Abundance of moisture is needed during the greater part of the year and plenty of shade. The pseudo-bulbs are large and stout and the leaves both broad and long. Spikes erect, many-flowered.

P. BICOLOR, *Lindl.*—Spikes up to two feet tall; flowers four inches broad, reddish-brown, with a white, rose-edged, yellow-throated lip. *Bot. Mag.*, t. 4078.

P. BLUMEI, *Lindl.*—More robust than *P. grandifolius* and with larger flowers, buff-yellow, suffused with red; lip white, with a crimson, yellow-edged front lobe. A native of Cochin China. Good varieties are ASSAMICA, BERNAYSII and SANDERIANUS.

P. FLAVUS, *Lindl.*—Flowers smaller than those of *P. grandifolius*; yellow, with red-brown marks on the front lobe of the lip.

P. GRANDIFOLIUS, *Lour.*—An old inhabitant of our glasshouses, introduced in 1778. Leaves often a yard long; spikes stout, erect, many-flowered, three to four feet tall. Flowers four inches broad; sepals and petals yellow-brown, their backs silvery-white; lip tubular, whitish on the exterior, light yellow-brown, the mouth rose-purple, edged with white; disc yellow, stained with reddish-purple. *Bot. Mag.*, t. 1924.

P. HUMBLOTII, *Rchb. f.*—A very beautiful species discovered in Madagascar about 1879 and introduced to cultivation shortly afterwards. It has roundish, rather small, pseudo-bulbs and broadly-lanceolate leaves fifteen to twenty-four inches long. The erect spike is as long, or longer than, the leaves and has from six to a dozen rounded flowers, each about two inches wide. The sepals and petals are broad and of about equal size, light rose-purple, shaded with white. Lip broad, crimped or goffered at the edges; side lobes red-brown, suffused with crimson; central lobe soft rose-purple, with a white centre on which there are two golden-yellow teeth. *Reichenbachia*, I, t. 17.

P. MACULATUS, *Lindl.*—Not so showy as many other species. A native of Northern India, it was introduced in 1882. The erect spike, up to a yard in length, carries several three-inch flowers, resembling those of *P. flavus*, but buff-yellow, with a chocolate-brown mark on the lip. A distinct feature of this species is the yellow spotting on the ample leaves. *Bot. Mag.*, t. 3960; *Orch. Alb.*, VIII, t. 381.

P. TUBERCULOSUS, *Blume*—Discovered by the brothers Humblot, in Madagascar, and introduced by Messrs. Sanders in 1880; it created a sensation among Orchid fanciers when first seen in flower a year later. The stem-like pseudo-bulbs are three or four-inches long; leaves oblong-lanceolate, ten to fifteen inches long; spike erect, up to two feet tall, with half a dozen three-inch flowers. The sepals and petals are white, the latter slightly broader and rounder than the former. Lip large, prominently three-lobed, side lobes orange-yellow, speckled with crimson-purple and studded with white hairs; central lobe deeply notched in the centre of the apex, white, blotched with rose; there is a deep yellow callus on the disk and, below it, a dense tuft of light yellow hairs. An extremely beautiful Orchid, but, like *P. Humblotii*, not too easily managed; both love considerable heat and abundant atmospheric moisture. *Orch. Alb.*, II, t. 91.

P. WALLICHII, *Lindl.*—Found in the Khasia Hills by Gibson, and introduced to Chatsworth in 1837. A robust, terrestrial species, with three yard-long leaves on five-inch pseudo-bulbs. Spike from three to five feet tall, stout, erect, with a dozen to twenty four-inch flowers. Sepals and petals tawny-buff, shaded with red; white on the exterior surfaces. Lip broadly-oval, white, with an orange-yellow base and red lines across the yellow disc. The variety MANNII has larger and more richly-coloured flowers. *Bot. Mag.*, t. 7023; *Mag. Bot.*, VI, p. 193.

PHAIUS WALLICHII

p. 156

PLATYCLINIS FILIFORMIS

PLEIONE LAGENARIA

HYBRIDS

The finest and most colourful of the several hybrids are P. COOK-
SONIAE (*P. grandifolius* × *P. Humblotii*); P. COOKSONII (*P. Wallichii* ×
P. tuberculosus); P. MARTHAE (*P. Blumei* × *P. tuberculosus*); P. NORMAN
(*P. Blumei var. Sanderianus* × *P. tuberculosus*); P. ORPHANUM (*P. grandi-
folius* × *P. Marthae*); P. OWENIANUS (*P. bicolor var. Oweniae* × *P.
Humblotii*), and P. PHOEBE (*P. Blumei var. Sanderianus* × *P. Humblotii*).

PHALAENOPSIS, *Blume*

Tribe, Vandeae; sub-tribe, Sarcantheae

Although by no means so widely distributed as the Dendrobiums,
Aerides and Vandas, the numerous species of Phalaenopsis—or Moth
Orchids—have a fairly wide range in the Far East. A few are found in
Assam, others in Siam, Malaya, Borneo, Celebes and in the Philippines.
A few come from moderate altitudes, but all need tropical conditions
under cultivation and should not be subjected to a lower temperature
than 60° in the coldest weather, while the day temperature at the height
of Summer may be 90° or over. Practically all species love rather dense
shade, and certainly an abundance of atmospheric moisture, with, of
course, less in dull, wintry weather than in the heat of Summer.

Somewhat shallow pans, or teak-wood baskets, are the best receptacles and these must be efficiently crocked. The compost may consist
very largely of Sphagnum moss, with a small amount of Osmunda
fibre. The old practice of placing them in upright, openwork, teak-wood
cylinders is rarely adopted now. Potting should be done when new roots
are being formed; the long roots may be placed among the crocks and
the compost filled in so that the crowns of the plants are eventually
slightly above the edge of the pan or basket. The following are the finest
species among many very beautiful Orchids. There are no pseudo-bulbs
and the leaves are broad or flat.

P. AMABILIS, *Blume*—A lovely Orchid, introduced from Java in 1846.
Leaves broadly obovate, six to twelve inches long; the arching spikes are
many-flowered. The wide-spread flowers are three or four inches wide,
with white sepals and petals, and a yellow base to the lip. Frequently
known as *P. grandiflora. Bot. Mag.*, t. 5184; *Orch. Alb.*, VI, 277.

P. APHRODITE, *Rchb. f.*—A native of the Philippines, with broad leaves, purple beneath, up to fifteen inches long. Spikes two to three feet long, ending in a loose, many-flowered panicle. Flowers white, two to three inches wide, with purple pencillings and yellow stains on the lip. *Bot. Mag.*, t. 4297; *Mag. Bot.*, VII, p. 49.

P. ESMERALDA, *Rchb. f.*—Leaves up to six inches long. Spikes erect, about eighteen inches tall, many-flowered. Flowers only about an inch wide, with amethyst-purple sepals and petals, often whitish, and a dark purple lip. A pretty Orchid. *Orch. Alb.*, VII, t. 321.

P. LOWII, *Rchb. f.*—A small grower, introduced from Moulmein in 1862. The many-flowered, paniculate spike is about a foot or so long. The rounded flowers are white, with purple bases; lip white, with a yellow spot on the side lobes and a purple central lobe. *Bot. Mag.*, t. 5361; *Sel. Orch.*, II, t. 15.

P. MARIAE, *Burbidge*—A Philippine species, with shortly-branched spikes of smallish flowers, white, tinged with purple and stained with purple at the bases of the sepals and petals; lip white and purple. *Bot. Mag.*, t. 6946; *Orch. Alb.*, II, t. 80.

P. ROSEA, *Lindl.*—A pretty Philippine species, with rather small leaves and many-flowered, branched spikes. Flowers about an inch and a half wide, with white, purple-stained sepals and petals and a rose-purple lip. *Bot. Mag.*, t. 5212.

P. SANDERIANA, *Rchb. f.*—A very beautiful species introduced from the Philippines in 1882. Possibly a natural hybrid from *P. Aphrodite* × *P. Schilleriana*. Leaves large, speckled with grey; spikes up to three feet long, with numerous three-inch flowers. Lip and dorsal sepal light rose-pink; lateral sepals pale rose, marked with white; lip white, yellow at the base and marked with purple on the front lobe. The lovely variety ALBA is white, except for some pale purple spots on the base of the side lobes of the lip, and a yellow-spotted crest. *Orch. Alb.*, V, t. 209.

P. SCHILLERIANA, *Rchb. f.*—An old favourite, introduced from the Philippines in 1858; more easily grown than most species. The broad leaves may be over a foot long, while the loosely-branched, slightly arching spike may be a yard or more in length. Flowers very numerous, about three inches wide, pale rose-purple, shading to white at the margins of the sepals and petals; lip paler, marked with yellow and red on the side lobes, and faintly dotted with purple on the whitish central lobe; crest yellow. *Bot. Mag.*, t. 5530; *Sel. Orch.*, I, t. 1.

P. STUARTIANA, *Rchb. f.*—Another popular, free-flowering species, introduced from Mindinao in 1881. Leaves drooping, up to a foot in length, heavily blotched with grey on the upper surface, purple beneath. Spikes branched, many-flowered, up to two feet long. Flowers rather less than three inches wide; petals and dorsal sepal white, finely dotted or stippled with purple towards their bases; lateral sepals white on the outer halves, yellow on the inner halves, spotted with red-purple; lip with yellow, red-dotted side lobes, and a yellowish, or whitish, purple-spotted central lobe.

OTHER SPECIES

Other noteworthy species, all beautiful but not very popular at present, include P. AMETHYSTINA, P. BOXALLI, P. CORNU-CERVI, P. INTERMEDIA, P. LUEDEMANNIANA, P. MANNII, P. PARISHII, P. SPECIOSA, P. SUMATRANA, P. TETRASPIS, P. VIOLACEA, and the much later introductions, P. DENEVEI and P. SERPENTILINGUA.

HYBRIDS

Many very beautiful hybrids have been raised and some of the best of the older ones are P. AMPHITRITE (*P. Stuartiana* × *P. Sanderiana*); P. ARTEMIS (*P. rosea* × *P. amabilis*); P. HARRIETTAE (*P. amabilis* × *P. violacea*); P. ROTHSCHILDIANA (*P. Schilleriana* × *P. amabilis*); P. SCHRÖDERAE (*P. leucorrhoda* × *P. intermedia var. Portei*); and P. VESTA (*P. Aphrodite* × *P. rosea var. leucaspis*).

Later elegant and robust hybrids include P. GILLES GRATIOT (*P. Aphrodite* × *P. Rimestadiana*); P. KATHERINE SIEGWART (*P. amabilis* × *P. Gilles Gratiot*); and P. RÊVE ROSE (*P. Algers* × *P. Schilleriana*).

PLATYCLINIS, *Bentham*
Tribe, Epidendreae; sub-tribe, Liparieae

A small genus of graceful, beautiful Orchids of lowly habit (formerly known as Dendrochilums), with very tiny flowers crowded together on the upper pendulous part of the slender spikes. Natives of Java and the Philippines. Well-drained pots or pans are necessary as the plants require plenty of moisture for the greater part of the year. An Intermediate House and an Odontoglossum compost suit them. Known popularly

as Golden Chain Orchids, although *P. uncata* does not fit into this
descriptive title. The lower part of the spike should be supported by a
thin wire, so that the "tassels" hang clear.

P. COBBIANA, *Hemsley*—Pseudo-bulbs small, leaves six inches long.
Spikes about a foot long; flowers tiny, straw-coloured, with an orange-
yellow lip.

P. FILIFORMIS, *Bentham*—Pseudo-bulbs very small; leaves six inches
long. Spikes a foot or more in length, the racemose portion bearing fifty
to eighty very tiny, fragrant, crowded, canary-yellow flowers. A most
delightful Orchid.

P. GLUMACEA, *Bentham*—A taller grower than other species, often with
fifteen-inch leaves, and a long, slender spike, half of which is racemose,
crowded with scores of small, fragrant, yellowish-white flowers. The
tiny segments are sharply pointed and their chaff-like form suggested the
name. The variety VALIDA has broader leaves and larger flowers. *Bot.
Mag.*, t. 4583, as *Dendrochilum glumaceum*.

P. UNCATA, *Bentham*—Somewhat smaller than *P. filiformis*, with very
small, greenish flowers.

PLEIONE, *D. Don.*

Tribe, Epidendreae; sub-tribe, Coelogyneae

A small group of small but exceedingly beautiful deciduous Orchids,
free-flowering and rarely exceeding a height of six inches. They are best
grown in shallow pans, amply drained, and in a compost of two-thirds
fibre and one-third Sphagnum moss, with some sand. Potting should be
done annually, soon after the plants have flowered, and it is a good
plan to twist a few strands of Sphagnum moss round the old pseudo-
bulbs (which are of annual duration only) and let a few ends depend so
that good anchorage may be obtained in the compost. Water carefully
until new growth is free, but after the leaves have fallen reduce the water
supply severely, almost entirely, until the flowers begin to appear from
the bases of the new pseudo-bulbs. The flowers are practically stemless
and rise singly or in pairs. The few species here included under Pleione
are often placed under Coelogyne, from which genus it differs horticulturally rather than botanically. These natives of Northern India are
known as Indian Crocuses; they occupy little space.

LAELIOCATTLEYA GOLDEN RADIANCE

P. HOOKERIANA, *Lindl.*—Pseudo-bulbs tiny, leaves a couple of inches long. Flowers two to three inches wide, rose-purple, lip lighter, with apical marks if brown-purple and a yellow throat. Var. BRACHYGLOSSA has a white lip, a yellow disc and brown spots. *Bot. Mag.*, t. 6388.

P. HUMILIS, *Lindl.*—Leaves about six inches long, flowers nearly three inches broad, blush-white, lip of similar colour, fringed with white hairs and spotted with amethyst-purple. *Bot. Mag.*, t. 5674.

P. LAGENARIA, *Lindl.*—A lovely little Orchid, with eight-inch leaves, and flowers about three inches wide. The sepals and petals are rosy-lilac; lip whitish, with purple stripes on the rosy-lilac side lobes, and barred and speckled with crimson-purple on the front lobe; disc yellow and red; throat yellow, marked with crimson. *Bot. Mag.*, t. 5370.

P. MACULATA, *Lindl.*—An Autumn-flowering species discovered in the Khasia Hills and introduced in 1849. Pseudo-bulbs not much more than an inch long; leaves six to ten inches long; flowers about two inches wide. The sepals, petals and lip are white; the side lobes of the lip are lined with purple, the front lobe freely marked with crimson-purple; disc yellow, lined with purple. One of the most distinct forms is VIRGINEA, white, with a yellow throat. *Bot. Mag.*, t. 4691.

P. PRAECOX, *Lindl.*—This Winter-flowering species, found in Northern India and Burma, has two-inch pseudo-bulbs and ten-inch leaves. Flowers three inches broad, rose-purple, with a pale rose or white lip that has a fringed central lobe and a yellow throat. The variety WALLICHIANA has larger flowers of deeper colouring. *Mag. Bot.*, XIV, p. 7; *Bot. Mag.*, t. 4496 (*Wallichiana*).

P. REICHENBACHIANA, *T. Moore*—Pseudo-bulbs up to three inches high; flowers about two inches wide. Very pretty and distinct; rather rare. The rosy-lilac sepals are stained with amethyst-purple; petals paler; lip white, spotted with purple in front; margins hairy. *Bot. Mag.*, t. 5753.

P. PRICEI, *Rolfe*—A native of Formosa, almost hardy; flowers purple, white and gold. *Bot. Mag.*, 8729.

RENANTHERA, *Loureiro*

Tribe, Vandeae; sub-tribe, Sarcantheae

A small family of tall-growing, free-flowering Orchids, with individually small flowers that are gorgeous in the mass. Cultivation should follow the lines adopted for the successful management of tropical Aerides and Vandas. Renantheras should be grown wherever there is adequate accommodation for them.

R. COCCINEA, *Loureiro*—Introduced from Cochin China in 1817 and flowered for the first time in 1827, at Chatsworth. The cylindric, leafy stems will, in Nature, become so long as ten feet. The oblong, four-inch leaves are very leathery. The spike appears from a point opposite to an upper leaf, two to three feet long, branched and paniculate. A well-developed inflorescence may have upwards of a hundred flowers, each about two inches wide and nearly four inches deep. The petals and the dorsal sepal are very narrow, deep, bright red, mottled with yellow; lateral sepals long and much broader than the petals, with slightly waved margins, clear vermilion-red; lip very tiny, yellow, tipped with red. *Bot. Mag.*, t. 2997–98; *Orch. Alb.*, II, t. 37.

R. IMSCHOOTIANA, *Rolfe*—Of similar habit to, but much dwarfer than, the previous species and therefore more easily accommodated. A Burmese species, introduced about 1899. Rarely more than two feet tall. Flowers a trifle larger than in *R. coccinea*, freely produced on sparingly-branched, paniculate spikes, vivid vermilion. *Bot. Mag.*, t. 7711.

R. MATUTINA, *Lindl.*—Discovered by Blume, in Java, in 1824, and introduced in 1846. Stems slender, about two feet tall. Spikes flexuose, branched and many-flowered. Flowers of the usual shape, smaller than those of the previous species, bright yellow, shaded with crimson.

R. STORIEI, *Rchb. f.*—Very like *R. coccinea* in habit, with larger leaves and broader flowers. The dorsal sepal and petals are deep orange; lateral sepals dark rich crimson, shaded with orange; lip small, crimson, marked with yellow and white. *Bot. Mag.*, t. 7537.

RESTREPIA, *Humboldt, Bonpland et Kunth*
Tribe, Vandeae; sub-tribe, Pleurothalleae

The genus Restrepia consists of about a dozen species of small plants, with slender stems which carry one rather broad and leathery leaf. The slender peduncles bear very beautiful flowers, with narrow sepals and connate petals that provide the chief attraction and are very large, considering the size of the plant, and usually of brilliant colour. Restrepias may be grown at the coolest end of the Intermediate House, in small pots or pans and in a compost of Sphagnum, Osmunda (or similar) fibre, placed over ample drainage. The plants do not require a definite resting season, but need far less water during the Winter and also for a short period after flowering.

Tropical America, from Brazil to Mexico, is the home of the genus, but the plants are found at considerable elevations, growing on the trees and rocks. The genus commemorates Joseph E. Restrep, a naturalist who explored the Antioquian Andes, and was named by Kunth in 1815. One peculiarity of the Restrepias is that they may flower from the same stem two or three times in one year, or may produce more than one peduncle from the stem, consequently if a few plants are cultivated the grower is seldom without a flower or two at any given period of the year. Amateurs who cannot provide accommodation for the taller and bulkier Orchids should certainly include Restrepias in their collection, as the majority do not exceed a height of four inches.

R. ANTENNIFERA, *Humboldt, Bonpland et Kunth.*—This sturdy and once very popular Orchid has the largest flowers in the genus. The narrow, curved dorsal sepal has a thickened apex and is light yellow, dotted with red. The petals are similar, but smaller. The two lower sepals are joined together, except at the tips, somewhat boat-shaped; the ground colour is yellow but this is almost hidden by the abundant, bright, brown-purple spots. The small lip has similar colouring and is therefore not very conspicuous, indeed, casual observers not infrequently mistake the connate sepals for the lip. Introduced about 1814. *Bot. Mag.,* t. 7930.

R. ELEGANS, *Karsten*—A very charming and pretty Orchid, of tufted habit, and smaller than the foregoing. It frequently produces a pair of peduncles. The long-tailed dorsal sepal is erect, whitish at the base and streaked with purple, the attenuated portion being yellow; connate sepals yellow, dotted with purple. Similar colour is found in the shorter petals. Lip shorter than the connate sepals and of the same colours. Introduced by M. Linden, about 1850. *Bot. Mag.,* t. 5966.

R. GUTTULATA, *Lindl.*—An attractive Orchid, in which the sepals are marked with crimson-purple on a white ground.

R. MACULATA, *Lindl.*—This has been granted specific rank, but is possibly a robust form of *R. antennifera,* with larger and yellower leaves. Collected by M. Linden, in Ecuador. *Bot. Mag.,* t. 6288.

R. PANDURATA, *Rchb. f.*—Another miniature beauty, from Colombia, and one that appears to have flowered for the first time, under cultivation, at the Glasnevin Botanic Gardens, Dublin. The joined lateral sepals are dull white, with fairly regular lines of crimson-purple dots.

R. SANGUINEA, *Rolfe*—Introduced from Colombia. This is a small species, with crimson flowers. R. GEMMA is a varietal form, more robust than the type, and with crimson-purple dots on the whitish ground-colour of the combined sepals.

R. STRIATA, *Rolfe*—A favourite with the author. The lateral sepals are united for rather more than half their length, yellow, striped with bright maroon. Found in Colombia. *Bot. Mag.*, t. 7233.

R. XANTHOPHTHALMA, *Rchb. f.*—A native of Central America with minute yellow and reddish brown flowers.

OTHER SPECIES

Several other members of this family of miniature and delightful Orchids have been described, but are rarely seen in cultivation. They include R. REICHENBACHIANA, from Costa Rica and R. TRICHOGLOSSA, from Colombia; R. DAYANA, R. OPHIOCEPHALA, R. FALKENBERGII, R. ASPACICENSIUM, R. LANSBERGII and R. ECUADORENSIS are very like R. *antennifera*, but differ somewhat in their colourings.

RHYNCHOSTYLIS, *Blume*

Tribe, Vandeae; sub-tribe, Sarcantheae

A small genus of very beautiful Orchids and although the flowers are small they are crowded in pendulous or erect racemes. The several species thrive with the Vandas and Aerides.

R. COELESTIS, *Rchb. f.*—Makes a sturdy, dwarf plant, furnished with fleshy, five-inch leaves. Spikes erect, racemose, crowded with small white and blue flowers. A rare and beautiful Orchid, found in Siam. *Orch. Alb.*, VIII, t. 631.

R. RETUSA, *Blume*—Seldom more than eight inches tall, with arching leaves about ten inches long. Spikes racemose, pendulous, crowded with flowers about three quarters of an inch in diameter. Sepals and petals white, spotted with bluish-purple; lip purple. Widely distributed in India, Burma and Java. One of the "Fox Brush" Orchids and an extremely beautiful, neat plant. Also known as *Saccolabium Blumei*, and

SACCOLABIUM LONGICALCARATUM

SELENIPEDIUM CARDINALE

figured as such in *Orch. Alb.*, IV, t. 169; *Bot. Mag.*, t. 4108 (*var. guttata*).

SACCOLABIUM, *Blume*

Tribe, *Vandeae; sub-tribe, Sarcantheae*

About fifty species are known, chiefly natives of India and Malaya. Most of them are dwarf and carry their smallish, often fleshy, flowers in short, pendulous spikes. May be grown with Vandas and Aerides and treated similarly. Several species are attractive horticulturally and interesting botanically.

S. ACUTIFOLIUM, *Lindl.*—Less than a foot tall, with rather long leaves. Spikes short; flowers less than an inch wide, light yellow, spotted with red-brown. *Bot. Mag.*, t. 4772.

S. AMPULLACEUM, *Lindl.*—A pretty Orchid, rarely six inches tall; leaves long and linear; spikes erect, crowded with flowers less than an inch wide; bright rose-carmine; lip short, column white. *Bot. Mag.*, t. 5595; *Orch. Alb.*, IV, t. 191.

S. BELLINUM, *Rchb. f.*—This Burmese species is particularly beautiful and rarely exceeds six inches in height, with stout, ten-inch leaves. The fleshy flowers are loosely clustered at the end of the short, sturdy spike; they are about an inch and a half wide. The yellow sepals and petals are heavily blotched with very dark purple; lip, bi-lobed, spreading, white, with an orange-yellow disc dotted with purple. *Bot. Mag.*, t. 7142; *Orch. Alb.*, IV, t. 156.

S. BIGIBBUM, *Rchb. f.*—Another little gem, with numerous small flowers clustered towards the end of a short spike. The colour is light yellow, with markings of pale red; lip comparatively large, white and fringed. A Burmese species. *Bot. Mag.*, t. 5767.

S. CURVIFOLIUM, *Lindl.*—A dwarf species, with inch-wide flowers crowded in an erect spike; bright cinnabar-red. Very showy. *Orch. Alb.*, III, t. 107.

S. GIGANTEUM, *Lindl.*—Notwithstanding its name this is a very dwarf species, with short leaves and equally short, drooping, racemose spikes of fragrant, comparatively large flowers, with white sepals and petals that are spotted with bright purple; lip light purple. *Bot. Mag.*, t. 5635; *Orch. Alb.*, II, t. 56.

S. HENDERSONIANUM, *Rchb. f.*—A dwarf species found in Borneo. The

M

small, bright rose flowers are numerous and carried on an erect spike; lip pale rose. *Bot. Mag.,* t. 6222; *Orch. Alb.,*VI, t. 275.

S. MINIATUM, *Lindl.*—A very dwarf Javanese species introduced in 1846 and still often grown. The erect spikes carry a dozen or more orange-red flowers, each three quarters of an inch wide. A very pretty Orchid.

S. VIOLACEUM, *Lindl.*—About a foot tall, with long, leathery leaves and pendulous spikes of inch-wide flowers, fragrant, white, with purple spots; lip bright purple. A native of the Philippines. *Bot. Reg.,* 1847, t. 30; as *Vanda violacea.*

OTHER SPECIES

Other species, chiefly of botanical interest, include S. CALCEOLARE, yellow, white and red ; S. GEMMATUM, S. LONGICALCARATUM, S. INTER-MEDIUM, S. MOOREANUM and S. PECHEI.

SCUTICARIA, *Lindley*
Tribe, Vandeae; sub-tribe, Maxillarieae

The very quaintness of the two well-known species of Scuticaria would place them among botanical Orchids, but the large, handsome flowers bring them into the horticultural grouping. The style of growth is very distinct, as the leaves are terete and the plants grow best when upside down, therefore it is a good plan to fix them to blocks or flat rafts of Teak wood and suspend them from the roof or against one of the upright supports of the house. Sphagnum moss and a small amount of fibre tucked among and over the roots will suffice for compost; but the temperature should be that of a Stove House and abundance of moisture is necessary, except during the dull and colder months of the year and after the completion of growth. The plants will withstand more sunshine than most Orchids.

S. HADWENII, *Planchon.*—Introduced from Rio de Janeiro in 1851, and, later, imported from Southern Brazil. It is not such a showy Orchid as its companion species, nevertheless the three-inch, fleshy flowers are attractively coloured, as the sepals and petals are yellowish-green, heavily marked with reddish-brown. The broad, pale yellow lip is spotted and blotched with light brown throughout the central area, and has whitish edges. *Bot. Mag.,* t. 4629.

S. STEELEI, *Lindl.*—Discovered in British Guiana in 1840–44 by the Schomburgk brothers, this species has longer terete, pendulous leaves than the previous species, indeed they may be four feet in length, but are seldom much more than two feet when grown in this country. The flowers are slightly larger than those of *S. Hadwenii*, light yellow, marked with bright red-brown; the lip has an orange crest that increases the attractiveness of the flowers. In both species from one to three flowers are carried on short spikes. *Orch. Alb.*, II, t. 65; *Bot. Reg.*, t. 1986.

SELENIPEDIUM, *Reichenbach filius*
Tribe, Cypripedieae; sub-tribe, Selenipedieae

The Selenipediums are natives of South America, at one time referred to the genus Cypripedium. They differ from their Old World relatives in several respects, but the chief differences from a purely horticultural point of view are their green, longer and thinner leaves, and their many-flowered spikes. The flowers do not last so long as those of Cypripediums but as they are produced in succession the display is continued over a long period. The shape of the flowers conforms to that found in Cypripediums, but in most species the petals are extended enormously, like long ribbons or tails. The majority of Selenipediums in general cultivation need rather warmer conditions than the majority of Cypripediums, they occupy more space and must receive ample shade in bright weather, otherwise the general treatment is the same.

S. CARICINUM, *Rchb. f.*—The deep green, Sedge-like leaves of this Bolivian species are from twelve to eighteen inches long and recurved towards the ends. The spike is usually about as long as the leaves and may have so many as half a dozen flowers which expand in steady succession. The graceful flowers are not very large, greenish-white, with yellowish veins; the petals are ribbon-like, lightly spirally twisted and about three inches long; lip pouched, yellowish-green, veined with darker green, and with purple dots on the ivory-white, infolding side lobes. *Bot. Mag.*, t. 5466, as *Cypripedium caricinum*.

S. CAUDATUM, *Rchb. f.*—Introduced from Peru in 1847, this is one of the most remarkable of all Orchids. The leaves are from twelve to eighteen inches long and the flowers are large, the dorsal sepal often six inches long, acuminate, and slightly twisted or wavy, pale yellowish-white, with bright, greenish-yellow, longitudinal veins; the ventral sepal, somewhat broader at the base, is similarly coloured and extended. The petals are marvellous developments and one wonders why a plant should use so much energy in producing them; half an inch wide at the base, they gradually decrease in breadth and extend flatly and ribbon-like to a length of from eighteen to thirty inches; the colour is brownish-green, bronzy-green or yellowish at the base. The spike may be eighteen inches tall and each flower is borne on a long pedicel so that the "tails" may hang clear of the foliage. Lip pouched, bronzy-green, with purple-spotted, infolding, ivory-white side lobes that expose the paler interior. Several varieties have been recorded, the most distinct being LUXEM-BOURG VAR., with yellow sepals; WALLISII, with smaller, almost white, flowers; and WARSCEWICZII, of dwarf habit and with more brightly-coloured rosy flowers. The variety LINDENII is so distinct that Lindley created a new genus—Uropedium—for it; the great distinction is that the lip is not pouched, but becomes a third ribbon-like petal. *Sel. Orch.*, II, t. 1, as *Cypripedium caudatum.*

S. KLOTZSCHIANUM, *Rchb. f.*—Very like *S. caricinum* in general habit; spikes two feet tall; flowers rather small, with a green, rose-tinted dorsal sepal, and narrow, green, purple-shaded petals about three inches long; lip cylindric, pale green. A rare plant at present.

S. LINDLEYANUM, *Rchb. f. et Warsc.*—Another rare species, introduced from British Guiana in 1881. The light green leaves are two to three inches broad and from eighteen to twenty-four inches long. Spikes up to more than a yard tall; flowers rather small, green, with red-brown veins.

S. LONGIFLORUM, *Rchb. f. et Warsc.*—A robust species introduced in 1867. The leaves are about two feet long; spikes of similar length, with six or more flowers, each from three to four inches wide. The sepals and petals are narrow, light greenish-yellow, shaded with rose and edged with white; lip yellowish-green, dotted with rose. The variety HARTWEGII is even more robust than the type and has larger flowers with much more rose or pink colour; it has been known in gardens as *S. Roezlii* or *Cypripedium Roezlii. Bot. Mag.*, t. 5970, as *C. longifolium; Bot. Mag.*, t. 6217 (*C. Roezlii*).

S. SCHLIMII, *Rchb. f.*—A very pretty Orchid introduced from Colombia in 1854. Seldom more than one foot tall, it has few-flowered spikes, but it is more or less continuously in flower when grown at the cool end of the Intermediate House. The species is remarkable because it is self-fertilizing and seeds freely, therefore the pedicel and ovary should be removed directly the flowers fade, otherwise the strain of seed production will debilitate the plant. The flowers are very neat and nicely proportioned, about two inches broad. The sepals and petals are white, flushed with rose, and the round, smooth, inflated lip is rose coloured, with carmine streaks around the small opening; staminode yellow. The variety ALBIFLORUM is pure white, except for a tinge of rose at the bases of the petals, and a bright yellow staminode. *Bot. Mag.*, t. 5614, as *Cypripedium Schlimii.*

S. VITTATUM, *Rchb. f.*—A Brazilian species, introduced in 1875, but now rarely seen in cultivation. Flowers about the same size as those of *S. Lindleyanum*; upper sepal whitish, spotted with red; petals three inches long, green and brown-purple; lip green and purple.

HYBRIDS

The earlier hybridists raised numerous hybrids and almost all of these are beautiful Orchids, with S. CARDINALE, S. GRANDE, S. LEUCORRHODUM, S. SCHRÖDERAE and S. SEDENII as probably the best.

S. AINSWORTHII (*S. longifolium var. Hartwegii* × *S. Sedenii*); S. ALBANENSE (*S. Schlimii* × *S. Sedenii*); S. ALBO-PURPUREUM (*S. Schlimii* × *S. Dominii*); S. CARDINALE (*S. Sedenii* × *S. Schlimii var. albiflorum*); S. DOMINYANUM (*S. caricinum* × *S. caudatum*); S. GRANDE (*S. longifolium var. Hartwegii* × *S. caudatum*); S. LEUCORRHODUM (*S. longifolium var. Hartwegii* × *S. Schlimii var. albiflorum*); S. SCHRÖDERAE (*S. caudatum* × *S. Sedenii*); and S. SEDENII (*S. Schlimii* × *S. longifolium*). S. CANDIDULUM is an ivory-white, rose-tinted form of the latter hybrid.

SOPHRONITIS, *Lindley*

Tribe, Epidendreae, sub-tribe, Laelieae

Although the genus Sophronitis is one of the smallest in number of species it is one of the most important, indeed S. GRANDIFLORA, of extremely dwarf habit, has such shapely and brilliant flowers that it has become a parent of three hybrid races, Sophrocattleya, Sophrolaelia and Sophrolaeliocattleya, and has added its brilliance to most of these Orchids. The few species in cultivation are only from one to three inches in height, with leathery, flattish leaves and short stems that carry from one to three flowers. All are natives of Brazil and are best grown at the cool end of an Intermediate House. Pans are the most suitable receptacles; these should be somewhat shallow and have ample drainage material, with a modest amount of compost consisting of equal parts of Osmunda fibre and Sphagnum moss. Abundance of atmospheric moisture is desirable, except in dull weather and when the temperature falls to 40°. The pans should be suspended from the roof glass.

S. CERNUA, *Lindl.*—The type species, introduced about 1825. The pseudo-bulbs are about half an inch long; leaves of about the same length; stem slightly longer, bearing two or three roundish and comparatively small, cinnabar-red flowers, with an orange base to the lip, and an orange column. *Bot. Mag.*, t. 3677; *Bot. Reg.*, t. 1129.

S. GRANDIFLORA, *Lindl.*—By far the most useful and beautiful species, introduced about 1840. The inch-long pseudo-bulbs have three-inch leaves, and stems of about the same length usually bearing one flower, but occasionally two. The very shapely flowers are widely expanded, about three inches broad, flattish, with brilliant scarlet sepals and petals and a three-lobed lip that has orange-marks on the side lobes and base. A most delightful Orchid, of easy culture, usually flowering in the Winter and early Spring. A few varietal forms have been named and the chief are COCCINEA with larger, rosy-scarlet flowers; MILITARIS, vivid scarlet-red; PURPUREA, carmine-purple; and ROSEA, deep rose, shaded with purple. *Bot. Mag.*, t. 3709; *Mag. Bot.*, IX, t. 194; *Sel. Orch.*, III, t. 3.

S. VIOLACEA, *Lindl.*—Leaves about three inches long; pseudo-bulbs small; stems shorter than the leaves, with one or two flowers, each rather more than an inch wide, violet-magenta, palest at the bases of the sepals and petals; lip broad. *Bot. Mag.*, t. 6880.

SPATHOGLOTTIS, *Blume*

Tribe, Vandeae; sub-tribe, Ereiae

This genus consists of a few terrestrial species of tall Orchids with long, grassy leaves, and rounded flowers about three inches broad, on erect spikes. Although not very popular now, they are very attractive and distinct. The pseudo-bulbs are small, corm-like, spaced along a creeping rhizome, from which the spike arises. Osmunda fibre and Sphagnum moss make a suitable rooting compost, but certain growers add some half-decayed leaves, and a few have used a small quantity of old, flaky cow manure. Ample drainage is necessary as an abundance of water is needed throughout the growing season, but very little after leaf-fall—just sufficient to keep the pseudo-bulbs from shrivelling. The temperature of the Intermediate House will suit them.

S. AUREA, *Lindl.*—Spikes about a yard tall, with several flowers, each three inches broad, and bright yellow; lip deep yellow, dotted with red.

S. FORTUNEI, *Lindl.*—A foot or more tall, with a spike of similar length, terminating in a raceme of six to eight yellow flowers, each an inch and a half broad, with red spots on the side lobes of the lip. A handsome Orchid introduced from Hong Kong by Robert Fortune in 1844. *Bot. Reg.*, 1845, t. 19.

S. KIMBALLIANA, *Sander*—About a yard tall, with several three-inch flowers of bright golden-yellow colour, with red markings on all the lobes of the lip.

S. LOBBII, *Rchb. f.*—Spikes up to two feet tall, with about six flowers, two inches broad, bright yellow, with red dots on the lip.

S. VIEILLARDI, *Rchb. f.*—A particularly robust species, with numerous two-inch flowers on an erect spike about two feet tall. The flowers open in succession from the bottom upwards and are white, flushed with rose; lip white, marked with red-brown. Very showy. *Bot. Mag.*, t. 7013.

HYBRIDS

S. AUREO-VIEILLARDI (*S. aurea* × *S. Vieillardi*); S. WIGANAE (*S. Kimballiana* × *S. Vieillardi*).

STANHOPEA, *Frost*
Tribe, *Vandeae*; sub-tribe, *Stanhopieae*

A genus of very wonderful Orchids, with pendant spikes of large, curiously-formed, gorgeously-coloured flowers that invariably arrest attention at exhibitions. Unfortunately, the fleshy flowers do not last long. The architecture of the flowers is not so extravagant as in Coryanthes, nevertheless the basal portion (hypochile), is bent downwards and then upwards into two pointed processes, with the apical portion (epichile) like a central lobe, varying in form.

Stanhopeas are found in Tropical America and, under cultivation, need plenty of warmth, and abundance of atmospheric moisture during the period of growth. As the flower spikes are pendulous, the plants should be grown in teak-wood baskets, so that the inflorescence finds no obstruction in its downward passage through a compost consisting mainly of Sphagnum moss. The short, ovoid pseudo-bulbs are clustered and the lanceolate leaves range from ten to fifteen inches in length. There are several species, but only the most important are described here.

S. BUCEPHALUS, *Lindl.*—Flowers fragrant, three inches broad, dull orange-yellow, irregularly spotted with deep red. Very showy when a raceme carries four or five flowers. *Bot. Mag.*, t. 5298.

S. DEVONIENSIS, *Lindl.*—Rare in cultivation, with larger flowers than in *S. Bucephalus*, fawn-yellow, spotted with brownish-crimson; lip ivory-white. Very handsome.

S. EBURNEA, *Lindl.*—A beautiful and fragrant Orchid with medium-sized, ivory-white flowers, and purple spots on the basal portion of the lip. *Bot. Mag.*, t. 3359; *Bot. Reg.*, t. 1529.

S. INSIGNIS, *Frost et Hook.*—Flowers fragrant, of medium size, pale yellow, with purple spots. Lip ivory-white, spotted sparingly with purple. Seldom has more than two flowers on the spike. *Bot. Mag.*, t. 2948; *Bot. Reg.*, t. 1837.

S. OCULATA, *Lindl.*—A showy, and probably the most variable, species. Flowers five or more on a spike, five inches broad, light-yellow, with red spots; lip orange-yellow and white, with red spots. *Bot. Mag.*, t. 5300.

S. TIGRINA, *Bateman*—A very handsome species, and at one period quite popular. Flowers five to seven inches broad and probably the largest found in the genus; red, with yellow markings and yellow tips to the sepals; petals narrower, wine-red, marked and tipped with yellow. Lip ivory-white, with purple spots. *Bot. Mag.*, t. 1839; *Lindenia*, II, t. 51.

S. WOODII, *Lindl.*—The reflexed sepals and petals of this very showy species are golden-yellow, spotted with reddish-purple; lip yellow and white, with a few red spots at the maroon base. Flowers large, very fragrant, usually five or six on the foot-long raceme. *Bot. Mag.*, t. 5287; *Lindenia*, VII, t. 315.

SELENIPEDIUM GRANDE VAR. ATRATUM

STANHOPEA OCULATA

VANDA KIMBALLIANA

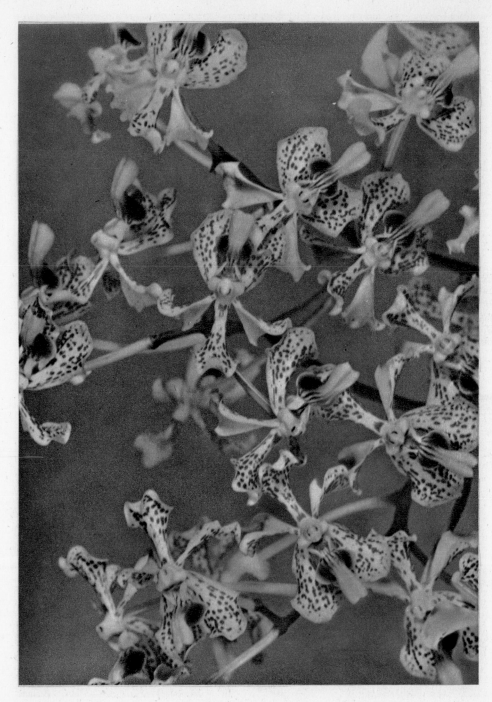

THUNIA, *Reichenbach filius*

Tribe, Vandeae; sub-tribe, Bletieae

Founded by the younger Reichenbach, the genus Thunia consists of a comparatively few species of rather tall, deciduous plants, natives of Burma and North India. They, and the hybrids, are easily grown in an intermediate temperature, but as rooting is free and growth rapid, they may be supplied with weak liquid manure so soon as thoroughly re-established. From three to nine flowers are carried, rather closely together, in a slightly pendulous raceme, at the tips of the growths. Excellent plants may be produced in 48-sized pots, or deep pans, but when larger specimens are desired and larger pots are used extreme care is necessary in the early stages of new growth, lest the rooting medium should become sodden with water, and the new roots killed. The stems, biennial and slightly jointed, may range from two to three feet in height; they are fleshy and furnished with opposite, somewhat thin, strongly-veined leaves. After the flowering period the leaves commence to fall, therefore the water supply must be reduced gradually and finally withheld, and while the plant is at rest a temperature of not lower than 50° will suffice. Annual potting is very desirable in the Spring, so soon as signs of new basal growths are apparent. Remove the old potting material and carefully separate the stems. Most of the old roots will have died, therefore each stem must be tied to a thin stake thrust firmly down among the crocks, so as to keep the base of the growth just below the surface of the compost. Given a moist atmosphere and comfortable warmth, the new growth will advance rapidly. Spraying with a Nicotine insecticide at fortnightly intervals will make the leafage safe against attacks of green fly and red spider.

T. ALBA, *Rchb. f.*—As the name suggests, this species has white flowers, but these have five raised, beautifully fringed, purple ridges on the lip. Discovered by Wallich and found in Nepal, Lower Burma and Moulmein. Introduced about 1836, *Bot. Mag.*, t. 3991.

T. BENSONIAE, *Hook.*—A handsome species, that has bright purple flowers, with fringed yellow ridges on the lip. Found by Col. Benson, near Rangoon, in 1866. First flowered at Kew and Chelsea in 1867. *Bot. Mag.*, t. 5964.

T. BRYMERIANA, *Rolfe*—Native of Upper Burma. A very beautiful

Orchid, with large flowers in which the sepals and petals are white, while the lip has radiations of purple and yellow and, often, red-tinted, fringed keels. Possibly a natural hybrid from *T. Marshalliae* × *T. alba*. *Reichenbachia*, Ser. II, t. 82.

T. MARSHALLIANA, *Rchb. f.*—From Burma: described in 1877. Very like *T. alba*, but has a shorter lip, with fringed, orange-yellow keels. A robust grower, with large white flowers. F.C., 1871. *Orch. Alb.*, t. 130.

T. WINNIANA, *L. Linden*—Very like *T. Bensoniae* in style of growth, but has larger very handsome flowers. The sepals and petals are deep rose-magenta, lip rose-magenta, with a crimson-purple, crested central lobe.

HYBRIDS

T. VEITCHIANA (*T. Marshalliana* × *T. Bensoniae*). Raised by Messrs. James Veitch & Sons. Flowers whitish, often flushed with purple; the central lobe of the lip is rose-purple, with orange yellow, fringed keels. BURFORD VAR., INVERSA and SUPERBA are varieties recorded and show some colour variations. *Orch. Alb.*, 326.

TRICHOPILIA, *Lindley*

Tribe, Vandeae; sub-tribe, Oncidieae

The Trichopilias are Orchids which will give pleasure to an amateur with modest accommodation for his plants. As compared with the popular hybrid Cymbidiums, Cypripediums and Odontoglossums, they have no great horticultural value, but a well-grown specimen with half a dozen attractive flowers displayed in a ring around the growths, and extended over the margin of the receptacle, is very attractive. The genus is a small one. Some of the species are rather rare at present and only the most beautiful are described below. The rather long, flattened, crowded pseudo-bulbs are monophyllous, but the leaves are short, leathery and deep green. Pans form the best receptacles and the usual Odontoglossum compost suits the plants, which should be accommodated in the Intermediate House, or the warmest end of the Cool House, with abundant atmospheric moisture during the growing season. A drier atmosphere is desirable when the plants are in bloom, otherwise the flowers will soon become spotted and lose their beauty.

T. COCCINEA, *Lindl.*—The deflexed spikes carry one large flower, with narrow, twisted, brownish-green sepals and petals and a long, trumpet-shaped lip that is white on the outside and cherry-red within. Several varieties have been recorded and the crimson and white CRISPA—sometimes given specific rank—was formerly very popular; others with crimson colouring are LEPIDA, MARGINATA and CHAMPLATREUX'S VAR., but this last has not been seen for a long time past. A native of Central America. *Fl. Gard.*, II, t. 54.

T. FRAGRANS, *Rchb. f.*—In this pretty species the semi-erect spikes carry from two to four very fragrant flowers; sepals and petals white; lip very conspicuous, white, with a spreading "mouth" and a yellow mark at the base. Thoroughly worthy of cultivation. Native of Colombia. *Bot. Mag.*, t. 5035, as *Pilumna fragrans*.

T. GALEOTTIANA, *A. Rich.*—Not seen for many years; spikes procumbent, usually one-flowered; sepals, petals and lip, yellow, the latter with a darker yellow, red-spotted disc. *Bot. Mag.*, t. 5550, as *T. Turialvae*.

T. SANGUINOLENTA, *Rchb. f.*—In this handsome, Ecuadorean species the short, erect spikes carry one smallish flower, with olive-green, red-spotted sepals and petals, and a whitish lip variously marked with red-purple. Has been known as *Helcia sanguinolenta*. *Bot. Mag.*, t. 7281.

T. SUAVIS, *Lindl.*—Discovered by Warscewicz, in Costa Rica, in 1848, this species has retained its old-time popularity. The spikes bear two or more flowers, and spread out almost horizontally below the rather large leaves. The flowers have a diameter of about four inches and are fragrant. Sepals and petals narrow, cream-white, very lightly spotted with pale rose; lip broadly funnel-shaped, white, with numerous spots of dark rose; the margins of the lip recurve slightly, and are frilled. *Bot. Mag.*, t. 4654; *Sel. Orch.*, III, t. 8.

T. TORTILIS, *Lindl.*—A Mexican species and the one on which Dr. Lindley founded the genus in 1836. It is an amusing Orchid, the contortionist of the family, with rose-coloured sepals and petals that are edged with yellowish-green and spirally twisted; lip white, freely marked with red-brown. *Bot. Mag.*, t. 3739; *Orch. Alb.*, VIII, t. 349.

OTHER SPECIES

T. ALBIDA, T. BREVIS, T. LAXA and T. ROSTRATA are other species of varying attractiveness.

TRICHOSMA, *Lindley*

Tribe, Epidendreae; sub-tribe, Coelogyneae

A monotypic genus, closely allied to Coelogyne and represented by T. suavis, which was discovered in the Cherra district of the Khasia Hills, in 1836, by Gibson, who was collecting for the Duke of Devonshire, in whose gardens, at Chatsworth, it first flowered in 1841.

T. suavis, *Lindl.*—A species of tufted habit, without pseudo-bulbs, the slender stems rising to about six inches, each bearing a pair of leaves from four to six inches long. The short racemes arise from between the leaves and carry from three to five fragrant flowers each about an inch broad. The sepals and petals are cream-coloured; lip white, with red-purple markings on the side lobes, and raised yellow lines, with a few purple-brown dots, on the central lobe. Can be grown under conditions suitable for Odontoglossums. *Bot. Mag.*, t. 3739; *Orch. Alb.*, VIII, 349.

VANDA, *R. Brown*

Tribe, Vandeae; sub-tribe, Sarcanthieae

A large genus of Tropical Orchids with considerable variation in habit and size and colour of the flowers. The geographical range is very much the same as for Aerides, therefore similar cultural methods will suit them, but a few species are found at considerable altitudes and require cooler treatment. Certain species grow very tall and lose their lower leaves, but usually emit aerial roots and may then be cut down so that the new roots may be inserted in the pot or pan. The roots are stout and brittle, consequently care is needed when a plant is disturbed.

V. BENSONI, *Bateman*—Found in Lower Burma and introduced in 1866. Stems about eighteen inches tall, with two ranks of ten-inch leaves. The spikes are racemose, sub-erect, and a foot or more in length, with a dozen or more two-inch flowers. Sepals and petals yellowish-green, reticulated and veined with reddish-brown; lip rose or purple; spur white. *Bot. Mag.*, t. 5611.

V. COERULEA, *Griffith*—The Queen of the family and as it failed to survive for more than a few years in most gardens it was imported in large quantities each year and stocks were thereby renewed. Now, however, it is being raised from seeds and no doubt the seedling plants will have a longer life under cultivation. A beautiful Orchid, with stems

VANDA SANDERIANA

from ten to eighteen inches tall, stiffly erect, and leaves six to nine inches long. Spikes sub-erect and variable in length, bearing several widely-expanded flowers three to four inches in diameter. Sepals and petals almost equal, shortly-narrow at the base, then spreading and rounded. The colour varies greatly, but usually light blue, mottled with darker blue; lip small, dark blue; column white; spur short. Numerous varietal forms have been named, but those most prized have deep blue colouring and broader sepals and petals. Discovered in the Khasia hills, by Griffith, in 1837. Thrives best in the Intermediate House. *Orch. Alb.*, VI, t. 282; *Sel. Orch.*, I, t. 18; *Reichenbachia*, II, t. 57.

V. COERULESCENS, *Griffith*—A small edition of *V. coerulea*. It is a native of Burma and has many small flowers on a sub-erect spike. Flowers bright blue; column blue. *Bot. Mag.*, t. 5834; *Orch. Alb.*, I, t. 48.

V. DENISONIANA, *Benson et Rchb. f.*—Very like *V. Bensoni*, but with longer leaves, shorter spikes and fewer flowers. The latter are about two and a half inches in vertical measurement, ivory-white; lip white, with yellow shading in the throat. *Bot. Mag.*, t. 5811.

V. HOOKERIANA, *Rchb. f.*—A species with terete stems and leaves, two to three feet tall. Spikes short, few-flowered. Flowers roundish, about two and a half inches broad; sepals white, the dorsal sepal short, and curved forward; petals broad, undulated, white, speckled with dark purple and often shaded with light purple. Lip wide, fan-shaped, slightly lobed, white, heavily flecked with amethyst-purple; side lobes purple. A handsome Malayan Orchid, introduced about 1879. Needs plenty of heat. *Orch. Alb.*, II, t. 73; *Reichenbachia*, II, t. 74.

V. KIMBALLIANA, *Rchb. f.*—A dainty Orchid, with cylindrical or almost terete leaves that are channelled on the face. Spikes about a foot long, with many two-inch flowers. Sepals and petals white, sometimes flecked with light purple; lip broad for the size of the flower, with pale purple side lobes and a deep bluish-purple central lobe. A native of Burma; introduced about 1886. *Bot. Mag.*, t. 7112.

V. LAMELLATA, *Lindl.*—Dwarf, with long, leathery leaves. Spikes erect, a foot to fifteen inches long, carrying numerous two-inch flowers, light yellow, marked with red-brown; lip white. In the variety BOXALLII, the longer spikes carry more numerous flowers, with cream-white sepals and petals. The lower halves of the lateral sepals are red-brown. *Orch. Alb.*, VIII, t. 338.

V. PARISHII, *Rchb. f.*—A dwarf species, discovered in Moulmein in 1862. Rarely more than nine inches tall, with broad, three-inch leaves, and stout, foot-long, sub-erect spikes of six to ten flowers. The rounded, two-inch flowers are fleshy, greenish-yellow, very freely spotted with red-brown; lip magenta-purple. The variety MARRIOTTIANA has fewer and rather smaller flowers, brown, shaded with yellow; lip magenta-purple, with white and rose-purple marks at the base. *Orch. Alb.*, I, t. 15; var. *Marriottiana* in *Orch. Alb.*, II, t. 61.

V. ROXBURGHII, *R. Brown*—Fairly widely distributed in Bengal, Burma, and Ceylon, this species is stated to have been cultivated by Sir Joseph Banks, at Springrove, Isleworth, about a hundred and thirty years ago, but it is now by no means common in cultivation. The stems are twelve to eighteen inches tall, and the spikes about ten inches long, slightly pendant, with five to a dozen two-inch flowers. The flowers are fragrant, and the light green sepals and petals are freely tessellated with brown, but white at the back; lip white, with a violet-purple central lobe. *Bot. Mag.*, t. 2245; *Orch. Alb.*, II, t. 59; *Mag. Bot.*, VII, t. 265.

V. SANDERIANA, *Rchb. f.*—An altogether remarkable and magnificent Orchid, discovered by Roebelin in Mindanao (Philippines), in 1882, and introduced by Messrs. Sanders. During recent years certain botanical authorities have created a new genus for it, and so it becomes EUANTHE SANDERIANA, although very many years must elapse before the old name gives place to the new in private and commercial collections. Unfortunately, it occupies a large amount of space, as the stout stems may be two feet tall, furnished with very stout, truncate, semi-erect leaves a foot or fifteen inches long. The spikes are sub-erect, stout, and may have from three to a dozen flowers. The latter are flat, shapely, and three to five inches in diameter. The dorsal sepal and the petals are broad, soft rose, shaded with white, the former rounded and the latter tawny-yellow, spotted with red. The lateral sepals are larger than the petals, tawny-yellow, with a beautiful network of crimson veins, or, to quote the Veitchian description, "with sanguineous red anastomosing prominent veins." *Bot. Mag.*, t. 6983; *Orch. Alb.*, III, t. 124; *Reichenbachia*, II, t. 62.

V. TERES, *Lindl.*—A very lovely Orchid, introduced about 1829; it has a wide distribution in India, Burma and the Malaya and is grown extensively out of doors in the gardens of the Far East. The stems are slender, terete, and may be from two feet to seven feet tall, with five-inch terete leaves. The spikes appear opposite the leaves, and are from eight inches to a foot long, with three to six beautiful flowers of very distinct form. The white sepals, often shaded with rose, form a fine setting for the broader, rose or rosy-magenta petals. Lip shortly and broadly spurred; side lobes orange-yellow, marked with red; central, and extended, bilobed central lobe dark magenta-purple. Needs more light than most species and has been grown successfully "planted out" in a box, containing little else than crocks and Sphagnum, placed inside the end of a warm house. So grown, six to a dozen plants, supported by teak stakes, are a fine sight when in bloom in the Spring. ALBA, ANDERSONII, AUROREA and CANDIDA are colour variations from the type. Roxburgh described it as *Dendrobium teres*. *Bot. Mag.*, t. 4114; *Sel. Orch.*, III, t. 2; *Reichenbachia*, I, t. 27.

V. TRICOLOR, *Lindl.*—Numerous Vandas have been grouped under this title because of their great similarity, but some of these have received the status of species. A native of Java, it was introduced in 1846. The stems are from eighteen inches to four or five feet tall, furnished with fifteen-inch, slightly recurving, stout leaves. The fragrant flowers are fleshy, and measure two to three inches vertically. The whitish or buff sepals and petals are freely spotted with deep purple; lip rose-purple, with a narrow, ridged central lobe. In the type the petals are sometimes so twisted at the base as to display the white under-surface. The rather short, stout spikes may have from three to eight or ten flowers. Var. PLANILABRIS has flatter and rounder flowers; SUAVIS is whiter, with red-purple spots; GOTTSCHALCKEI, now rare, is more robust and more densely spotted; DALKEITH var. has light yellow sepals and petals, and crimson markings. *Bot. Mag.*, t. 4432; *Orch. Alb.*, II, t. 77; *V. suavis*, in *Bot. Mag.*, t. 5174 and *Orch. Alb.*, IV, t. 180.

HYBRIDS

V. CHARLESWORTHII, probably a natural hybrid from *V. caerulea* × *V. Bensoni;* very much like *V. coerulea*; V. MISS JOAQUIM (*V. teres* × *V. Hookerianiana*), a very beautiful hybrid raised in Java by the lady whose name it bears; habit as in *V. teres*; easily grown and free-flowering; extremely popular among Orchid growers in the East Indies.

ZYGOPETALUM, *Hook.*

Tribe, Vandeae, sub-tribe, Cyrtopodieae

A genus of sturdy, Cool-House Orchids, with long-lasting flowers of distinct colouring and therefore extremely useful for grouping with other and more brilliant species. Fairly easily grown in the usual Odonto-glossum compost.

Z. BRACHYPETALUM, *Lindl.*—A Winter-flowering species introduced from Brazil in 1847. Grows rather tall, the sturdy spikes carrying six to eight flowers of stout texture. The brown and green sepals and petals provide a good background for the broad, mauvy-blue, white-edged central lobe of the lip. By no means common in cultivation.

Z. BURKEI, *Bentham*—A very distinct and handsome species, with four-inch flowers that have broad, but pointed, spreading sepals and petals and a red-brown, white-based lip. Also known as *Batemania Burkei*. Very rarely seen at present and the larger, brighter variety WALLISII even more rarely. *Bot. Mag.*, t. 6003.

Z. CANDIDUM, *Rchb. f.*—A dwarf species, without pseudo-bulbs, and formerly known as *Warscewiczella candida*, *Huntleya candida* and *Warrea candida*. The two-inch flowers are white, with a white edging to the violet-blue lip. Requires rather warmer treatment than most Zygopetalums.

Z. CERINUM, *Rchb. f.*—A dwarf species, without pseudo-bulbs from Panama, and known formerly as *Huntleya cerina*, and *Pescatorea cerina*. The leaves are about eight or ten inches long, but the spike is barely four inches long, and carries one three-inch flower. The colour is light citron-yellow but the lip is brighter yellow, with red ridges. *Bot. Mag.*, t. 5598; *Orch. Alb.*, IX, t. 394.

Z. COCHLEARE, *Lindl.*—The leaves are about ten inches long and the spike much shorter, with one very fragrant, white flower in which the lip is white, lined with violet-purple. Has been known and figured as *Z. flabelliformis*, *Z. Gibbesiae*, *Huntleya imbricata*, and *Warscewiczella cochlearis*.

Z. GAUTIERI, *Lemaire*—Although sometimes recorded as a variety of *Z. maxillare*, this is a distinct and valuable horticultural Orchid, but one not frequently seen now. It is more robust than *Z. maxillare*, with broader flowers in which the blue colouring is emphasised. *Orch. Alb.*, I, t. 28.

ZYGOPETALUM MACKAYII

p. 181

Z. GRAMINEUM, *Lindl.*—The grassy leaves of this pseudo-bulbless species, from Colombia, have short, one-flower edspikes. The flowers are yellowish-green, with rows of red-brown spots; lip yellow, dotted with red-purple; crest red-purple. Has been known as *Kefersteinia graminea. Bot. Mag.*, t. 5046.

Z. GRAMINIFOLIUM, *Rolfe*—In this species the pseudo-bulbs are very small and each carries several narrow leaves at its apex. The sturdy, erect spikes carry about half a dozen flowers, with dark, bronzy-brown markings on the green sepals and petals; lip violet-blue, with white streaks, and a light blue crest. A useful Brazilian Orchid. *Lindenia*, VIII, t. 339.

Z. GRANDIFLORUM, *Bentham*—Introduced from New Granada and now somewhat rare in cultivation, this species has short, diphyllous pseudo-bulbs and erect, short spikes of several three-inch flowers. The light green sepals and petals are freely marked with longitudinal brown bands; lip white, with raised red-purple lines. Known also as *Batemania grandiflora. Bot. Mag.*, 5567.

Z. INTERMEDIUM, *Lodd.*—An Autumn-flowering Brazilian species, with long leaves and short pseudo-bulbs, and erect, eighteen-inch spikes. The flowers have green, brown-blotched sepals and petals, and a white, bilobed lip with radiating lines and spots of violet-purple. *Reichenbachia*, I, t. 16.

Z. MACKAYII, *Hook.*—One of the most handsome of all true Zygopetalums. The ovoid pseudo-bulbs have eighteen-inch leaves and even taller spikes of several fragrant, three-inch flowers. The yellowish-green sepals and petals are blotched with purple-brown, and the broad, white lip has violet-purple lines and spots. *Bot. Mag.*, t. 2748; *Orch. Alb.*, IX, t. 427.

Z. MAXILLARE, *Lodd.*—A species with narrow leaves, short pseudo-bulbs and a semi-erect spike of several neat, smallish flowers. The bronzy-brown sepals and petals have transverse markings of green. The lip is violet-blue, with paler margins and a blue crest. Introduced from Rio de Janeiro in 1829. *Bot. Mag.*, t. 3686.

Z. ROSTRATUM, *Hook.*—A native of British Guiana, with short pseudo-bulbs, eight-inch leaves and short spikes of one or two flowers. The latter are four inches across, with greenish sepals and petals, white at the base and shaded with rosy-brown; lip large, white, with purple streaks

N

and a yellow crest. A handsome Orchid when grown well. *Bot. Mag.*, t. 2819; *Orch. Alb.*, II, t. 78.

Z. WAILESIANUM, *Rchb. f.*—A member of the Warscewiczella or pseudo-bulbless group. A rare plant, of dwarf habit, with two-inch, creamy-white sepals and petals and a white lip, with blue stains on the base and on the crest.   Also known as *Warrea Wailesiana.*

Z. WENDLANDI, *Rchb. f.*—A rare species, without pseudo-bulbs, found in Costa Rica by Wendland in 1858–59. The sepals and petals are yellowish-green and the lip is violet-blue, with a white margin and crisped edges. Also known as *Warscewiczella Wendlandi. Orch. Alb.,* III, t. 126; *Reichenbachia*, II, t. 53.

Z. XANTHINUM, *Rchb. f.*—A very pretty, lowly Orchid, and probably better known under its former popular name of *Promenea xanthina.* Lindley named it *Maxillaria xanthina.* Has short pseudo-bulbs and leaves, and semi-pendulous, one-flowered spikes. The roundish, two-inch flowers are bright citron-yellow, with a large yellow, red-spotted lip. *Orch. Alb.,* I, t. 7; *Reichenbachia*, 2nd Ser., I, t. 11.

OTHER SPECIES

Other species either of less horticultural value, or very rare, are Z. BURTII, Z. DISCOLOR, Z. DORMANNIANA, Z. GAIRIANUM, Z. GARDNERIANUM, Z. KLABOCHORUM, Z. LALINDEI, Z. LEHMANNI, Z. LINDENI, Z. LUCIDUM, Z. MARGINATUM, Z. MELEAGRIS, Z. MICROPTERUM, Z. PATINII, Z. STAPELIOIDES, Z. VENUSTUM and Z. WALLISII.

HYBRIDS

Raisers have not been very busy among Zygopetalums, therefore the number of hybrids is small. Z. SEDENII (*Z. maxillare* × *Z. Mackayii*) raised at Chelsea by John Seden, was the first hybrid to appear and it flowered in 1874; a particularly graceful Orchid, with several fine flowers on an arching spike; the striated, violet-blue lip is very attractive.

Col. Clay raised Z. CLAYII (*Z. crinitum* × *Z. maxillare*), while hybrids of later date, all more or less attractive, include Z. ARMSTRONGIAE (*Z. Mackayii* × *Z. rostratum*); Z. BLACKII (*Z. crinitum* × *Z. Perrenoudii*); Z. PERRENOUDII (*Z. Gautieri* × *Z. intermedium*); Z. SANDERI (*Z. Mackayii* × *Z. Perrenoudii*); and Z. ROEBLINGIANUM (*Z. rostratum* × *Z. Gautieri*).

ORCHIDS OF BOTANICAL INTEREST

D URING the past quarter of a century there has been a remarkable development of the purely horticultural interest in Orchids.
Both in commercial and private establishments certain races
of Orchids are cultivated for home decoration or for the cut-flower
trade. This applies particularly to Cymbidiums, certain types of Cypripediums, Odontoglossums and Laeliocattleyas, consequently a gardener
in charge of a private establishment of some importance must be able
to cultivate these Orchids equally as well as Carnations, Primulas and
Chrysanthemums. In each case there are enthusiasts—"fanciers," to
use an old horticultural expression—always waiting to purchase new
and improved varieties. No one can properly complain of this development, but there are hundreds, indeed thousands of Orchids that do not
come under the not easily determined description of "horticultural".
Nevertheless, these are intensely interesting and often extremely beautiful, though modest. Every known plant is of botanical interest and
amateur Orchid growers will find an abiding pleasure in the genera and
species grouped in this section. Those who love the rare, the mysterious,
the fascination of Nature's intriguing developments of form and habit,
and have the desire to grow plants which are not repeated by hundreds
in other collections, will not be disappointed if they devote some of
their skill and accommodation to what, for lack of a better term, are
classed as "botanical" Orchids. To separate the "botanical" from the
"horticultural" is no easy task and, after all, the dividing line is readily
overstepped either way, according to the taste of the grower. The
separation is a purely arbitrary matter and the author is entirely
responsible for the present arrangement, but would draw attention to
observations made in connection with numerous species described in
the previous section of this work.

ACACALLIS, *Lindley*

Tribe, Vandeae; sub-tribe, Cyrtopodieae

It is a pity that the lovely little Brazilian ACACALLIS CYANEA, *Lindl.*, is
such a rare plant, as it is one of the few Orchids with blue flowers. Of

lowly growth, it needs only a small upright Teak-wood raft on which to grow, with a small amount of peat fibre, or Osmunda fibre and Sphagnum, tucked among and around its roots. The best place for it is in a very warm house, where the atmosphere is continuously moist. The flowers might easily be mistaken for those of an Odontoglossum; they are bright blue, and extremely attractive. A remarkable specimen was exhibited before the war at a Ghent Quinquennial Show in May, where, although a very small item in a large display made by Messrs. Sanders, it arrested the attention and received the admiration of thousands of people who had little or no knowledge of Orchids. Introduced from Brazil in 1853. *Bot. Mag.*, t. 8678.

ACAMPE, *Lindley*

Tribe, Vandeae; sub-tribe, Aerideae

An unimportant genus of epiphytes, containing several species from India, chiefly South India and China. All need treatment similar to that suitable for Vandas, to which they are closely allied. In most species the flowers are some shade of yellow, with red spots or shading.

The best known species are ACAMPE CONGESTA, *Lindl.;* A. DENTATA, *Lindl.;* A. LONGIFOLIA, *Lindl.;* A. MULTIFLORA, *Lindl.;* A. PACHYGLOSSA, *Reichb. f.;* A. PAPILLOSA, *Lindl.* (*Bot. Reg.*, t. 1552); and A. WIGHTIANA, *Lindl.;* but it is doubtful whether all these are in cultivation at present.

ACANTHOPHIPPIUM, *Blume*

Tribe, Epidendreae; sub-tribe, Bletieae

Comparatively few species of Acanthophippium are found in cultivation, although several were to be found in the older and larger collections of Orchids. The plants are terrestrial, with oblong pseudo-bulbs and markedly ribbed leaves. The spikes are erect and carry several fairly large and spurred flowers. The colouring varies, some being yellow, others white, with rose, red, or purple spottings.

A. BICOLOR, *Lindl.*, yellow, marked with red-purple (*Bot. Reg.*, t. 1730) ; A. CURTISII, *Rchb. f.*, yellow, marked with rose-purple ; A. JAVANICUM, *Blume*, yellow, marked with red-purple (*Bot. Mag.*, t. 4492;

ODONTIODA SAXA, SUTHERLAND VARIETY

Bot. Reg., XXXII, t. 47); A. STRIATUM, *Lindl.*, white, lightly marked and shaded with red (*Bot. Reg.*, 1838, t. 47); and A. SYLHETENSE, *Lindl.*,white, striped and spotted with purple, have all been in cultivation.

Acanthophippiums are rather widely distributed, geographically, being found in Ceylon, India, Java and Malaya.

ACINETA, *Lindley*

Tribe, Vandeae; sub-tribe, Stanhopieae

The species that make up the genus ACINETA, *Lindl.*, are very like *Stanhopeas* in their style of growth, manner of flowering, and general cultural requirements; indeed, botanists place them under the sub-tribe *Stanhopeae*. Wooden baskets are the best receptacles. The drainage material may very well consist of sterilized Bracken rhizomes cut into small pieces, as this will allow the pendulous flower spikes to emerge without hindrance, as they are produced from the base of the pseudo-bulb and extend in a downward direction. Obviously, the baskets should be suspended from the roof.

From four to a dozen fragrant flowers may be borne on the ten-inch or twelve-inch spikes; each one is rounded, fleshy, and bears a distinct resemblance to a *Peristeria*. It is necessary to keep a close watch upon the plants as the flowering season approaches, as an excess of water might cause an incipient spike to rot.

A. BARKERI, *Lindl.*—A Summer-flowering species with large, golden-yellow flowers that have dark red spots in the centre of the lip. Mexico. *Bot. Mag.*, t. 4203; *Mag. Bot.*, XIV, t. 145.

A. CHRYSANTHA, *Lindl.*—A Mexican species with yellow flowers borne on pendulous spikes; attractive and Summer-flowering.

A. DENSA, *Lindl.*—An attractive Central American Orchid with bright yellow sepals, crimson-spotted petals, and rich red markings on the lip. *Bot. Mag.*, t. 7143.

A. HUMBOLDTII, *Lindl.*—Possibly the best species, but the very long spikes of handsome flowers are of short duration; the lightly spotted sepals are chocolate-purple, and the petals rose-red. A native of Colombia. *Bot. Reg.*, 1843, t. 18; *Orch. Alb.*, VII, t. 297.

A. ERYTHROXANTHA, *Rchb. f.*, is synonymous with *A. densa*, as is *A. Warscewiczii*; and *A. superba* with *A. Humboldtii*. A. HOUBYANA,

Rchb. f., from Colombia (New Granada), is recorded as having ivory-white, purple-spotted flowers.

AERANTHES, *Lindley*

Tribe, Vandeae; sub-tribe, Sarcantheae

A small genus of tropical Orchids, natives of Madagascar, and now very popular among Orchid growers throughout the East Indies, where they need no artificial heat or protection. They are nearly related to *Angraecums*, but are of small horticultural interest. Sometimes known under the generic title of Aeranthus.

A. CAUDATUS, *Rolfe* and A. GRANDIFLORUS, *Lindl.*, are the best known species; the latter has white, yellow-tipped flowers and is figured in *Bot. Reg.*, t. 817.

AGANISIA, *Lindley*

Tribe, Vandeae; sub-tribe, Cyrtopodieae

A small genus of lowly Colombian Orchids that are pretty, but of more botanical than horticultural value. The principal species are A. CYANEA, *Bentham*, with blue shading on the white sepals and petals, and a white-based blue lip; A. IONOPTERA, *Nicholson*, with white sepals, violet-blue, white-tipped petals, and violet-purple spots on the white lip; and A. PULCHELLA, *Lindl.*, a charming little Orchid, with white sepals and petals and a divided lip with red spots, white margin, and a yellow crest.

ANCISTROCHILUS, *Rolfe*

Tribe, Epidendreae; sub-tribe, Erieae

A. THOMSONIANUS, *Rolfe*—A native of West tropical Africa, and a very beautiful Orchid that at once suggests affinity with Coelogyne. The pseudo-bulbs are orbicular, squat, about an inch wide, and the solitary leaf is six to eight inches long. The flower spikes are produced from the base of the pseudo-bulb, and are rather shorter than the leaf. There are usually two flowers, each three inches broad, pure white except for the red streaks on the elongated and pointed central lobe of the lip. *Bot. Mag.*, t. 6471 as *Pachystoma Thomsonianum*.

ANSELLIA, *Lindley*

Tribe, Vandeae; sub-tribe, Cymbidieae

Mostly natives of Western tropical Africa, the Ansellias are Orchids of rather tall growth, but few of them are of first rate horticultural value. The most desirable species have tall, branched spikes which carry numerous, sometimes hundreds, of flowers of modest size and of yellow or yellowish colouring. Useful for grouping with other subjects, or with other Orchids in an exhibition group. Generally, the flowering period is early in the New Year, but the plants are a trifle erratic in this respect.

Fairly large pots are desirable as Ansellias root very freely and an established plant will often have a thicket of more or less erect roots surmounting the pot and hugging the pseudo-bulbs. They may be treated like Cymbidiums, but prefer a rather higher temperature and a more definite resting period. Plenty of head room is needed as the spikes may be from 3 ft. to 4 ft. tall, therefore they are not Orchids for the amateur who has low-roofed houses.

A. AFRICANA, *Lindl.*—Where it can be accommodated this is a very useful Orchid and under good cultivation it may produce a branched spike 4 ft. tall, with fifty to one hundred roundish, yellow, red-barred flowers. Introduced from tropical Africa, in 1844. *Bot. Mag.,* t. 4965; *Bot. Reg.,* 1846, t. 30. The variety LUTEA has, smaller, lighter yellow flowers but more sparsely spotted. *Bot. Mag.,* t. 4965.

A. CONFUSA, *N.E. Br.*—A strong grower that may produce over eighty flowers on a spike. The colour is yellowish-green, with brown-purple spots. A native of West tropical Africa. *Bot. Mag.,* t. 4965.

A. CONGOENSIS, *Rodigas*—A free-flowering species, with yellow, brown-spotted flowers over an inch broad. *Lindenia,* II, t. 64.

A. GIGANTEA, *Rchb. f.*—This has somewhat smaller flowers than those of *A. africana,* pale yellow, with red-brown bars; lip yellow. Fragrant. Possibly a form of *A. africana.* Introduced from Natal in 1847.

A. NILOTICA, *N.E. Br.*—Botanists have doubted the validity of this comparatively dwarf species. J. G. Baker made it a variety of *A. africana,* while others have considered it might be typical *A. africana* and A. NILOTICA a varietal form of it. The flowers are yellow and the plant is very showy when well grown. A native of tropical East Africa.

ARUNDINA, *Blume*

Tribe, Epidendreae; sub-tribe, Coelogyneae

A small family of terrestrial Orchids, of Reed-like habit and with pretty but rather fugitive flowers; of no particular horticultural interest. The plants have no pseudo-bulbs and may be grown with Sobralias.

A. BAMBUSIFOLIA, *Lindl.*—A native of Northern India and Upper Burma, introduced about 1840 and quite popular half a century ago. Will thrive under the same conditions as Sobralias. From two to four feet tall, with narrow, foot-long leaves and short, terminal, few-flowered spikes. Flowers two to three inches broad, with rosy-lilac sepals and petals, and a broad, purple lip with a white disc.*O rch. Alb.*, III, t. 139. The correct name is A. GRAMINIFOLIA (*D. Don*) *Hochreutiner*.

A. DENSA, *Lindl.*—The sweetly-scented flowers of this yard-high plant are carried in clusters at the apex of the growths. They are rosy-violet and have a crimson margin to the lip. *Bot. Reg.*, t. 38.

ASPASIA, *Lindley*

Tribe, Vandeae; Sub-tribe, Oncidieae

A genus of about a dozen species, found chiefly in Brazil, which should be grown with the richly-coloured Miltonias. The only species seen during late years is A. LUNATA.

A. LUNATA, *Lindl.*—A very pretty Orchid, seldom exceeding twelve inches in height, producing racemes of white, brown-spotted flowers in Spring; worth taking some trouble to grow successfully.

OTHER SPECIES

Other species recorded are A. BIBRIANA, *Rchb. f.;* A. LYRATA, *Rchb. f.;* A. PAPILIONACEA, *Rchb. f.* from Costa Rica ; A. PRINCIPISSIMA, *Rchb. f.;* and A. VARIEGATA, *Lindl. Bot. Reg.*, XXII, t. 1907.

BARTHOLINA, *R. Brown*

Tribe, Ophrydeae; sub-tribe, Habenarieae

A very small genus, and not a popular one.

B. PECTINATA, *R. Br.*—The best known species; from Southern Africa. The flowers are pale blue, and laciniated; leaves reniform and fleshy. A terrestrial Orchid. A small plant was exhibited by Lord Rothschild as long ago as 1899, but Aiton recorded it in the second edition of his *Hortus Kewensis.*

BATEMANIA, *Lindley*

Tribe, Vandeae; sub-tribe, Cyrtopodieae

Several Orchids formerly bearing the generic title of *Batemania*—occasionally mis-spelt *Batemannia*—are now referred to *Zygopetalum*, with which genus they may be grown. One is of particular horticultural interest.

B. COLLEYI, *Lindl.*—This has short, four-angled, monophyllous pseudo-bulbs; leaves broad, eight or ten inches long; flowers three inches wide, borne on a few-flowered pendulous raceme. Sepals and petals wine-purple, shaded with brown; lip white, stained with red. *Bot. Mag.*, t. 3818; *Orch. Alb.*, VIII, t. 341.

BULBOPHYLLUM, *Thouars*

Tribe, Epidendreae; sub-tribe, Dendrobieae

A large genus, widely distributed in the East Indies, Malaya, Central and South America, and even in Australia and New Zealand; the species differ widely in their size and form. Some are beautiful, while others are almost repulsive, but all are intensely interesting, be they large or small. The majority need a humid atmosphere and a fairly high temperature with plenty of Sphagnum in the potting compost.

B. BARBIGERUM, *Lindl.*—A small grower, only a few inches tall, this species has tiny, monophyllous pseudo-bulbs and a few-flowered raceme. The petals are very small, mere scales, but the brownish sepals are prominent, while the narrow lip is softly felted with yellow, and has a beard that ends in a fanned-out, brush-like arrangement with long, purple hairs. It is a remarkable Orchid in a remarkable family, and is particularly interesting because the lip is articulated with the column, and the slightest breath of air will set it rocking, and at the same time make the slender filaments of the "brush" wave about. Not infrequently a specimen is exhibited at Chelsea Show, and those who know how to excite the flower into activity are apt to make it work overtime. "It's alive!" is a common expression from novices, who fancy they see in

B. BARBIGERUM a link between the animal and vegetable kingdoms. Worth cultivating for its sensitiveness. *Bot. Mag.*, t. 6567.

B. BECCARII, *Rchb. f.*—The giant of the family, but "the flowers emit an odour so loathsome as to permanently exclude the plant from general cultivation". Nevertheless, those who are keenly interested in the wonders of Nature, and have room for it in a tropical house, have endeavoured to cultivate it, and on rare occasions it is exhibited. The thick rhizome creeps or climbs by means of roots from the lower surface, and bears widely-spaced, stout pseudo-bulbs, each surmounted by a single leaf a foot or more in length and somewhat less in width, very thick and leathery. The pendulous raceme is crowded with flowers; these are about a third of an inch wide, dull yellow, with red reticulations on the sepals, a red central band on the petals, and a red-ribbed, yellow lip. Discovered by Thomas Lobb in Borneo in 1853; but he failed to send home living plants. Prof Beccari rediscovered it in 1867. *Bot. Mag.*, t. 6567.

B. COMOSUM, *Hemsl.*—A small, deciduous species with a number of whitish, long-tailed flowers. Quite interesting and attractive. Found in Burma. *Bot. Mag.*, t. 7283.

B. DEARII, *Hort.*—An attractive species, with small, clustered, monophyllous pseudo-bulbs and solitary flowers, borne on erect peduncles about six inches tall. For the size of the plant the flowers are large; the dorsal sepal has red spots on a dull yellow ground, and the lateral sepals are marked with purple. The yellow lip has veins of deeper hue, some purplish spots and a whitish crest. The lip is articulate and rocks rapidly when the plant is moved. Originally known as *Sarcopodium Dearei*.

B. ERICSSONII, *Kränzlin*—A remarkable and striking species found by Ericsson in New Guinea, about 1890, and appears to have been first exhibited by the Hon. Walter Rothschild in 1897. The umbellate inflorescence bears up to a dozen flowers, with tail-like extensions of the dull white, brown-speckled sepals and petals, and a red lip. The umbel and the "tails" present the appearance of a *Cirrhopetalum*.

B. GRANDIFLORUM, *Blume*—Flowers large, often five inches long; dorsal sepal two inches broad, greenish-yellow, spotted with white; lower sepals reddish-brown, prettily reticulated. A plant with several flowers is very attractive. A native of New Guinea. *Bot. Mag.*, t. 7787.

B. LEMNISCATUM, *Parish*—A tiny plant, with small flowers crowded on a pendulous spike not more than six inches long. The colour is deep purple, and there are long hairs on the sepals; petals white, with a purple stripe; lip bright purple. A pretty species, discovered by the Rev. C. Parish, in 1868, at Moulmein. *Bot. Mag.*, t. 5961.

B. LOBBII, *Lindl.*—This delightful species is free-flowering and easily cultivated in an intermediate house in an Odontoglossum compost. The pseudo-bulbs are small and the single leaf is six inches long; the single-flowered scape is rather shorter than the leaves, but the individual flowers may be as much as four inches across. The broad buff-yellow dorsal sepal has several lines of purple spots; the lateral sepals have purple shading and the centre of the lip is yellow, spotted with purple. A specimen carrying several flowers is always an attraction. Found in Java, by Thomas Lobb, in 1846. *Bot. Mag.*, t. 4532; *Bot. Reg.*, 1847, t. 29.

The variety SIAMENSE is larger than the type and has lighter yellow flowers with bright crimson spots and veins. Other varieties are COLOSSUM and BURFORDIENSE.

B. UMBELLATUM, *Lindl.*—Found by Wallich, or his collectors, in Nepal, in 1821. A lowly plant, with small, yellow, red-spotted flowers, and a tiny, white, purple-blotched lip. There are several flowers in an umbellate inflorescence. A somewhat rare species. *Bot. Mag.*, t. 4267; *Bot. Reg.*, 1845, t. 44.

OTHER SPECIES

Other species of merit or interest are B. DAYANUM, B. MODESTUM and B. SALTATORIUM.

CHONDRORHYNCHA, *Lindley*
Tribe, Vandeae; sub-tribe, Cyrtopodieae

In this very small group of tufted Colombian Orchids, the best known species is C. CHESTERTONII, *Rchb. f.*, a very pretty plant with comparatively large yellow flowers and a beautifully fringed lip. A lovely Orchid. *Lindenia*, t. 405.

Several other species have been, and are, in cultivation, notably the sulphur-yellow, brown-spotted C. FIMBRIATA, *Rchb. f.;* the pale yellow C. LENDYANA, *Rchb. f.* and C. ALBICANS, *Rolfe*, with greenish-white flowers.

COELIA, *Lindley*

Tribe, Epidendreae; sub-tribe, Erieae

A small group of South American species that are pretty, but of botanical rather than horticultural interest. All are pseudo-bulbous, with narrow leaves and short, erect spikes of bright, and usually fragrant, flowers.

C. BAUERIANA, *Lindl.*—Introduced from Mexico. Has dense racemes of whitish, sweetly-scented flowers; summer-flowering. *Bot. Reg.*, 1841, t. 36.

C. BELLA, *Rchb. f.*—From Guatemala ; flowers fairly large, creamy-white, with a yellow lip, and borne on a few-flowered spike; fragrant. *Bot. Mag.*, t. 6628.

C. MACROSTACHYA, *Lindl.*—From Mexico. The flowers, of bright rose-red colour, are placed closely on a tall, erect spike. *Bot. Mag.*, t. 4712.

COELIOPSIS, *Reichenbach filius*

Tribe, Vandeae; sub-tribe, Oncidieae

A monotypic genus; its only species was found in Panama. It is a pretty plant, modest but distinguished.

C. HYACINTHOSMA, *Rchb. f.*—A lowly plant with fairly broad leaves, and a short, semi-pendulous spike of closely-set, smallish flowers of a pretty shade of pink. The compression of the flowers into a dense cluster suggests that the plant is too modest to extend its spike and space its flowers sufficiently widely to display them better. A delightful little Orchid that is best grown in an intermediate temperature, and one worthy of cultivation by those who are not entirely wedded to spectacular Orchids.

COLAX, *Lindley*

Tribe, Vandeae; sub-tribe, Oncidieae

Although Lindley is the authority for Colax jugosus, he had previously placed this Orchid in Maxillaria, while Bentham placed it in Lycaste. The one species recognized by horticulturists is a native of Brazil, and has been in cultivation since 1840; it is cultivated in many modern collections of Orchids, and is therefore retained under its most popular designation.

ODONTIODA LAURETTE

C. JUGOSUS, *Lindl.*—A lowly plant, with short, diphyllous pseudo-bulbs. The six-inch spikes carry two or three rounded flowers that are about two inches wide, with broad white sepals that provide a fine setting for the rather broad, dull white petals, on which there are transverse bars and blotches of bright violet-purple. The lip is of similar colouring, but usually darker, with whitish base and side-lobes. Will succeed at the warmest end of the cool house. *Bot. Mag.*, t. 5661; *Bot. Reg.*, 1843, p. 51.

COMPARETTIA, *Poeppig et Endlicher*
Tribe, Vandeae; sub-tribe, Oncidieae

In this small genus of South American Orchids the species are few, and easily grown at the warm end of the Cool House, but near the glass. Although pretty, the Comparettias are of no great horticultural value.

C. COCCINEA, *Lindl.*—The two-inch stems have two or three leaves, each about three inches long. The nodding spikes carry about half a dozen inch-wide flowers, bright yellow, edged with orange. The small, three-lobed lip is scarlet. Rare in cultivation. *Bot. Reg.*, 1838, t. 88.

C. FALCATA, *Poeppig et Endl.*—The small diphyllous pseudo-bulbs are clustered, and the slender spikes carry several small crimson flowers. Discovered in Ecuador in 1835 by Poppig, and the type species of the genus. Sometimes known as *C. rosea. Bot. Mag.*, t. 4980; *Orch. Alb.*, VIII, t. 359.

C. MACROPLECTRON, *Rchb. f.*—Once fairly popular because it has the largest flowers in the genus, these being two inches wide, and borne on a slender spike eighteen inches or more in length. The whitish, purple-spotted sepals are very small, but the lip is very large, clawed, with a spreading, slightly bi-lobed apex that is white, veined and dotted with purple. A long and slender spur extends from the back of the lateral sepals. Discovered in Colombia and introduced in 1878. *Orch. Alb.*, II, t. 65.

C. SPECIOSA, *Rchb. f.*—Discovered in Ecuador in 1877, with medium-sized, bright scarlet flowers on a loose raceme. The spur is even longer than in *C. macroplectron. Orch. Alb.*, V. t. 233.

CORYANTHES, *Hooker*

Tribe, Vandeae, sub-tribe, Stanhopieae

South American Orchids, remarkable for the size and fantastic formation of their flowers, the several species are seldom seen in cultivation, but when a plant does flower it is certain to be a centre of interest. The spikes are pendant, therefore teak baskets are the best receptacles; a moist atmosphere and high temperature are needed.

C. MACRANTHA, *Hook.*—The stout pseudo-bulbs may have two or three broad leaves. In a well-grown plant the spike may carry two or three flowers, each six inches wide, yellow, spotted with dull purple. The sepals and petals are thin, and appear floppy, but the lip is fleshy, very large, roughly bucket-shaped for the most part, and holding the nectar, which drips from the horn-like processes attached to the base of the column. An Orchid well worth growing for the extraordinary shape of its flowers. *Bot. Mag.*, t. 3102; *Mag. Bot.*, V, p. 31.

C. MACULATA, *Hook.*—Of similar structure to those of *C. macrantha*, the flowers of C. MACULATA, are a trifle smaller, with a yellow, purple-spotted "bucket", and dull yellow sepals and petals. *Bot. Mag.*, t. 3102; *Orch. Alb.*, VIII, t. 755.

C. LEUCOCORYS, *Rolfe*—A Peruvian species with yellow sepals, white petals, an ivory-white helmet, and rose-purple "bucket".

Several other species have been recorded, but these, and also those cited above, are very rare plants.

CYCNOCHES, *Lindley*

Tribe, Vandeae; sub-tribe, Stanhopieae

Although it cannot be denied that many Cycnoches flowers are handsome, and all are of intense botanical interest by reason of the long, arching column which has suggested the popular title of "Swan's Neck Orchids", it must be confessed that few species find a home in modern Orchid collections. Their cultivation is similar to that found favourable to Stanhopeas. Male and female flowers are on different racemes.

C. CHLOROCHILON, *Klotzsch*—Found in Central America, and introduced about 1838, this is probably the best known species. The slender pseudo-bulbs are about eight inches long; leaves numerous. Spikes rather short, usually with two to four inverted six-inch flowers. Sepals and petals reddish-yellow, and so arranged that they bear some resemblance to a swan; column long and curved. *Orch. Alb.*, VI, t. 203; *Reichenbachia*, I, t. 39.

C. EGERTONIANUM, *Bateman*—This has pendulous racemes twelve to fifteen inches long, with numerous flowers, each an inch and a half in breadth. Sepals and petals dull purple, green at the base; column long, slender, purple. *Bot. Reg.*, 1843, p. 77.

C. PENTADACTYLON, *Lindl.*—The racemes of male flowers are pendulous, those of female flowers erect and few-flowered. The sepals and petals are reflexed, greenish-yellow or dull white, heavily marked with red-brown. *Fl. Gard.*, III, t. 75.

OTHER SPECIES

Other species that have found favour in the past are C. AUREUM, C. LODDIGESII, C. MACULATUM, C. PERUVIANUM and C. VERSICOLOR.

CYPERORCHIS, *Blume*
Tribe, Vandeae; sub-tribe, Eulophieae

A small genus, closely allied to Cymbidium and needing similar cultural conditions; natives of Northern India, but only two species find favour.

C. ELEGANS, *Blume*—About eighteen inches tall, with long, rich green leaves and somewhat shorter pendulous spikes of numerous, small, closely-placed, pale yellow flowers, sometimes with a red mark on the lip. *Bot. Mag.*, t. 7007.

C. MASTERSII, *Bentham*—Although of dwarf growth the erect spikes of this quite attractive species may be twenty inches tall, with six or more white flowers. The lip has rose-purple spots and a yellow crest. Frequently figured and described as *Cymbidium Mastersii. Bot. Reg.*, 1845, t. 50; *Orch. Alb.*, III, t. 140.

CRYPTOPHORANTHUS, *Barbosa Rodrigues*
Tribe, Epidendreae; sub-tribe, Pleurothalleae

Weird and wonderful Orchids of intense botanical interest and placed in Pleurothallis or Masdevallia by certain authorities, but we leave them under the name by which they were known for very many years.

C. DAYANUM, *Rolfe*—Stems two or three inches high, with a leaf three or four inches long by about three inches in breadth. The short stem arises from the base of the leaf, with one pale yellow flower freely chequered with reddish-purple. The flowers are very quaintly formed, the upper sepal being joined to the two lateral sepals at base and apex, thus forming an opening which has given the species the name of Window Orchid. Also known as *Masdevallia Dayana*.

C. ATROPURPUREUM, *Rolfe*—A few inches tall, with much smaller and less inflated purplish-brown flowers. *Bot. Mag.*, t. 4164, as *Masdevallia fenestrata*.

ERIOPSIS, *Lindley*

Tribe, Vandeae; sub-tribe, Cyrtopodieae

A very small genus of South American Orchids needing intermediate conditions, but seldom cultivated. The small flowers are carried on erect spikes upwards of twelve inches tall. The most prominent species are E. BILOBA, *Lindl*, with tawny-yellow sepals and petals, edged with red-brown, lip yellow, dotted with purple; and E. RUTIDOBULBON, *Hook*, with orange-yellow, purple-edged sepals and petals, and purple spots on the orange lip.

EULOPHIA, *R. Brown*

Tribe, Vandeae; sub-tribe, Eulophieae

Upwards of fifty species of Eulophia have been described but very few are of horticultural value. They are natives of tropical Africa and the Indo-Malayan region and consequently they need the warmth of the hottest house, except when at rest. Ample drainage and a compost of Osmunda or peat-fibre and Sphagnum moss will suffice. They have short pseudo-bulbs, long, rather narrow leaves, and tall, erect, greenish, white or purple-marked flowers. Two species are occasionally cultivated.

E. GUINEENSIS, *R. Brown.*—Spikes two to three feet tall, with six to ten smallish flowers; the sepals and petals are narrow, purplish-green; lip white, with lines of crimson. The variety PURPURATA has more and brighter colouring. *Bot. Mag.*, t. 2467; *Orch. Alb.*, II, t. 89.

E. MACULATA, *Rchb. f.*—Smaller than the former, with erect spikes of reddish-brown, white-lipped flowers.

BULBOPHYLLUM LOBBII

EPIDENDRUM HARTII

EULOPHIELLA, *Rolfe*

Tribe, Vandeae; sub-tribe, Cyrtopodieae

A small genus of tropical Orchids founded by Rolfe, but although the flowers are of fair size and brightly coloured, the plants do not take very kindly to cultivation, although fine specimens have been seen occasionally. The species seem to enjoy the warmest position in the warmest house, with abundance of atmospheric moisture and plenty of freely-percolating water at their roots. A suitable compost consists of peat or Osmunda fibre, loam fibre, Sphagnum, some flaky, semi-decayed leaves, and sand or finely broken crocks. Wide pans or baskets are the best receptacles and may be suspended from the roof in a house where Phalaenopses flourish. When growth has finished for the season, the supplies of moisture should be reduced, but not withheld. Both species are normally spring-flowering. Growth extends by means of stout rhizomes which carry the widely-placed pseudo-bulbs.

E. ELIZABETHAE, *Rolfe*—Leaves rather broad and up to three feet tall. Flowers about three inches wide, white, with bright yellow markings on the lip and red-purple shading on the outer sides of the sepals. The spikes may carry as many as twenty flowers and before the buds expand the whole inflorescence is reddish-purple. The species is a native of Madagascar, where it was discovered by M. Hamelin, *Bot. Mag.*, t. 7387.

E. PEETERSIANA, *Kränzlin*—Also a native of Madagascar, and a much stronger grower than *E. Elizabethae*. Collected by M. Ocoris, who sent plants to M. Peeters, of St. Gilles, Brussels, in 1897, some of which were subsequently offered for sale by them to Messrs. Sanders, St. Albans. The yard-long flower stems may carry as many as twenty or twenty-five beautiful flowers, in which the sepals are bright purple, with tips of much deeper hue; the petals are purple, while the lip is white, bordered with purple, and has a crested disc and some orange markings in the throat.

GALEANDRA, *Lindley*

Tribe, Vandeae; sub-tribe, Eulophieae

Warmth-loving Orchids, from tropical America, with rather thin foliage that is very liable to be attacked by thrips. A pretty but not popular genus, of which few species are in cultivation.

o

G. BAUERI, *Lindl.*—Stems about eighteen inches tall, with terminal, semi-drooping spikes of several two-inch, yellow, brown-tinted flowers, with a funnel-shaped yellow, purple-lined lip. *Bot. Mag.*, t. 4701.

G. DEVONIANA, *Lindl.*—Formerly quite common in British collections, this native of the Amazon region has stems upwards of eighteen inches tall, bearing a few-flowered, terminal spike. The sepals and petals are brownish-green and the tubular lip is white, with purple marks. *Bot. Mag.*, t. 4610; *Sel. Orch.*, I, t. 37.

G. NIVALIS, *Hort.*—Dwarfer than the foregoing species, this has slender, drooping, terminal spikes of three or four flowers, each about two inches broad, with upright, olive-green sepals and petals and a wide-mouthed, tubular, white lip on which there is a bright violet-purple blotch.

G. D'ESCAGNOLLEANA, and G. LAGOENSIS, *Reich.* have been in cultivation but we have not seen them.

GOMESA, *R. Brown*

Tribe, Vandeae; sub-tribe, Oncidieae

A small genus of Brazilian Orchids, but of botanical interest only. The narrow pseudo-bulbs are diphyllous and the inflorescences are loosely racemose, about six inches long. The older botanists found some difficulty in defining the genus, consequently certain species have been recorded by various authorities under *Miltonia, Odontoglossum, Rodriguezia* and *Pleurothallis,* and illustrated under these titles. May be grown with Miltonias.

G. BARKERI, *Bentham*—Racemes many-flowered; flowers small, yellowish-green, with some red spots on the lip. *Bot. Mag.*, t. 3497, as *Rodriguezia Barkeri.*

G. PLANIFOLIA, *Lindl.*—The species most frequently seen nowadays; racemes about six inches long, carrying numerous small, greenish-yellow, fragrant flowers; lip short. *Bot. Mag.*, t. 3504, as *Rodriguezia planifolia.*

Other species of interest are G. FOLIOSA and G. RECURVA, the latter very like G. PLANIFOLIA.

GRAMMANGIS, *Reichenbach filius*

Tribe, Vandeae; sub-tribe, Eulophiae

Probably the only member of this small genus now found in British collections is the robust G. ELLISII, which commemorates the Rev. W. Ellis, who discovered it in Madagascar prior to 1862 and introduced it to cultivation. Needs plenty of warmth and moisture.

G. ELLISII, *Rchb. f.*—The thick, four-angled stems have numerous long and broad leaves towards the apex. Produced from the base of the stem, the tall, arching spikes carry about a dozen three-inch, fleshy, fragrant flowers that are tawny-yellow, barred or profusely spotted with red-brown and have a yellow bar across the upper part of the sepals; the petals are very small; lip hollowed, with short lobes, pale yellow or white, with white ridges and crimson furrows. *Bot. Mag.*, t. 5179; *Orch. Alb.*, IV, 147.

HOULLETIA, *Brongiart*

Tribe, Vandeae; sub-tribe, Stanhopieae

A small genus of South American Orchids with very much the habit of Phaius. The stout, ovoid pseudo-bulbs carry single, large leaves on long foot-stalks. The erect, stout spikes are up to twenty-four inches tall, with six to ten three-inch flowers. The plants need an intermediate temperature and a fairly substantial compost.

H. BROCKLEHURSTIANA, *Lindl.*—The sepals and petals are light reddish-brown, streaked with yellow and spotted with red-brown. Lip whitish, with a warted, blackish surface and some yellow reticulations. *Bot. Mag.*, t. 4072; *Orch. Alb.*, VIII, t. 337.

H. ODORATISSIMA, *Lindl.*—This species resembles *H. Brocklehurstiana* in habit, but the three-inch flowers are chocolate-red, with white markings on the lip. *Lindenia*, VII, t. 324.

IONOPSIS, *Humboldt and Kunth*

Tribe, Vandeae; sub-tribe, Oncidieae

A small genus of tropical American Orchids, of tufted habit, with stout leaves and arching, many-flowered spikes of small flowers that are an inch or less in diameter. Graceful and pretty Orchids but not grown so freely now as in earlier years. They need intermediate conditions, but if allowed to do so, will "flower themselves to death." Pans are the best receptacles.

I. PANICULATA, *Lindl.*—Sepals and petals white, large for the size of the flowers; lip bi-lobed, white, with a yellow mark on the rose-purple base. *Bot. Mag.*, t. 5541.

I. UTRICULARIOIDES, *Lindl.*—A pretty species of lowlier habit than the former. Flowers small, numerous, on a panicled, foot-long spike; white, with a rose-purple spot at the base of the lip. *Bot. Reg.*, t. 1904, as *I. tenera.*

IPSEA, *Lindley*

Tribe, Vandeae; sub-tribe, Erieae

The only species in cultivation is a native of Ceylon and was introduced in 1866. It will succeed under the same cultural conditions as Pleiones.

I. SPECIOSA, *Lindl.*—A terrestrial, deciduous Orchid, with tuberous roots; leaves five to eight inches long; spikes a foot or more long, erect, carrying several three-inch, bright yellow, fragrant flowers, with some red lines on the three-lobed lip. A rare plant. *Bot. Mag.*, t. 5701.

LAELIOPSIS, *Lindley*

Tribe, Epidendreae; sub-tribe, Laelieae

A very small genus of West Indian Orchids, closely allied to the Laelias, and with long, slender spikes. The species cited is occasionally seen in collections. May be grown with *Laelia rubescens* and *L. anceps.*

L. DOMINGENSIS, *Lindl.*—Pseudo-bulbs short, diphyllous; leaves thick, about five inches long. Spikes slender, eighteen inches tall, often sparingly branched at the end and carrying from six to a dozen flowers, each nearly three inches broad. The sepals and petals are rose-mauve, with purple veins; lip, rose-purple, with darker veins and a yellow throat. A graceful and pretty Orchid known also as *Cattleya domingensis* and *Bletia domingensis. Orch. Alb.*, V, t. 199; *Fl. Gard.*, III, t. 105.

LISSOCHILUS, *R. Brown*

Tribe, Vandeae; sub-tribe, Eulophieae

A genus of robust, tall and stately plants found in Tropical Africa and occupying more room than most growers can provide. They are robust, and the stout, erect spikes carry numerous three-inch flowers that are not without attraction. Abundance of water is needed during the growing and flowering seasons and the rooting medium should be fairly substantial, over ample drainage. In their native swamps the species of Lissochilus make a fine display.

L. GIGANTEUS, *Welwitsch*—A giant Orchid, with spikes six to twelve feet tall, bearing upwards of twenty rosy-lilac flowers in which the sepals are turned back and the petals erect. The purplish lip is veined with deeper colour, and has three yellow keels in the throat. A majestic Orchid when well grown. *Orch. Alb.*, X, t. 457.

L. HORSFALLII, *Bateman*—About six feet tall when in flower. The purple sepals are shaded with chocolate-brown, the petals white, shaded with rose, and the lip purplish-crimson, with white marks on the crimson disc. *Bot. Mag.*, t. 5486.

L. KREBSII, *Rchb. f.*—Comparatively dwarf, with spikes from two to four feet tall. The red-brown sepals are marked with green, and the petals very bright yellow; lip red-brown, with a bright yellow front lobe, and purple markings. The variety PURPURATUS has larger purple-brown flowers. *Bot. Mag.*, t. 5861.

L. ROSEUS, *Lindl.*—Rather less than four feet tall, this species has dusky-brown sepals and petals and a rose-coloured, gold-crested lip.

MORMODES, *Lindley*
Tribe, Vandeae; sub-tribe, Stanhopieae

Although of little horticultural value, the numerous species of Mormodes will compare favourably in interest with any other Orchids. The pseudo-bulbs vary in height from three to nine inches and the plicate, deciduous leaves range from six inches to nearly two feet in length. The spikes may be from six to fifteen inches long, erect or pendulous, few- or many-flowered. The shape of the flowers varies somewhat, but is always extraordinary and indicates the fairly close relationship of Mormodes with Catasetum and Cycnoches, with which they may be cultivated. Perhaps the most remarkable thing about species of Mormodes is the way in which the pollen masses are distributed, literally ejected. The anther case is articulated with the column and is so sensitive "that when the beak is touched ever so lightly, the whole of the pollinary

apparatus is released and tossed upwards with a jerk to some distance."
The Catasetums also are able to eject their pollen masses.

Not many species are in cultivation to-day except in botanical gardens;
a few of the most attractive are M. BUCCINATOR, *Lindl.;* M. CARTONII,
Hook.; M. COLOSSUS, *Rchb. f.;* M. LAWRENCEANA, *Rolfe ;* M. LUXATUM,
Lindl.; M. OCANAE, *Lindl.;* M. PARDINA, *Bateman;* M. ROLFEANA,
Linden ; M. UNCIA, *Rchb. f.;* and M. VERNIXIA.

ORNITHOCEPHALUS, *Hooker*

Tribe, Vandeae; sub-tribe, Oncidieae

The tropical American Orchids included in this genus will appeal only
to those who take a scientific or botanical interest in plants. The flowers
are not showy, but they are peculiarly constructed, the curved column
and the extended, thread-like rostellum being distinct from those of other
Orchids. As seen on the racemose spike, the flowers look like tiny
birds or coloured bats. Only one among the score of species finds a place
in collections.

O. GRANDIFLORUS, *Lindl.*—Growth tufted; leaves four to six inches
long, hiding the tiny pseudo-bulbs. Spike arching, about eight inches
long, produced from the axil of the last-made leaf. Flowers numerous,
three quarters of an inch broad, white, with green at the base of the
sepals and petals; lip white, with a green base. Half a century ago this
was a quite common Orchid. *Orch. Alb.,* t. 472.

PACHYSTOMA, *Blume*

Tribe, Epidendreae; sub-tribe, Erieae

A curious genus of terrestrial Orchids found in the East Indies. Only
one species is of horticultural interest and this is beautiful when represented by a specimen carrying half a dozen flowers. The small, flattish,
Onion-shaped pseudo-bulbs are surmounted by a pair of lanceolate
leaves, about six inches long. The stems are slender, of similar length to
the leaves, and carry from two to four flowers.

P. THOMSONIANUM, *Rchb. f.*—Introduced from West Africa about
1875. It is found at a considerable altitude, but needs a Warm House.
Shallow pans are the best receptacles and an Osmunda compost suits it.
It needs plenty of moisture, except during the resting period. Quite

ODONTONIA GOLDEN RAY

frequently two flowering stems arise from the base of the last-made pseudo-bulb. Flowers white, rather starry, with a slender, recurved purplish lip. *Bot. Mag.*, t. 6471 ; *Orch. Alb.*, V, t. 220.

PAPHINIA, *Lindley*
Tribe, *Vandeae; sub-tribe, Ortopodieae*

For purely horticultural reasons this genus of dwarf, South American Orchids has been retained, but botanists have referred some species to Lycaste and Maxillaria. Although not lacking in attractions, these Orchids are of botanical interest rather than horticultural value. All have small, clustered pseudo-bulbs and lanceolate leaves varying from four to ten inches in length, and all have rather short, pendulous, few-flowered racemes. The Warm House suits them best, with abundant atmospheric moisture and fairly dense shade. The usual Odontoglossum compost, but with a larger proportion of Sphagnum moss, will suffice; shallow pans are better receptacles than pots.

P. CRISTATA, *Lindl.*—Flowers three to four inches broad; sepals and petals yellowish, with transverse markings of reddish-brown on the basal halves and some brown shading. Lip short, fleshy, reddish-purple, with a small tuft of white hairs at the tip. *Bot. Mag.*, t. 4836; *Orch. Alb.*, I, t. 34. The variety MODIGLIANIANA is white, with a yellow-tipped column; var. RANDII is reddish-brown, with white margins to the sepals and petals.

P. GRANDIFLORA, *Rodrigues*—The most attractive and best-known species. Flowers larger than those of *P. cristata;* dorsal sepal pale yellow at the basal half, banded with reddish-purple; upper half reddish-purple, with a cream-yellow edging. Lip very dark purple, with white hairs on the fleshy, central lobe. *Orch. Alb.*, IV, t. 145, as *P. grandis.*

P. RUGOSA, *Rchb. f.*—Flowers smaller than those of other species ; sepals and petals yellow, dotted with red; lip red-purple, with an apical tuft of white hairs or bristles. *Reichenbachia*, 2nd Ser., I, t. 8.

PLEUROTHALLIS, *R. Brown*
Tribe, *Epidendreae; sub-tribe, Pleurothalleae*

So far as numbers are concerned the genus *Pleurothallis* has probably more species than any other family of Orchids, but it must be confessed that comparatively few have any horticultural value or are cultivated for their attractive flowers. Nevertheless it is a fascinating genus and the species show such a wide range of form, habit and colour that various authorities have placed them in such genera as Masdevallia, and even Rodriguezia. They have slender stems, usually with a single leaf and few-flowered racemes, but some have clusters of flowers, and others solitary flowers. Limits of space forbid the inclusion of more than a few of the most distinct species, and as they are mostly natives of the mountainous regions of tropical America, they may be grown at the warmest end of the Cool House, in small pots containing an Odonto-glossum compost.

P. BARBERIANA, *Rchb. f.*—A very tiny plant, about half an inch high; spikes up to five inches long, many-flowered, nodding; flowers small, white and purple. *Bot. Mag.*, t. 6886.

P. GROBYI, *Lindl.*—Flowers small, yellow, marked with crimson. Height about four inches. *Bot. Reg.*, 1797.

P. INSIGNIS, *Rolfe*—Five or six inches tall, with one or two fairly large flowers on a spike; whitish-green, marked with red-purple. *Bot. Mag.*, 6936.

P. PICTA, *Lindl.*—Flowers small, very pretty, on very slender spikes, yellow and red. *Bot. Reg.*, t. 1825.

P. PUNCTULATA,—Flowers nearly two inches wide, yellow, red and purple.

P. ROEZLII, *Rchb. f.*—One of the best species, about fifteen inches tall, with pendulous flowers on six-inch spikes; dark reddish-purple. *Orch. Alb.*, t. 476.

P. RUBENS, *Lindl.*—About eight inches tall; spikes with several fairly large flowers; yellowish-green.

P. SCAPHA, *Rchb. f.*—Plants up to one foot tall, with several comparatively large flowers on a long spike; yellowish-white, with purple marks, lower sepals brownish. The various segments are extended into slender "tails". *Bot. Mag.*, t. 7431.

POLYSTACHYA, *Hooker*

Tribe, Vandeae; sub-tribe, Cymbidieae

A genus of small, attractive Orchids found chiefly in the East Indies, but a few come from tropical America and South Africa. Although interesting and sometimes pretty, most species are of botanical rather than horticultural interest.

P. OTTONIANA, *Rchb. f.*—This has small, white flowers, with a yellow mark on the disc.

P. PUBESCENS, *Rchb. f.*—This also has small pseudo-bulbs, and numerous yellowish flowers on a racemose spike. There are red marks on the sepals. *Bot. Mag.*, t. 5586.

RODRIGUEZIA, *Ruiz et Pavon*

Tribe, Vandeae; sub-tribe, Oncideae

Very pretty and mostly East Indian Orchids, but not regarded as possessing much horticultural value. All are of dwarf growth, with more or less pendulous, few-flowered racemes. They are best accommodated in the Intermediate House, in a compost consisting chiefly of Sphagnum moss, and in well-drained pans or baskets. Many of the species have also been known as Burlingtonias.

R. BATEMANI, *Lindl.*—A species with short pseudo-bulbs and leaves. Racemes somewhat pendulous, few-flowered. The sepals and petals are white, the latter broader than the former and marked with rose-purple; lip white, with rose-purple streaks. *Bot. Reg.*, t. 1927.

R. CANDIDA, *Rchb. f.*—Pseudo-bulbs very small; leaves four to six inches long; racemes pendulous, and with about six fragrant flowers, each nearly three inches broad, white, with a bright yellow central mark on the lip. *Bot. Reg.*, t. 1927 and *Orch. Alb.*, I, t. 13, as *Burlingtonia candida.*

R. DECORA, *Rchb. f.*—Taller than most species and with long, terminal, many-flowered racemes of small flowers. The sepals and petals are white, with brown spots; lip white. *Bot. Mag.*, t. 4834.

R. GRANADENSIS, *Rchb. f.*—A lowly, monophyllous species, with pendulous, many-flowered racemes. Flowers small, white; lip white, with a yellow blotch at the base. Also known as *Burlingtonia granadensis.*

R. PUBESCENS, *Rchb. f.*—A Brazilian species.—Leaves long and leathery; racemes pendulous, with a dozen or more small flowers; white with a yellow mark at the base of the lip. *Lindenia*, VII, t. 306.

R. SECUNDA, *Humb., Bonpl. et Kunth.*—A very old inhabitant, introduced from Trinidad in 1818. A pretty Orchid, with small monophyllous pseudo-bulbs; spikes nodding, many flowered, flowers small, rose-pink; lip of deeper colour. *Bot. Mag.*, t. 3524; *Bot. Reg.*, t. 930 ; *Orch. Alb.*, VIII, t. 351.

R. VENUSTA, *Rchb. f.*—A tufted species, without pseudo-bulbs. The small flowers are numerous, on pendulous racemes. Flowers fragrant, white, with a yellow blotch on the broad lip. *Bot Reg.*, t. 1927; and *Orch. Alb.*, VIII, t. 363, as *Burlingtonia fragrans.*

SARCOCHILUS, *R. Brown*
Tribe, Vandeae; sub-tribe, Sarcantheae

The species of Sarcochilus have a wide geographical distribution, considering how few there are. All are dwarf plants, but they vary so greatly in habit, and more so in floral shape, that botanists have at various times placed the species in Thrixspermum, Microphera, Dendrocholla, Chiloschista, Gunnia, Camarotis and Aerides, and it was left to Reichenbach to unite them in Sarcochilus. None is of much horticultural value, but S. FITZGERALDII is a charming subject when in flower.

S. BERKELEYI, *Hook. f.*—About six inches tall, with six-inch leaves. Spike six to eight inches long, pendulous, crowded with flowers about an inch and a half wide; cream-white, with a purple blotch on the short lip. *Orch. Alb.*, t. 436.

S. FITZGERALDII, *F. Muell.*—A low-growing species from Queensland. A charming little Orchid with a half a dozen inch-wide, rounded flowers on a slender, drooping spike. The gem-like flowers are white, with dense rose-purple spotting at the bases of the sepals and petals; lip small and of similar colouring.

S. HARTMANNI, *F. Muell.*—Somewhat like the former species, but the smaller flowers are spotted with red. *Bot. Mag.*, t. 7010.

S. LUNIFERUS, *Hook. f.*—An extraordinary and very dwarf plant, as the short, flat leaves are rarely seen and, in any case, are short-lived. Spikes racemose, drooping; flowers numerous, about half an inch broad, yellow, with white spots; lip small, white. *Bot. Mag.*, t. 7044.

S. PURPUREUS, *Bentham*—Much taller than other species, often two feet in height, with four-inch, linear leaves. The numerous inch-wide flowers are crowded on a six-inch spike; they are rose-purple, with a darker lip. *Mag. Bot.*, VII, p. 35. Known also as *Camarotis purpureus.*

SCHOMBURGKIA, *Lindley*

Tribe, Epidendreae; sub-tribe, Laelieae

A genus of robust Orchids from Central and Southern America. Attractive when in flower, but probably occupying too much room to become really popular. May be grown with Laelias and Cattleyas.

S. CRISPA, *Lindl.*—Stems fusiform, diphyllous; leaves up to ten inches long, leathery. Spikes a yard or more long, with several flowers at the end; flowers about three inches broad, with brown, yellow-shaded sepals and petals; lip white, shaded with rose. The sepals and petals are crisped, hence the specific name. *Bot. Mag.*, t. 3729; *Bot. Reg.*, 1844, t. 23.

S. HUMBOLDTII, *Rchb. f.*—Pseudo-bulbs long, diphyllous, furrowed. Spikes about four feet tall, with numerous three-inch flowers on purple pedicels. The undulate sepals and petals are soft lilac, shaded with purple at the tips; lip purple, with lighter markings and a yellow disc. Known as *Epidendrum Humboldtii* and *Bletia Humboldtii*.

S. LYONSII, *Lindl.*—An attractive species, with tall pseudo-bulbs and long, narrow leaves. Spikes about three or four feet long, ending in a raceme of from six to fifteen flowers. The latter are two inches broad, white, marked with purple. *Bot. Mag.*, t. 5172.

S. THOMSONIANA, *Rchb. f.*—Flowers about three inches broad, cream-yellow, with buff tips to the sepals and petals; lip red-purple.

S. SANDERIANA, *Rolfe*—A strong grower, with several three-inch, rose-purple flowers; lip rose purple. *Reichenbachia*, Ser. II, t. 59.

S. TIBICINIS, *Bateman*—A well-known, robust species, introduced from Central America in 1836. The terminal spikes may be from three to six feet long, with numerous three-inch flowers at the top. Sepals and petals undulate, brown, shaded with purple; lip with broad yellow, purple lines and a short, excerted, central lobe, white, stained with yellow and purple. Good specimens are not infrequently seen in large exhibits of Orchids. The old and hollow pseudo-bulbs, often twelve to eighteen inches tall, make a congenial home for ants, both in Nature and under cultivation. *Bot. Mag.*, t. 4476; *Orch. Alb.*, V, t. 295.

S. UNDULATA, *Lindl.*—Rather like *S. tibicinis* in habit and size. Spikes a yard long, racemose at the end, with numerous rather small flowers that are rich red, shaded with brown, with very pronounced undulations on the sepals and petals; lip rose and purple, with a white, longitudinally ridged disc. *Sel. Orch.*, II, t. 21.

STAUROPSIS, *Reichenbach filius*

Tribe, Vandeae; sub-tribe, Sarcantheae

A small genus of tall, robust Orchids with broad, spreading leaves and more or less erect spikes of large, fleshy flowers. The plants are too large for most collections and S. LISSOCHILOIDES is probably the one with the greatest horticultural value.

S. FASCIATA, *Bentham*—Spikes erect, with a few two-inch flowers, chestnut-brown, barred with yellow; lip white, with red spots. *Orch. Alb.*, V, t. 208.

S. GIGANTEA, *Bentham*—Spikes racemose, about a foot long, with several three-inch yellow, brown-spotted flowers, shaded with purple. *Bot. Mag.*, t. 5198.

S. LISSOCHILOIDES, *Bentham*—Spikes sub-erect, with ten to twenty three-inch flowers that are yellow, freely spotted with red-purple. Very attractive when grown well. *Bot. Reg.*, 1846, t. 59 as *Vanda Batemanii*.

TETRAMICRA, *Lindley*

Tribe, Epidendreae; sub-tribe, Laelieae

Small, dwarf, Tropical American Orchids that have been placed by different authorities in Bletia, Leptotes, Laelia, Laeliopsis and Schomburgkia, but we retain the name by which the prettiest and most frequently grown species is known in gardens, although the title of Leptotes is almost as popular.

T. BICOLOR, *Rolfe*—Stems terete, about two inches long, on creeping rhizomes ; monophyllous ; leaves six inches long, green above and purple below. Spikes short, with three or four flowers, each about two inches broad. Sepals and petals white; lip purple, edged with white. Very pretty when flowering freely. Best grown in pans in the Intermediate House. *Bot. Mag.*, t. 3734; and *Bot. Reg.*, t. 1625, as *Leptotes bicolor*.

VUYLSTEKEARA CAMBRIA, BORDE HILL VARIETY

TRICHOCENTRUM, *Poeppig et Endlicher*

Tribe, Vandeae; sub-tribe, Oncidieae

Natives of Central America, the dozen or more species of Tricho-centrum are allied to Comparettia. The plants are dwarf, have no pseudo-bulbs, and the base of the lip of the small flowers is extended to form a slender spur. They are not difficult Orchids to manage in an Intermediate House, in an Odontoglossum compost and shallow pans. Although pretty Orchids, the Trichocentrums are of small horticultural value.

T. ALBO-PURPUREUM, *Rchb. f.*—The short spikes extend horizontally between the flat, fleshy leaves, and carry one or two flat, two-inch flowers. The spreading and almost equal sepals and petals are purple-brown, tipped with green; lip and column white, the former widespread at the apex, with a rose-purple mark on each side. *Orch. Alb.*, V, t. 204; *Bot. Mag.*, t. 5688.

T. MACULATUM, *Lindl.*—A rare species, discovered in 1842. Of similar habit to the above. The smaller flowers are white, freely spotted with rose; lip of similar colour, with a yellow, red-dotted disk.

T. PFAVII, *Rchb. f.*—Not seen by the author. Flowers small, white, with basal markings of brown ; lip white, marked at the base with brown.

T. TIGRINUM, *Lindl.*—Leaves specked with red; flowers about two inches broad, fragrant, greenish-yellow, marked with purple-brown; lip white, with a yellow crest. *Bot. Mag.*, t. 5688.

T. TRIQUETRUM, *Rolfe*—Leaves upright; flowers straw-yellow; lip yellow, with orange markings. *Lindenia*, VII, t. 311.

OTHER SPECIES

Other species recorded include T. FUSCUM, T. HARTII, T. PORPHYRIO and T. ORTHOPLECTRON.

VANILLA, *Swartz*

Tribe, Neottieae ; Sub-tribe, Vanilliae

With the exception of a few species of Orchis—many of them British plants—no Orchid other than the Vanilla has, of itself, any economic value. From some species of Orchis a starchy, mucilaginous substance is produced which bears the name of Salep.

VANILLA PLANIFOLIA, *Andr.*, a native of Central America, is cultivated in several parts of the tropical world for the long pods which, after fertilization, follow the greenish-white, unattractive flowers. The "pods" are from six to ten inches long, slender, and when they burst the Vanilla fragrance is very strong and penetrating. These provide the Vanilla of commerce.

The plants consist of a stout, succulent stem, many feet in length, furnished with fleshy leaves five or six inches long. They are climbers that need stout supports and a high temperature. There are numerous species of Vanilla, but only V. PLANIFOLIA is of special interest. *Bot. Mag.*, t. 7167.

EPIDENDRUM

In addition to those mentioned on pp. 111–116, two species of botanical interest are E. HARTII, *Rolfe*, from Jamaica, which has graceful spikes of fragrant, whitish-yellow flowers ; and E. PENTOTIS, *Rchb. f.*, from Minas Geraes, somewhat like *E. fragrans*, with creamy-yellow flowers that have purple lines on the lip. These species are illustrated from Miss Walkden's collection at Sale.

ERIA, *Lindley*

Tribe, Epidendreae; sub-tribe, Erieae

A very large genus, indeed one of the largest, as it contains over four hundred species, distributed throughout tropical Asia, but few are of horticultural value. Most of them thrive in an Intermediate House and in a compost suitable for Dendrobiums.

E. CONFUSA, *Hook, fils.*—Pseudo-bulbs eight inches tall, bearing three or four stout, persistent leaves; flowers small, pale buff, borne in erect spikes that rise among the leaves. *Hook. Ic. Pl., xix, t.* 1850.

E. HYACINTHOIDES, *Lindl.*—A robust species that produces eight-inch spikes of small, white flowers from the bases of the previous year's pseudo-bulbs. An attractive Orchid. *Bot. Mag., t.* 8229.

INTERGENERIC HYBRIDS

ABOUT forty years ago the late Mr. Charles Harman Payne wrote an article for the Christmas number of *The Gardeners' Magazine;* it was a fanciful, Wellsian story in which he attempted to forecast the possibilities of generic Orchid hybrids. He specialized in Chrysanthemums and Pelargoniums, and his botanical knowledge of Orchids was practically nil. If he were alive to-day he would find that some of his fanciful prophecies had come true, but—if memory serves aright—he foretold a combination of Cypripedium and Odontoglossum, with Cypripedium sepals and petals, and an Odonto-glossum lip!

Such a combination is unlikely, but other combinations of genera that appeared equally unlikely in those days, have produced races of very beautiful Orchids, as witness the Odontiodas, Laeliocattleyas, Brasso-cattleyas, Sophrocattleyas, and Odontonias. Moreover, many of these hybrids are easily grown and all add to the beauty and interest of gardens, while the majority possess high horticultural value, apart from their appeal to specialists. In the case of the more popular generic hybrids it is quite impossible to cite, within the limits of this book, all that have been raised, therefore those mentioned are such as have made the strongest appeal to the writer, or show some special distinction in form or colour, but the selection given will serve as a guide to novices. Moreover, all known generic combinations have been included for the purpose of indicating what has been accomplished by raisers.

BIGENERIC HYBRIDS

ADAGLOSSUM

Ada × Odontoglossum

A. JUNO.—A curious hybrid raised by Messrs. J. & A. McBean. It was exhibited at a meeting of the Royal Horticultural Society on September 9, 1913. The parentage is *Ada aurantiaca × Odontoglossum Edwardii*, and those who saw it wondered why a larger-flowered species of Odontoglossum had not been chosen. The flowers are small and *O. Edwardii* impressed its character in the shape and colour, reddish-purple, of the flowers. An Orchid of little horticultural value.

ADIODA

Ada × Cochlioda

A. ST. FUSCIEN.—Raised at St. Fuscien, Armiens, by M. Henri Graire, and recorded in 1911, this is the result of crossing *Ada aurantiaca* with *Cochlioda Noezliana*. A curious little plant, with deep red sepals and a three-lobed, yellowish, red-tinged lip. First seen at the R.H.S. meeting of August 29, 1911, and probably the first hybrid derived from *Ada aurantiaca*.

AERIDOPSIS

Aerides × Phalaenopsis

A hybrid raised in the Shinjiku Imperial Garden of Japan by crossing *Aerides japonicum* with *Phalaenopsis Leda*.

AERIDOVANDA

Aerides × Vanda

Two hybrids have been recorded: *A. Vandarum × Vanda teres*, named A. MUNDYI; and *A. crassifolium × Vanda cristata*, named A. RUTH. These were registered in 1918 and 1944 respectively.

EPIDENDRUM PENTOTIS

ERIA CONFUSA

ERIA HYACINTHOIDES

LAELIOCATTLEYA ANACONDA

ANGULOCASTE

Anguloa × Lycaste

A curious bigeneric hybrid between Anguloa × Lycaste; more curious than beautiful.

A. BIEVREANA (*Anguloa Ruckeri × Lycaste Skinneri*).—Raised by M. de Bievre, gardener to the King of Belgium, Laeken, Brussels. It flowered in 1903, and has large, deep yellow flowers, with red spots on the petals and column. When it appeared, doubts were raised concerning the parentage of this interesting hybrid.

ANOECTOMARIA

Anoectochilus × Haemaria

When the low-growing species of the Anoectochilus group were popular by reason of their beautiful leaves, several hybrids were raised between the genera composing this group. The following hybrid combines Anoectochilus and Haemaria.

A. DOMINYI (*Anoectochilus Roxburghii × Haemaria discolor.*).— Raised by Messrs. Veitch, and commemorates one of the earliest hybridists.

ARACHNOPSIS

Arachnis × Phalaenopsis

A. ROSEA is the only hybrid recorded at present; its parents are *Arachnis Maingayi* and *Phalaenopsis Schilleriana*.

ARANDA

Arachnis × Vanda

About a dozen hybrids have been recorded. Two were raised at the Singapore Botanic Gardens—A. DEBORAH (*Arachnis Hookeriana × Vanda lamellata*); and A. NANCY (*A. Hookeriana × V. Dearei*). Several others were raised in Java, *Arachnis alba* being used as one parent in each case.

P

ARANTHERA

Arachnis × Renanthera

Renanthera Storiei and *R. coccinea* were used as parents in the production of several hybrids raised at Singapore, the other parents being *A. Maingayi* and *A. Hookeriana.*

BRASSOCATTLEYA

Brassavola × Cattleya

A group of handsome Orchids, but many of the modern hybrids have been so intercrossed or crossed back into Cattleyas that they have lost a great deal of the Brassavola influence, particularly in the lip, for the beautiful fringing has been reduced until it has almost disappeared. In cultivation, they may be grown with the Cattleyas. The first of these bigeneric Orchids was raised by John Seden at Messrs. James Veitch & Sons' Nurseries, Chelsea, and the memory of that first magnificent flower remains with the writer. It is still a very fine Orchid, originally named Bc. DIGBYANO-MOSSIAE, but has frequently been known as Bc. VEITCHII.

The number of Brassocattleyas is now so large that to name a quarter of those recorded would occupy far more space than is available in this work. The following are all good.

Bc. CLIFTONII (*Bc. Digbyano-Mossiae × Cattleya Trianae*); Bc. DIETRICHIANA (*Bc. Mrs. J. Leemann × C. Fabia*); Bc. DIGBYANO-MENDELII (*B. Digbyana × C. Schröderae*); Bc. HEATONENSIS (*B. Digbyana × C. Hardyana*); Bc. MINERVA (*Bc. Mrs. J. Leemann × C. Dowiana*); Bc. MRS. J. LEEMANN (*B. Digbyana × C. Dowiana*); Bc. THORNTONII (*B. Digbyana × C. Gaskelliana*); Bc. VILMORINIANA (*Bc. Mrs. J. Leemann × C. Mossiae*); and Bc. HEATHERWOOD (*Bc. Ilene × C. Octave Dion*).

BRASSODIACRIUM

Brassavola × Diacrium

One hybrid, BRASSODIACRIUM COLMANII, was raised from *Brassavola nodosa × Diacrium bicornutum.* It was registered by Sir Jeremiah Colman in 1909.

BRASSOEPIDENDRUM

Brassavola × Epidendrum

This particular combination has not been exploited to any great extent. An example is BE. STAMFORDIENSE (*B. glauca × E. Parkinsonianum*).

BRASSOLAELIA

Brassavola × Laelia

This combination has not proved so popular as Brassocattleya, nevertheless it has produced some beautiful Orchids, of which the best at Bl. DIGBYANO-PURPURATA (*B. Digbyana × L. purpurata*); and Bl. MRS. M. GRATRIX (*B. Digbyana × L. cinnabarina*).

CHONDROBOLLEA

Chondrorhyncha × Bollea

Presumed to be a natural hybrid between *Chondrorhyncha Chestertonii* and *Bollea coelestis*, a plant has been recorded as CHONDROBOLLEA FROEBELIANA; probably not now in cultivation.

CHONDROPETALUM

Chondrorhyncha × Zygopetalum

Many years ago Messrs. Sanders succeeded in crossing *Chrondrorhyncha Chestertonii* with *Zygopetalum Mackayi* and produced a curious hybrid named CHONDROPETALUM FLETCHERI; not seen by the author and may not be in cultivation.

DIACATTLEYA

Diacrium × Cattleya

Interesting and pretty hybrids in which the influence of the Diacrium parent is shown distinctly.

DC. COLMANIAE (*D. bicornutum × Cattleya intermedia* var. *nivea*); DC. SANDERAE (*D. bicornutum × C. Mendelii*).

DIALAELIA

Diacrium × Laelia

About thirty years ago Messrs. James Veitch & Sons raised hybrids of this parentage and again the Diacrium influence was very much in evidence.

DL. LANGLEYENSIS (*Diacrium bicornutum × Laelia purpurata*); DL. VEITCHII (*D. bicornutum × L. cinnabarina*).

DOSSINIMARIA

Dossinia × Haemaria

A very old bigeneric hybrid and possibly not now in cultivation.—
D. DOMINYI (*Dossinia marmorata × Haemaria discolor*).

EPICATTLEYA

Epidendrum × Cattleya

Pretty Orchids, but few in number.

EC. MATUTINA (*Cattleya Bowringiana × Epidendrum radicans*); EC. PENTOMOS (*C. Mossiae × E. pentotis*); EC. RADIATO-BOWRINGIANA (*E. radiatum × C. Bowringiana*); and EC. WOLTERI (*C. Loddigesii × E. vitellinum*).

EPIDIACRIUM

Epidendrum × Diacrium

A curious combination, but the hybrids have little horticultural value.

ED. BONADII (*Diacrium bicornutum × E. Ellisii*); ED. COLMANII (*D. bicornutum × E. ciliare*); ED. GATTONENSE (*D. bicornutum × E. radicans*).

EPILAELIA

Epidendrum × Laelia

Not all the hybrids between Epidendrum and Laelia have been successful from a horticultural point of view, but some are quite interesting and not lacking in beauty. The following are the most distinct.

EL. CHARLESWORTHII (*Epidendrum radicans* × *Laelio cinnabarina*); EL. FLETCHERIANUM (*E. atropurpureum* × *L. harpophylla*); EL. HEATON- ENSIS (*E. Wallisii* × *L. cinnabarina*); EL. SYLVIA (*E. Cooperiana* × *L. cinnabarina*); EL. THALIA (*E. atropurpureum* × *L. cinnabarina*); and EL. VITA-BROSA (*E. vitellinum* × *L. tenebrosa*).

EPIPHRONITIS

Epidendrum × *Sophronitis*

Very pretty and brightly coloured hybrids.

E. ORPETII (*Epidendrum O'Brienianum* × *Sophronitis violacea*); E. VEITCHII (*E. radicans* × *S. grandiflora*).

LAELIOCATTLEYA

Laelia × *Cattleya*

The early hybridists found that many of the more robust species of Laelia could be successfully mated with Cattleyas, and they used L. purpurata and C. labiata varieties for the purpose. Later, raisers have used other species, and crossed and intercrossed the hybrids until there is now available a wide range of useful Orchids, varied in their season of flowering, in size and colour, and which usually thrive under conditions suitable for the most dominant parent.

LAELIOCATTLEYA ELEGANS (*Laelia elegans, Reich.*).—Very popular with an earlier generation of enthusiasts, and a strong grower, but as it showed considerable variation in floral colour, doubts were thrown upon its *bona fides* as a species, and it was subsequently found to be a natural hybrid between *Laelia purpurata* and *Cattleya Leopoldii*. The large flowers may be white, pale rose, deep rose or purple, but always with a prominent purple-tipped lip.

LC. CALLISTOGLOSSA (*L. purpurata* × *C. gigas*).—An old and valuable free-flowering Veitchian hybrid, with a fine purple and yellow lip. LC. BELLA (*L. purpurata* × *C. labiata vera*), raised by John Seden, about 1884, held favour for a long period, and, like LC. CALLISTOGLOSSA, is still cultivated in many collections.

As the mere citation of Laeliocattleyas recorded up to 1915 occupied about a dozen pages in *Sanders List of Hybrids*, it is possible only to name a few of the most attractive. LC. ANACONDA (*C. Dowiana* ×

Lc. Pallas), a gorgeous, free-flowering, orange and ruby hybrid ; Lc. ACONCAGUA (*Lc. Schröderae × C. Maggie Raphael var. alba*), a grand Orchid ; Lc. APHRODITE (*C. Mendelii × L. purpurata);* Lc. AUREOLE (*C. Iris × Lc. Luminosa);* Lc. CANHAMIANA (*C. Mossiae × L. purpurata);* Lc. C. G. ROEBLING (*C. Gaskelliana × L. purpurata);* Lc. CANHAMIANA (*L. purpurata × C. Mossiae);* Lc. CHOLLETIANA (*C. Mossiae × L. superbiens);* Lc. EUNICE (*L. anceps × C. chocoensis var. alba);* Lc. FASCINATOR (*C. Schröderae × L. purpurata);* Lc. GEORGE WOODHAMS (*C. Hardyana × Lc. callistoglossa);* Lc. GOLDEN ORIOLE (*C. Dowiana var. aurea × Lc. Charlesworthii);* Lc. H. G. ALEXANDER (*Lc. Moloch × Lc. Momus);* Lc. GOLDEN RAY (*C. fulvescens × Lc. Golden Gleam);* Lc. G. S. BALL (*C. Schröderae × L. cinnabarina);* Lc. LEONIAE (*Lc. Pyramus × Lc. Serbia);* Lc. LUMINOSA (*L. tenebrosa × C. Dowiana var. aurea);* Lc. MRS. MEDO (*C. Venus × Lc. Luminosa);* Lc. PALLAS (*C. Dowiana × L. crispa);* Lc. PROFUSION (*Lc. Serbia × C. Hardyana);* Lc. SARGON (*C. Hardyana × Lc. Lustre);* Lc. TRIMYA (*C. Trianae × Lc. Myra);* and Lc. GOLDEN RADIANCE.

LEPTOLAELIA

Leptotes (Tetramicra) × Laelia

The original combination of these genera was made about fifty years ago.

L. VEITCHII (*Leptotes bicolor × Laelia cinnabarina*).

MACOMARIA

Macodes × Haemaria

More interesting botanically than horticulturally.

M. VEITCHII (*Haemaria discolor × Macodes petola*).

MILTONIDIUM

Miltonia × Oncidium

M. ARISTOCRAT (*Miltonia Schröderiana × Oncidium leucochilum, Hanbury's var.*), was recorded by Messrs. Mansell and Hatcher in 1940.

LAELIOCATTLEYA ANACONDA

MILTONIODA

Miltonia × *Cochlioda*

Handsome hybrids of dwarf habit and bright colours.

M. Ellwoodiae (*Miltonia Charlesworthii* × *Mda. Harwoodii*); M. Ajax (*M. Schröderiana* × *C. Noezliana*); M. Harwoodii (*M. vexillaria* × *C. Noezliana*); and M. Actaea (*M. Bleuana* × *C. Noezliana*).

ODONTIODA

Odontoglossum × *Cochlioda*

Although it was so long ago as 1904 that the first Odontioda appeared there are many who remember the sensation it created at the Temple Show of that year, but they could not have imagined the wonderful development to follow from further combinations of Odontoglossum and Cochlioda, and by the frequent intercrossing of the hybrids and by crossing hybrids back on to species. Oda. Vuylstekeae—the first Odontioda—was raised by M. Charles Vuylsteke, of Loochristy, Belgium, who brought it to London and was awarded a Silver-gilt Lindley Medal in addition to a First Class Certificate. The species used as parents were *Odontoglossum nobile* (*Pescatorei*) × *Cochlioda Noezliana*. The flower had the shape of the Odontoglossum parent, but the rose and salmon-red colouring betrayed the influence of the Cochlioda.

Now, Odontiodas are to be seen in almost every group of Orchids exhibited publicly, and no private collection of Orchids is considered complete without a fair representation of these beautiful and useful members of a hybrid race not yet fifty years of age. Odontiodas may be grown successfully with, and under the same treatment as, Odontoglossums and they are easily managed. The most brilliantly coloured Odontiodas retain much of the habit and size of the Cochlioda, but some recent hybrids have quite large flowers of beautiful form and colour, and, floriculturally, they are scarlet Odontoglossums. Most of the lighter coloured hybrids have larger flowers and spikes, and are difficult to distinguish from Odontoglossums.

Some of the most brilliantly coloured Odontiodas are O. Brad-shawiae (*C. Noezliana* × *O. crispum*); O. Cardinale (*Oda. Vuylstekeae*

× *O. crispo-Harryanum);* O. CHANTICLEER (*C. Noezliana* × *Oda Cooksoniae);* O. CHARLESWORTHII (*C. Noezliana* × *O. Harryanum);* O. COOKSONIAE (*C. Noezliana* × *O. ardentissimum);* O. FLAMINGO (*C. Noezliana* × *Oda. Bradshawiae);* O. KEIGHEYENSIS (*C. Noezliana* × *O. cirrhosum);* O. LOOCHISTIENSIS (*C. Noezliana* × *O. gloriosum);* O. ST. FUSCIEN (*C. Noezliana* × *O. Adrianae);* O. SEYMOURIAE (*Oda. Bradshawiae* × *Oda. Charlesworthii);* and the new O. WEDDING BELLS (*Oda. Topa* × *Oda. Chantos).*

The following selection of Odontiodas is sufficiently varied to suit most tastes, but novices might like to start with some of the older hybrids, such as the brilliant O. CHANTICLEER and O. CARDINALE ; O. BRADSHAWIAE; O. COOKSONIAE; the smaller but free-flowering O. DEVOSSIANA and O. KEIGHLEYENSIS ; O. FLAMINGO; O. FLAMBEAU; O. LAMBEAUIANA; the variable O. PAULINE; O. PURPLE EMPEROR; O. RED ADMIRAL; O. ST. FUSCIEN; O. VANESSA; O. VESUVIUS; O. VUYLSTEKEAE; and O. YOLANDE. There are, however, many hundreds of hybrids to choose from.

Crimson Hybrids.—O. ASTA (*O. Acis* × *O. Rona);* O. CHARLETTE (*O. Charlesworthii* × *O. Marie Antoinette);* O. MARGIA (*O. Argia* × *O. Marie Antoinette);* O. SEBASTIA (*O. Dante* × *O. Esme);* O. REFULCIS (*O. Acis* × *O. Refulgens);* and O. TOPA (*O. Laura* × *O. Marie Antoinette).*

Pink Hybrids.—O. BRENDA (*O .Maureen* × *Odontoglossum crispum);* O. CETURA (*O. Clusia* × *O. Esme);* O. JANINA (*O. Columbus* × *O. Olenus);* O. MARIANA (*O. Argia* × *O. Geisha);* O. MELINA (*O. Victoria* × *Odontoglossum crispum);* and O. VIVIENNE (*O. Cooksoniae* × *Odontoglossum crispum).*

Purple Hybrids.—O. ACIDA (*O. Acis* × *O. Florida);* O. ALOMA (*O. Hemera* × *Odontoglossum crispum);* O. AYSHA (*O. Aleshea* × *O. Argia);* O. DIDYMA (*O. Columbia* × *O. Nerissa);* O. MINOSHA (*O. Geisha* × *O. Minos);* O. NATA (*O. Acis* × *Odontoglossum Purple Emperor)* ; and O. OLEGIA (*O. Argia* × *O. Olenus).*

Mauve Hybrids.—O. ASTARGIA (*O. Argia* × *O. Astoria)* ; O. ASTORIA (*O. Pittiae* × *Odontoglossum crispum);* O. A. E. NICHOLSON (*O. Marie Antoinette* × *O. Pittiae);* O. FRANCES (*O. Acis* × *O. Pittiae);* O. GILBARA (*O. Dante* × *O. Pittiae);* and O. SAXA (*O. Marie Antoinette* × *O. Mem. Pantia Ralli).*

LAELIOCATTLEYA GOLDEN RAY

LAELIOCATTLEYA LEONIAE VAR. LEBRONZE

MILTONIDIUM ARISTOCRAT

SOPHROI ÆLIOCATTLEYA TRIZAC.

Scarlet Hybrids.—*O.* AXERA (*O. Argia* × *O. Jeanette*); O. COLUMBIA (*O. Alcanatara* × *Odontoglossum St. James*); C. IDOS (*O. Iduna* × *O. Minos*); O. JEANETTE (*O. Cardinale* × *O. Sheila*); O. LAURETTE (*O. Jeanette* × *O. Laura*); and O. REFULGENS (*O. Brewii* × *O. Cardinale*).

ODONTOCIDIUM

Odontoglossum × *Oncidium*

Beautiful generic hybrids.—OC. FOWLERIANUM (*Od. cirrhosum* × *Onc. Forbesii*); OC. GRAIRIEANUM) *Od. Thompsonianum* × *Onc. macranthum*); OC. HEBE (*Od. cirrhosum* × *Onc. incurvum*).

ODONTONIA

Odontoglossum × *Miltonia*

Hybrids between these two genera are now becoming numerous and many of them are particularly beautiful and easily grown, mostly with flattish flowers that betray their Miltonia parentage. Here is a small selection.

ODONTONIA AMPHEA (*Odo. Duchess of York* × *Odont. Clonius*); ODO. BARONESS SCHRÖDER (*M. Bleuana* × *Od. The Czar*); ODO. CHARLESWORTHII (*Odont. Uro-Skinneri* × *M. vexillaria*); ODO. IBRANA (*Odo. Dorena* × *Odont. Serapis*); ODO. LUNA (*O. crispum var. xanthotes* × *Odo. Magali Sander*); ODO. LAMBEAUIANA (*Odont. Lambeauianum* × *M. Warcewiczii*); ODO. OLGA (*Odo. Thisbe* × *Odont. crispum*), one of the best; ODO. OPHELIA (*Odo. Aurata* × *Odont. Arcania*); ODO. PIERRE CHOLLET (*Odo. brugensis* × *M. vexillaria*); ODO. MAGALI SANDER (*Odont. ardentissimum* × *M. Warscewiczii*); and ODO. GOLDEN RAY.

ONCIDIODA

Oncidium × *Cochlioda*

Several of the numerous hybrids derived from this combination are very pretty and suggest further possibilities.

O. BELLA (*Oncidium Marshallianum* × *Cochlioda Noezliana*); O. CHARLESWORTHII (*Onc. incurvum* × *C. Noezliana*); O. COOKSONIAE (*C. Noezliana* × *Oncidium macranthum*); O. CYBELE (*Onc. sarcodes* × *C. Noezliana*); O. MARJORIE (*Onc. Forbesii* × *C. Noezliana*); O. PENELOPE (*Onc. leucochilum* × *C. Noezliana*); and O. STUART LOW

(*Oncidioda Cooksoniae* × *Onc. macranthum*), crimson and scarlet, a brilliant hybrid with a branching spike as found in the last named parent.

PHAIOCALANTHE

Phaius × *Calanthe*

A dozen or more of these bigeneric Orchids have been raised, but they cannot be considered popular.

Pc. ARNOLDIAE (*P. grandifolius* × *C. Regmerii*); Pc. COLMANII (*P. Norman* × *C. Regnierii*); Pc. IRRORATA (*P. grandifolius* × *C. vestita*); Pc. RUBY (*P. Sanderianus* × *C. Ruby*); Pc. SEDENIANA (*P. grandifolius* × *C. Veitchii*).

PHAIOCYMBIDIUM

Phaius × *Cymbidium*

When this bigeneric cross was first seen in flower it created a great deal of interest.

Pc. CHARDWARENSE (*P. grandifolius* × *C. giganteum*).

RENANTANDA

Renanthera × *Vanda*

A few hybrids have been recorded from the Far East and two were raised in France by Messrs. Vacherot Le Coufle. These are R. METEORE (*Renanthera Imschootiana* × *Vanda teres*) ; and R. TITAN (*R. Imschootiana* × *V. Sanderiana*). Messrs. Sanders, St. Albans, have raised R. SANDERI (*R. Imschootiana* × *V. Suavis*).

SCHOMBOLAELIA

Schomburgkia × *Laelia*

A curious hybrid that has probably disappeared from cultivation.

Sc. TIBIBROSA (*Schomburgkia Tibicinis* × *Laelia tenebrosa*).

SCHOMBOCATTLEYA

Schomburgkia × *Cattleya*

Of no particular horticultural value.

S. SPIRALIS (*Schomburgkia Tibicinis* × *Cattleya Mossiae*).

SELENOCYPRIPEDIUM

Selenipedium × Cypripedium

The only record of this cross appears to be S. MALHOUITRI, 1912, raised from *Selenipedium Schlimii × Cypripedium Harrissianum.*

SOPHROCATTLEYA

Sophronitis × Cattleya

A race of hybrids that, for the most part, are very beautiful, dwarf, and brightly coloured.

Sc. ANDROMEDA (*Sophronitis grandiflora × Cattleya Octave Doin*); Sc. ANNETTE (*S. grandiflora × C. granulosa*); Sc. ARIADNE (*S. grandiflora × C. Schilleriana*); Sc. BLACKII (*S. grandiflora × C. Hardyana*); Sc. DOREA (*Sc. Doris × C. Dowiana*); Sc. HEATHII (*S. grandiflora × C. Schröderae*); Sc. PEARL (*Sc. Doris × C. Portia*); Sc. SAXA (*S. grandiflora × Sc. Doris*); and Sc. DORIS (*S. grandiflora × C. Dowiana*).

SOPHROLAELIA

Sophronitis × Laelia

Another race of dwarf and pretty Orchids, mostly with bright colouring.

SL. FELECIA (*Sl. heatonensis × Laelia pumila*); SL. GRATRIXIAE (*Sophronitis grandiflora × L. tenebrosa*); SL. HEATONENSIS (*S. grandiflora × L. purpurata*); SL. LEDA (*Sl. Gratrixiae × L. pumila*); SL. MARRIOTT-IANA (*S. grandiflora × L. flava*); SL. PSYCHE (*S. grandiflora × L. cinnabarina*); and SL. SUNRAY (*Sl. Marriottiana × L. cinnabrosa*).

ZYGOBATEMANIA

Zygopetalum × Batemania

Many species formerly grouped under Batemania (frequently misspelled Batemannia) are now merged in the genus Zygopetalum, but one hybrid has been recorded between *Batemania Colleyi* and *Z. crinitum.* This was named ZYOBATEMANIA MASTERSII, and is probably not now in cultivation ; it was more interesting than beautiful.

ZYGOCOLAX

Zygopetalum × Colax

The few hybrids derived from mating Zygopetalum with Colax are very pretty Orchids, and although they have no particular commercial value they are valued by those who love to grow plants not found in the majority of collections. Two of the earliest hybrids were raised in Messrs. James Veitch & Sons' nurseries at Chelsea, over sixty years ago; these are Z. LEOPARDINUS (*Zyg. maxillare × C. jugosus*) of dwarf habit, with shortish racemes of three to five two-inch flowers in which the indigo colour of the lip is very conspicuous; and Z. VEITCHII (*Zyg. Mackayi × C. jugosus*), with shorter and fewer-flowered racemes, but with larger flowers in which the whitish lip has radiating lines and marginal strictions of violet-purple.

Variations of form and the amount and shade of the blue colour in the lip are to be found in Z. AMESIANUS (*Zyg. brachypetalum × C. jugosus*); Z. CHARLESWORTHII (*Zyg. Perrenoudii × C. jugosus*); and Z. WIGANIANUS (*Zyg. intermedium × C. jugosus*).

ZYGONISIA

Aganisia × Zygopetalum

There is little to be written in favour of this combination, but the hybrids raised long ago by Messrs. Sanders gained some notoriety. These were Z. ROLFEANA (*A. lepida × Z. Gautierii*), and Z. SANDERI (*A. lepida × Z. Perrenoudii*).

RENANTANDA SANDERI

TRIGENERIC HYBRIDS

BRASSOLAELIOCATTLEYA

Brassavola × *Laelia* × *Cattleya*

A very large group of, for the most part, very beautiful Orchids, showing a wide range of colours and considerable differences of form. Here again, there has been crossing and recrossing, consequently many hybrids show little indication of their Brassavola parentage. Some of the most attractive are listed below.

BLC. AUREOLE (*Brassocattleya Mrs. M. Gratrix* × *Laeliocattleya Luminosa*); BLC. GORDON HIGHLANDER (*Bc. Mdme. Charles Maron* × *Lc. Aphrodite*); BLC. POLYMELA (*Bc. Muriel* (× *Lc. Laguna*); BLC. SEAFORTH HIGHLANDER (*Bc. Mrs. J. Leemann* × *Lc. Aphrodite*); BLC. TRUFFAUTIANA (*Bc. Mrs. J. Leemann* × *Lc. Luminosa*); and BLC. THE BARONESS (*Bc. Mrs. J. Leemann* × *Lc. Ophir*). Hybrids of later origin include BLC. BOADICEA (*Blc. Queen of the Belgians* × *C. Mendelii*); BLC. SNOWDON (*Bc. Digbyano-Mossiae* × *Lc. Isabel Sander*); and BC. VENUS (*Bc. Mrs. J. Leemann* × *Lc. Britannia*).

CHARLESWORTHEARA

Miltonia × *Cochlioda* × *Ondidium*

This is a small group of interesting hybrids combining three genera and commemorating Mr. Joseph Charlesworth, founder of Messrs. Charlesworth & Co.

C. NOBILIS (*Miltonioda Ajax* × *Epidendrum macranthum*); C. RAJAH (*Miltonioda Ajax* × *Epidendrum monachicum*).

DIACATLAELIA

Diacrium × *Laelia* × *Cattleya*

An interesting hybrid raised by Sir Jeremiah Colman and recorded in 1910.

DCL. GATTON ROSE (*Diacrium bicornutum* × *Laeliocattleya Cappei*).

LOWIARA

Brassavola × *Laelia* × *Sophronitis*

Several of these remarkable combinations have appeared; the title commemorates Mr. Stuart Low.

L. INSIGNIS (*Brassolaelia Helen* × *Sophronitis grandiflora*); and L. PAUL (*Bl. Mrs. M. Gratrix* × *Sophrolaelia Psyche*).

ROLFEARA

Brassavola × *Cattleya* × *Sophronitis*

An interesting combination that commemorates Mr. R. A. Rolfe, founder and former Editor of *The Orchid Review*.

More than a dozen hybrids are recorded and in almost every instance a Brassocattleya has been used as one parent, with a Sophrocattleya as the second parent. The Sophronitis colouring prevails in most crosses.

A few of the notable successes are R. CERES (*Bc. Mrs. J. Leemann* × *Sc. Saxa*); R. EXCELSIOR (*Bc. Cliftonii* × *Sc. S.W. Flory*); R. QUEEN NEFERTITI (*Bc. Ilene* × *Sc. Thwaitesii*); and R. TIVIVES (*R. Excelsior* × *Cattleya Mossiae*).

SANDERARA

Cochlioda × *Brassia* × *Odontoglossum*

S. ALPHA (*Brassia Lawrenceana* × *Odontioda Grenadier*) was raised by Messrs. Sanders and recorded in 1937, when the combination indicated was named SANDERARA.

SOPHROLAELIOCATTLEYA

Sophronitis × *Laelia* × *Cattleya*

Now a numerous race and many of the hybrids are handsome, rather dwarf, and beautiful Orchids.

SLC. ELISSA (*Sophrolaelia Gratrixiae* × *Cattleya Hardyana*); SLC. HEBE (*Sl. Gratrixiae* × *Laeliocattleya Haroldiana*); SLC. NIOBE (*Sl. Felicia* × *Lc. Gottoiana*); SLC. TRIZAC (*Slc. Anzac* × *C. Trianae*); SLC. SIBYL (*Sl. heatonensis* × *Lc. Haroldiana*); SLC. THALIA (*S. grandiflora* × *Lc. Cappei*); and SLC. VENUS (*Sl. Psyche* × *C. Mendelii*).

VUYLSTEKEARA

Cochlioda × *Miltonia* × *Odontoglossum*

Beautiful Orchids, of which the following is a small selection.

V. Hyeana (*C. Noezliana* × *Odontonia Lairesseae*); V. insignis (*Odontioda Charlesworthii* × *Miltonia Bleuana*); V. Edna (*Miltonioda Harwoodii* × *Oda. Charlesworthii*); V. Estella Jewel (*V. Aspasia* × *M. Wm. Pitt*); V. Ganesta (*Oda. Ganesa* × *Odontonia Nesta*); V. Veronica (*V. Zena* × *M. Mem. H. T. Pitt*); V. Tyalda (*Oda. Geralda* × *Odtna. Tyana*); V. Avreisha (*Oda. Geisha* × *Odtna. Avril Gay*); and V. Cambria and its Borde Hill var. (*V. Rudra* × *Odont. Clonius*).

This " hybrid group " is named after M. Charles Vuylsteke, Loochristy, Ghent, who was the first person to raise an Odontioda.

WILSONARA

Odontoglossum × *Cochlioda* × *Oncidium*

Very distinct trigeneric Orchids of considerable beauty, and W. Wendy has become quite popular. The colouring, as might be expected, is very bright.

W. Deception (*Odontioda Charlesworthii* × *Oncidium macranthum*), W. majalis (*Oda. Chanticler* × *Onc. corynophorum*); W. tigrina (*Oda. Charlesworthii* × *Onc. tigrinum*); and W. Wendy (*Odontoglossum Lambeauianum* × *Oncidioda Cooksoniae*).

Wilsonara was named to honour Mr. Gurney Wilson, Chairman of the Royal Horticultural Society's Orchid Committee and previously Secretary to the Committee for many years.

QUADRIGENERIC HYBRIDS

BURRAGEARA

Cochlioda × *Miltonia* × *Odontoglossum* × *Oncidium*

At present a very small group named after Mr. Burrage, an American enthusiast.

B. LYOTH (*Charleswortheara nobilis* × *Odontoglossum Felicia*), was raised by Messrs. Charlesworth & Co.; B. WINDSOR (*Odontonia Firminii* × *Oncidioda Cooksoniae*), was raised by Messrs. Black & Flory.

POTINARA

Brassavola × *Cattleya* × *Laelia* × *Sophronitis*

A combination, named after M. Potin, a French grower, that contains steadily increasing numbers of showy hybrids. A few that have attracted special attention include P. ANISE (*Blc. Empire* × *Slc. Hermes*); P. DOROTHY (*Blc. maculata* × *Slc. Prince Hirohito*); P. ELECTRA (*Bc. Madame C. Maron* × *Slc. His Majesty*); P. JULIETTAE (*Bc. Ena* × *Slc. Marathon*); P. MEDEA (*Slc. Cleopatra* × *Blc. Beatrice*); P. NEPTUNE (*Bc. Admiral Jellicoe* var. *Rosita* × *Slc. Isabella*); P. ROSITA (*Bc. Rosita* × *Slc. langleyensis*); P. TASSA (*Bc. British Queen* × *Slc. Isabella*); and P. YANDRA (*Bc. Cliftonii* × *Slc. Meuse*).

VUYLSTEKEARA EDNA

p. 227

POTINARA MEDEA

MONTHLY REMINDERS

JANUARY

Good intentions get us nowhere. Very soon there will be much potting to be done, and if clean pots, clean crocks and the various potting materials are not at hand the work will be delayed.

See that the houses, stages, pots and moisture-holding materials are cleansed, not forgetting the spaces behind and beneath the hot-water pipes. There is great satisfaction in getting this work done before potting begins.

Check up on all tools, labels, blinds, and insecticides, so that everything is present and in its right place. Longer hours of daylight and brighter sunshine create more work, for which we should be fully prepared.

Take stock of the plants, visualize the extra room needed for favourite subjects and get rid of less desirable plants. Overcrowding is not good for plants or human beings; it increases work and anxiety.

Watch the weather carefully and restrict the amount of damping when the nights promise to be cold. Cold and wet do more harm than cold and dry.

Little ventilation will be needed but fresh air should be admitted on every favourable occasion. Never permit draughts or drip.

FEBRUARY

It is full early to pot Cattleyas or hybrids therefrom unless sufficient artificial heat is available to keep them comfortably warm.

Cypripediums should be examined carefully. Plants relieved of their flowers several weeks ago may be making new roots, and in such cases potting may proceed.

Provide supports for Cymbidium spikes but always bear in mind the habit of the hybrid; allow those of drooping habit to display their elegance.

Never allow Miltonias to become dry at their roots otherwise the flower spikes will be short. Keep them in the Intermediate House for the present.

While Calanthes are in flower keep them slightly cooler and in a somewhat drier atmosphere, to prevent the flowers from becoming spotted.

Remember that Cymbidiums love fresh air; they are cool-house Orchids and will not thrive in a stuffy atmosphere.

MARCH

Shading in some form must be provided as sunshine may be very bright in March; a grower who has lath blinds on his houses has an advantage over one who must depend upon Summer Cloud for shading.

Cypripediums are very uncomfortable when exposed to bright light, but keep them in a warm house.

Pot Calanthes directly new growths and new roots appear.

Newly-potted plants need special attention and particularly so during variable weather; it is fatally easy to overwater them.

Spray all flower spikes with a Nicotine solution before the buds expand.

Re-pot Oncidium varicosum var. Rogersii if the plants need new rooting materials.

APRIL

Shading and damping will need close attention. A moderate thickness of Summer Cloud will be desirable where blinds are not available, especially in southern districts.

During kindly weather begin to ventilate early but close early for the purpose of conserving sun-heat.

All Cattleyas that need more root space or new compost should be dealt with as speedily as possible, so that the plants may have a long season and good conditions of weather in which to become re-established before Autumn arrives.

Cypripediums with mottled leaves will need extra shading. Pot all green-leafed hybrids that need this attention.

Finish the potting of Calanthes.

Re-pot all Odontoglossums and Odontiodas that need more root room; it is a mistake to leave this work until warm weather arrives.

MAY

Considerable time will be occupied by shading, ventilating, watering and damping now that the days are longer and brighter.

Cattleyas enjoy the brighter and warmer conditions; endeavour to complete all necessary re-potting during the present month.

Pot Dendrobiums of the D. nobile group so soon as new growths and roots appear, and place them in the warmest house until growth is completed.

Newly-potted Orchids need little water until their roots are working freely in the new compost, but spray them gently overhead twice a day in fine weather and maintain a moist atmosphere.

The earlier flowering Cymbidiums that have had a brief rest, after being relieved of their flower spikes, will be showing signs of renewed vitality, and those that need it should be potted. It is a distinct advantage to keep up with this work, and not wait until all the plants require attention at the potting bench.

The same remarks apply equally to Miltonias; those in flower may be given slightly cooler and drier conditions until the flowering period is over.

JUNE

The longer hours of daylight, higher outdoor temperatures and increasing sunshine combine to occupy much of the grower's time. Watering, damping, ventilation and shading all demand more and more attention.

No fire heat should be needed for Odontoglossums, indeed during warm, calm evenings the lower ventilators may remain open all night.

Miltonias still need slightly warmer conditions than Odontoglossums.

Calanthes need fairly heavy shading, but it is too early to give them manurial stimulants.

Complete the potting of Dendrobiums; keep them moist and warm, but do not shade too heavily, or very early or very late in the day.

Proceed as rapidly as possible with all necessary re-potting among Cattleyas and their allies; plants dealt with now have an excellent chance of becoming re-established before the cooler weather of Autumn arrives; they respond readily to the light and warmth of Summer.

Finish all necessary potting of Cypripediums; if the work is delayed the brittle roots may suffer. Very little artificial heat will be needed provided the house is closed early to conserve warmth created by the sun.

Complete the potting of Cymbidiums as they, too, need a long season of growth if they are to flower freely next year.

Overhead spraying once or twice a day is beneficial to most Orchids at this season of the year.

Watch out for attacks of green fly, thrips and red spider. A fortnightly spraying with a Nicotine insecticide, taking care to moisten the under-sides of the leaves, will save much worry and trouble.

JULY

Provided July maintains its usual reputation for brilliance and warmth there will be little need for stoking, but much time will be occupied in watering, damping, ventilating and shading.

Start ventilating the houses quite early on bright, sunny days and get all necessary watering done early. If permanent shading is in use, watch the weather and ventilate accordingly. Houses so shaded do not warm up so quickly as those fitted with blinds, but they get much hotter as the day proceeds and the sun shines directly upon the glass.

Follow watering with a liberal damping and an overhead spraying for most Orchids. Three or four dampings per day will be needed. Maintain a moist and buoyant atmosphere, but remember that all cool Orchids will need more ventilation and damping than others.

Thin down the permanent shading over Dendrobiums that are well advanced in growth and have become re-established after the disturbance of re-potting.

Calanthes may be watered with weak liquid cow manure once a week.

Finish the re-potting of Cattleyas and keep the plants warm.

Watch the density of Summer Cloud and, if necessary, increase it over Cypripediums.

Use every effort to keep Odontoglossums as cool as possible and to prevent dry atmospheric conditions in the houses. Hose the surround-ings two or three times a day in hot weather, and also in the evening if real July weather prevails.

BRASSOLAELIOCATTLEYA POLYMELA

All Miltonias that need such attention should be potted without delay; never over-pot them.

AUGUST

Examine the stock of Cattleyas and their allies, and immediately re-pot any plants that cannot safely be left until another season.

Much the same attention to watering, damping, shading and ventilation will be needed as in July, but remember that the days are shortening.

Calanthes will need abundance of water and occasional manurial assistance. They must be kept warm while making up their big pseudo-bulbs.

Use the bottom ventilators freely in the long, warm evenings, especially in all houses devoted to cool Orchids.

Thrips blow in from outside, therefore do not neglect occasional sprayings with Nicotine insecticide, but use it while the Sphagnum surfaces are moist, and preferably towards evening.

Cymbidiums will now need an abundance of moisture at the roots and overhead; ventilate freely, but judiciously.

SEPTEMBER

The days are definitely shorter and the nights longer, therefore ventilation and shading become very important items in the routine of work.

Unless the weather is particularly bright and warm, ventilation should commence later in the morning, and be reduced earlier in the evening in houses containing Cattleyas, Vandas, Calanthes and Dendrobiums.

Maintain cool and moist conditions for Cool-House Orchids, especially for Odontoglossums and Cymbidiums, but watch for sudden falls in temperature at night, as frosts are not unknown towards the end of the month.

Most Orchids will need less shading. All additional light that can be admitted safely will assist the plants to form up growths and pseudo-bulbs before the chills of Autumn arrive.

The need for watering and damping will decline, and if there is no fire-heat available care must be taken to close the houses early and not permit any excess of atmospheric moisture at nightfall.

Where Cypripediums are already showing flower buds make certain the plants receive ample supplies of root moisture, as any loss in this direction will mean short flower stems.

Continue to feed Calanthes with liquid manure once a week, but gradually reduce the water supply so soon as the pseudo-bulbs are fully developed and the leaves begin to turn yellow.

Proceed with the re-potting of all Odontoglossums that need more root-room or new materials to root in. This is a suitable time for such work, but it should not be delayed unduly.

Fairly heavy shading will be necessary for Miltonias that have been re-potted this season.

OCTOBER

Keep Cattleyas comfortably warm and allow them more light, but do no more re-potting for this season. The plants will, for the most part, need less root-moisture from now until the New Year is advanced.

So soon as the leaves of Calanthes turn yellow, reduce the supply of water to the roots and cease the use of liquid manure.

Cypripediums coming into flower need special attention. It is a good plan to sponge the foliage, and clean the pots and the inside of the house before the flower stems extend very far. Overhead spraying should cease.

Fire heat will be necessary in most Orchid houses as the nights are often very cold at this season. Only use so much artificial heat as is absolutely necessary.

Thin down the Summer Cloud shading on the Cymbidium house and water the plants very carefully. Plants on which flower spikes are appearing must not be allowed to remain dry at the roots for long.

Complete the re-potting of Odontoglossums and their allies. Winter will soon arrive and newly disturbed plants will not readily re-establish themselves if cold and dull weather sets in.

Beware of permitting any excess of atmospheric moisture at night.

NOVEMBER

Dull skies and cold nights point to the need for much less damping and watering in all Orchid houses. Use fire heat sparingly; over-heated pipes are the cause of much trouble.

Ventilation must receive close attention. Prevent draughts but use every suitable opportunity to admit fresh air, even for an hour or less.

A combination of cold and damp conditions causes far more harm than cold and dry ones.

As the flowers of Cypripediums begin to open the benefits of clean surroundings will be apparent. Support the flower stems of such hybrids as need this assistance. Keep the plants just comfortably moist at the roots.

Wash the roof glass of all Orchid houses as the plants will now appreciate all the available light.

Allow Cattleyas to become moderately dry at the roots before giving a further supply of water. They will not dry out very rapidly during this and the next three months, and during this period they resent an excess of root moisture.

Overhead spraying should cease, but occasional sprays with an insecticide must not be omitted.

Routine work will be very considerably reduced, therefore the work of thoroughly cleansing the houses may begin.

DECEMBER

See that all Orchids in all sections are kept comfortable. Maintain the necessary warmth, but be extremely careful in the use of fire heat. Keep the temperatures just above the safety line, but no more.

The need for damping and watering will now be reduced to their minimum, but never allow dry spaces to develop behind and below the hot-water pipes.

Cleansing the houses—roof, staging, moisture-holding materials and pots—can and should be done now, while other work is less exacting.

Watch for and make good any repairs in glass, wood-work and iron work.

Examine all implements—sprayers, thermometers, water-cans, tanks, etc., and order any necessary new ones.

Sort out, wash and stack pots, pans and crocks and see that stocks are sufficient for future needs. Place all under cover and in the handiest possible place.

Fibrous loam, peat fibre, Osmunda fibre, Oak and Beech leaves, coarse sand, charcoal, finely broken crocks, and other materials needed for potting should be collected and placed under cover, but do not purchase Sphagnum moss until shortly before it is needed.

Labels, stakes in several sizes, wire, tying materials, and insecticides are best secured while there are few distractions. Supplies, ever ready and handy, save time and irritation.

Take stock and record every plant in a loose-leaf note book; particulars regarding date of acquisition, price, time and quality of flowering, are all helpful and prove interesting and instructive.

ADDENDUM

BRASSAVOLA, *R. Brown*

Tribe, Epidendreae ; sub-tribe Laelieae

A small genus of Laelia-like plants that are found in Brazil and the West Indies, and are easily grown with the majority of Laelias and Cattleyas and need similar treatment. From a horticultural point of view, only one species is important—*Brassavola Digbyana*, which, because of its large and beautifully fringed lip, has filled a very conspicuous place in the creation of handsome hybrids. It is mainly responsible for the beauty of Brassocattleyas and Brassolaelias.

B. DIGBYANA, *Lindl.*—The stem-like pseudo-bulbs carry a single, thick elliptic leaf, of glaucous-green colour. The inflorescence has one large flower, with greenish-white sepals and petals, and an enormous, cream-white, purple-tipped lip that is exquisitely and deeply fringed. A good flower is six inches broad and lasts for about three weeks. *Bot. Mag.* to 4474 ; *Bot. Reg.*, 1846, t. 53 ; *Orch. Alb.* VI, t. 241.

B. GLAUCA, *Lindl.*—A species of compact habit, and comparatively dwarf, with short, single-leafed, pseudo-bulbs. The solitary flowers are pale green and the lip is white, streaked with pink in the throat. *Bot. Mag.*, t. 4033 ; *Bot. Reg.*, 1840, t. 44 ; *Orch. Alb.* IX t 415.

B. NODOSA, *Lindl.*—This rarely exceeds a foot in height and the pseudo bulbs are rather closely placed on the rhizome. The flowers are white, the lip broad. *Bot. Mag.*, t. 4021.

Other species less attractive, are B. CUCULLATA, *R. Br.* (*Bot. Mag.*, t. 543), B. LINEATA, *Hook.* (*Bot. Mag.*, t. 4734) ; B. *Perrinii, Lindl.* (*Bot. Mag.*, t. 3761) ; and B. TUBERCULATA, *Hook.* (*Bot. Mag.*, t. 2818).

AN ORCHID BIBLIOGRAPHY

The great majority of known books on Orchids are listed in this Bibliography, from which, however, numerous pamphlets have been omitted.

AMES, OAKES.—*An Enumeration of the Orchids of the United States and Canada.* 8vo. Boston, U.S.A., 1924.

AMES, OAKES.—*Contribution to our Knowledge of the Orchid Flora of Southern Florida.* Illus., 8vo. Cambridge, Massachusetts, U.S.A., 1904.

AMES, OAKES.—*Notes on the Philippine Orchids.* 8vo. U.S.A., 1909-1911.

AMES, OAKES.—*Orchidaceae Halconenses ; an Enumeration of the Orchids collected on and near Mount Halcon, Mindoro.* Manila, 1907. *Philippine Journ. Sci.*, vol. II, No. 4.

AMES, OAKES.—*Orchidaceae: Illustrations and Studies in the Orchidae.* Illus., 1. 8vo. Boston, U.S.A., 1905.

APPLEBY, THOMAS.—*The Orchid Manual, for the Cultivation of Stove, Greenhouse and Hardy Orchids.* Illus. 8vo. N.D. ; Second Edition, 1864.

BALDWIN, HENRY. *The Orchids of New England ; a Popular Monograph.* Illus., 8vo. New York, 1884.

BARBOSA-RODRIGUES, JOÄS.—*Genera et Species Orchidearum Novarum.* Illus., 8vo. Rio de Janeiro, 1881.

BARBOSA-RODRIGUES, JOÄS.—*Structure des Orchidées.* Rio de Janeiro, 1883.

BARIA, GIAMBATTISTA.—*Flore Illustré de Nice et des Alpes-Maritimes.* Nice, 1868.

BATEMAN, JAMES.—*A Second Century of Orchidaceous Plants.* 4to. Illus., col. plts., London, 1867. *See also* Hooker, Sir W. J.

BATEMAN, JAMES.—*Monograph of Odontoglossum.* Illus., col. plts., fol. London, 1864-1874.

BATEMAN, JAMES. *The Orchidaceae of Mexico and Guatemala.* Illus., col. plts., eleph. fol. London, 1837–1843.

BAUER, FRANZ ANDREAS and LINDLEY, J.—*Illustrations of Orchidaceous Plants ; with notes and prefatory remarks by John Lindley.* Illus., col. plts., fol. London. 1830–1838.

BEAN, W. J. (*see* Watson, Wm.).

BEDFORD, E. J.—*Some Rare Sussex Orchids.* Illus., 4to, London, 1912. (*Knowledge*, xxxv.)

BEER, JOHANN GEORG.—*Beiträge zur Morphologie und Biologie der Familie der Orchideen.* Illus., fol. Vienna, 1863.

BEER, JOHANN GEORG.—*Praktische Studien an der Familie der Orchideen, nebst Kulturanweisungen und Beschreibung aller schönbluhenden tropischen Orchideen.* Illus., 8vo. Vienna, 1854.

BEER, JOHANN GEORG.—*Ueber das Vorkommen eines Schleuderorganes in den Früchten verschiedener Orchideen.* 8vo. Vienna, 1857.

BENTHAM, GEORGE.—*Notes on Orchidaceae.* Illus., 8vo. London, 1881. *Trans. Linn. Soc.*

BERGEN, PAUL. *See* Camus, E. G.

BLUME, KARL LUDWIG.—*Collection des Orchidées les plus Remarquable de l'Archipel Indien et du Japan.* Illus., col. plts., fol. Amsterdam, 1858–1859.

BLUME, KARL LUDWIG.—*Flora Javae, Orchideae.* Illus., fol. Brussels, 1858.

BLUME, KARL LUDWIG.—*Tabellen en Platen voor de Javaansche Orchideen.* Illus., fol. Batavia, 1825.

BOHNHOF, E.—*Dictionary of Orchid Hybrids.* 8vo. Paris, 1895.

BOIS, DÉSIRÉ and GIBAULT, GEORGES.—*Tableau Synoptique des Principaux Genres d'Orchidées Cultivées.* Illus., 1902. (*Journ. Soc., Nat. d'Hort., France.*)

BOLUS, HARRY.—*Icones Orchidearum Austro-Africanarum, with Descriptions of South African Orchids.* Illus., col. plts., 8vo. Capetown, 1893–1913.

BOLUS, HARRY, *Orchids of the Cape Peninsula.* Illus., col. plts., 8vo. Cape Town, 1888. *Trans. South African Philosophical Society.*

BOYLE, FREDERICK.—*About Orchids.* Illus., col. plts., 8vo. London, 1893.

BOYLE, FREDERICK.—*The Culture of Greenhouse Orchids, Old System and New.* Illus., col. plts., 8vo. London, 1902.

BOYLE, FREDERICK.—*The Woodlands Orchids, Described and Illustrated, with Stories of Orchid-Collecting.* Illus., col. plts., 8vo. London, 1901.

BRÄCKLEIN, A.—*Die Orchideen und ihre Kultur in Zimmer.* Illus., 8vo. Berlin, 1904.

BREDA, JACQUES G. SAMUEL VAN.—*Genera et Species Orchidearum quas in Java Colligerunt Kuhl et van Hasselt.* Fol. Ghent, 1827.

BRITTEN, JAMES, and GOWER, W. H.—*Orchids for Amateurs.* Illus. London, *Circa* 1889.

BROWN, ROBERT.—*Genera et Species Orchidearum in Horto Kewensi.* 8vo. London, 1830.

BROWN, ROBERT.—*Observations on the Fecundation in Orchideae.* 8vo. London, 1834. *Trans. Linn. Soc.,* xvi.

BURBERRY, H. A.—*The Amateur Orchid Cultivators' Guide Book.* Illus., 8vo. Liverpool, 1894; Second Edition, col. plts., Liverpool, 1895.

BURBIDGE, FREDERICK WILLIAM.—*Cool Orchids and How to Grow Them.* Illus., 8vo. Liverpool, 1874.

BURGEFF, HANS.—*Die Wurzelpilze der Orchideen, ihre Kultur und ihre Leben in der Pflanze.* Illus., 8vo. Jena, 1909.

BURRAGE, A. C.—*A Catalogue of the Orchid Plants at Orchidvale, Beverley Farms, Massachusetts.* 8vo. Massachusetts, 1924.

CAMUS, EDMOND GUSTAVE.—*Iconographie des Orchidées d'Europe et du Bassin Mediterranéen.* Fol., Illus., col. plts. Paris, 1921.

CAMUS, EDMOND GUSTAVE.—*Monographie des Orchidées de l'Europe, de l'Afrique Septrionale, de l'Asie Mineure, et des Provinces Russes Transcaspiennes.* 4to, illus., col. plts. Paris, 1908.

CAMUS, EDMOND GUSTAVE.—*Monographie des Orchidées de France.* Atlas, illus., col. plts. Paris, 1944. *Journ. Bot.*

CASTLE, LEWIS.—*Orchids, Their Structure, History and Culture.* Illus., 8vo. London, 1886; another issue, 1887.

CHAPMAN, HARRY J.—*New and Revised Edition of " Orchids : their Culture and Management."* Illus., col. plts., 8vo. London, 1903. *See also* W. Watson.

COGNIAUX, ALFRED CÉLESTIN.—*Chronique Orchidéenne.* (Supplement to the *Dictionnaire Iconographique des Orchidées.*) 8vo. Brussels, 1897–1907.

COGNIAUX, ALFRED CÉLESTIN (and others).—*Dictionnaire Iconographique des Orchidées.* 8vo., illus., col. plts. Brussels, 1897–1907; 1896–1902.

COGNIAUX, ALFRED CÉLESTIN.—*Genre Cypripedium.* 8vo., illus., col. plts. Brussels, 1896–1902. *Dictionnaire Iconographique des Orchidées.*

COGNIAUX, ALFRED CÉLESTIN.—*Notes sur les Orchidées du Brésil et des Regions Voisines.* 8vo. *Bulletin Soc. Roy Bot., Belge.* Brussels, 1907.

COGNIAUX, ALFRED CÉLESTIN.—*Orchidaceae Florae Brasiliensis.* Fol., illus. Munich, 1890–1906.

COLMAN, SIR JEREMIAH, BT.—*Hybridization of Orchids.* 4to, illus. Reigate, 1933. Printed for private circulation.

CORREVON, HENRI.—*Album des Orchidées de l'Europe Centrale et Septrionale.* Illus., col. plts., 8vo. Geneva, 1889.

CORREVON, HENRI.—*Les Orchidées Rustiques.* Illus., 8vo. Geneva, 1893.

CURTIS, CHARLES H.—*Orchids for Everyone.* Illus., col. plts., 4to. London, 1910.

CURTIS, CHARLES H.—*See Orchid Review.*

DARWIN, CHARLES ROBERT.—*Fertilization of Orchids.* (On the Various Contrivances by which . . . Orchids are Fertilized by Insects and on the Good Effects of Intercrossing.) Illus., 8vo. London, 1862.

DARWIN, CHARLES ROBERT.—*Notes on the Fertilization of Orchids.* 8vo. London, 1869. *Ann. and Mag. Nat. Hist.*

DEUTSCHE GESELLSCHAFT FÜR ORCHID-KUNDE.—Fol., illus., col. plts., 8vo. Berlin, 1906–1908. Subsequently issued as an Appendix to *Gartenflora.*

DIELS, LUDWIG.—*Die Orchideen.* Illus., col. plts., vol. 4 of *Die Natur,* 8vo. Osterweick, n.d.

DU BUYSSON, COMTE FRANÇOIS.—*Traité Théoretique et Pratique sur la Culture des Orchidées.* Illus., 8vo. Paris, 1878. *L'Orchidophile.*

DUCHARTRE, PIERRE ETIENNE.—*Note sur deux Orchidées (Angraecum sesquipedale et Oncidium splendidum).* 4to. Paris, 1862. *Bull. Soc. Bot. Fr. IX.*

DUCHARTRE, PIERRE ETIENNE.—*Note sur le Cattleya Trianae.* 4to. Paris, 1860. *Journ. Soc. Imp. et Centr. Hort., Paris.*

DUCHARTRE, PIERRE ETIENNE.—*Note sur le Phalaenopsis Schilleriana.* 4to. Paris, 1862. *Journ. Soc. Imp. et Centr. Hort.*

DUMORTIER, BARTHÉLEMY CHARLES.—*Notice sur le Genre*

Maelenia de la Famille des Orchidées. 4to. Brussels, 1834. *Mém. Acad. Roy. Sci. Brux.*

DUTHIE, JOHN FIRMINGER.—*Descriptions of some New Species of Orchidacea from North West and Central India.* 8vo. Calcutta, 1902. *Journ. Asiat. Soc., Bengal.*

DUTHIE, JOHN FIRMINGER.—*The Orchids of North West Himalaya.* Illus., fol. Calcutta, 1906. *Annals Royal Botanic Gardens, Calcutta,* vol. 9, part 2.

DUVAL, LÉON.—*Les Odontoglossum.* Illus., 12mo. Paris, 1895.

DUVAL, LÉON.—*Petit Guide Pratique de la Culture des Orchidées.* Illus., 12mo. Paris, n.d.

DUVAL, LÉON.—*Traité de Culture Pratique des Cattleyas.* Illus., 8vo. Paris, 1907.

FABER, F. C. VON.—*Beiträge sur vergleichenden Anatomie der Cypripediinae.* Illus., 8vo. Stuttgart, 1904.

FARWELL, OLIVER ATKINS.—*The Yellow-Flowered Cypripediums.* 4to. *Rept. Mich. Acad. Sci. XX, Lansing.* Michigan, 1918.

FITZGERALD, ROBERT DAVID.—*Australian Orchids.* Illus., fol. Sydney, 1874–1888.

FITZGERALD, ROBERT DAVID.—*Australian Orchids.* Only vol. I and part of vol. II published. Illus., fol. Sydney, 1874–1894.

GODEFROY-LEBEUF, A., and BROWN, N. E.—*Les Cypripediées.* 4to. Argenteuil, 1888.

GODEFROY-LEBEUF, A.—*L'Orchidophile.* Illus., col. plts., 8vo. Argenteuil, 1881–1893.

GOESSENS, A.—Artist for *Dictionnaire Iconographique des Orchidées.*

GOWER, W. H., *See* Britten and Gower.

GRANT, BARTLE.—*The Orchids of Burma, including the Andaman Islands.* 8vo. Rangoon, 1895.

GRINDON, LEOPOLD HARTLEY.—*The Fairfield Orchids : a descriptive Catalogue of the Species and Varieties grown by James Brook & Co., Fairfield Nurseries.* 8vo. Manchester, 1872.

HANDTWIG, GUSTAV CHRISTIAN.—*De Orchide.* 4to. Rostock, 1747.

HANSEN, GEORGE.—*The Orchid Hybrids, up to 1895.* 8vo. London and Berlin, 1895. Supplement, 1897.

HARRISON, C. AYLWYN.—*Commercial Orchid Growing.* Illus., 8vo. London, 1914.

HARRISON, C. AYLWYN.—*Orchids for Amateurs* (Ed. by T. W. Sanders). Illus. 8vo. London, 1911.

HEFKA, ANTON.—*Cattleyen und Laelien, Samenzucht und Pflege.* Illus., 8vo. Vienna and Leipzig, 1914.

HENDERSON, ARTHUR & CO.—*Catalogue of Orchids, etc.* 8vo. London, 1835. (*Bot. Pam. at R.H.S.*)

HENSHALL, JOHN.—*A Practical Treatise on the Cultivation of Orchidaceous Plants and Geographical Distribution.* Illus., col. plts., 8vo. London, 1845.

HERDMAN, SIR WILLIAM ABBOTT.—*Notes on Coryanthus maculata.* 8vo. Liverpool, 1884. (*Bot. Pam. at R.H.S.*)

HERDMAN, SIR WILLIAM ABBOTT.—*Remarks on Angraecum sesquipedale.* 8vo. 1885. (*Bot. Pam. at R.H.S.*)

HOFFMANNSEGG, JOHANN C., GRAF VON.—*Verzeichniss seiner Orchideen.* 8vo. Dresden, 1842.

HOOKER, SIR JOSEPH DALTON.—*A Century of Indian Orchids.* Illus., col. plts., 4to. Calcutta, 1849–1867. *Annals Royal Botanic Gardens, Calcutta, Vol. 5, Part 1.*

HOOKER, SIR WM. JACKSON.—*A Century of Orchidaceous Plants.* Illus., col. plts., 4to. 1851.

HOOKER, SIR WM. JACKSON, and LYONS, J. C.—*A First Century of Orchidaceous Plants.* Illus., col. plts., 4to. London, 1849.

HOROWITZ, A.—*Ueber den anatomischen Bau und das Aufspringen der Orchideenfruecht.* Illus., 8vo. 1902.

HUEGEL, KARL, FREIHERR VON.—*Orchideen-sammlung im Frühjahre.* 8vo. Vienna, 1845.

HURST, CHARLES CHAMBERLAIN.—*Mendel's Principles Applied to Orchid Hybrids.* Journ., R.H.S., xxvii. London, 1902. *Bot. Pam. at R.H.S.*

HURST, CHARLES CHAMBERLAIN.—*Notes on some Curiosities of Orchid Breeding.* Illus., 8vo. London, 1898. *Journ. R.H.S., xxi.*

IMTHURN, SIR EVERARD F.—*Sketches of Wild Orchids in Guiana.* 8vo. London, 1898. *Journ., R.H.S., xxii.*

IRMISCH, THILO.—*Beiträge zur Biologie und Morphologie der Orchideen.* Illus., 4to. Leipzig, 1853.

JENISCH (?).—*Katalog seiner Orchideensammlung zu Flottbeck*. 8vo. Hamburg, 1845.

JENNINGS, SAMUEL.—*Orchids and How to Grow Them in India and other Tropical Climates.* Illus., Col. plts., 8vo. London, 1875.

JOST, FRANZ.—*Beschreibung und Kultur tropischer Orchideen.* 8vo. Prague, 1852.

JOURNAL DES ORCHIDÉES.—*Published by Lucien Linden.* Ghent, 1890–1896; Subsequently merged into *La Semaine Horticole.*

KERCHOVE DE DENTERGHEM, COUNT OSWALD DE.— *Le Livre des Orchidées.* Illus., col. plts., 8vo. Ghent and Paris, 1894.

KERNER, ANTON JOSEPH.—*Die Hybriden Orchideen der Oster-reichischen Flora.* 8vo. Innsbruck, 1865.

KEW.—*Orchids Cultivated in The Royal Botanic Gardens.* 8vo. Kew, 1896 ; Second Edition, 1904.

KING, SIR GEORGE, and PANTLING, R.—*Some New Orchids from Sikkim.* 8vo. Calcutta, 1935. *Journ. Asiatic Society, Bengal.* (*Bot. Pam. at R.H.S.*)

KING, SIR GEORGE AND PANTLING, R.—*The Orchids of the Sikkim Himalaya.* 8vo. 1895. *Annals. Royal Botanic Gardens, Calcutta.* Vol. 8, Parts 1-4.

KLINGE, JOHANNES.—*Diagnoses Orchidearum Novarum in Cali-daris Horti Imperialis Botanici Petropolitani Cultarum.* Illus., 8vo. S. Petersburg, 1898. Acta Horti. Petrop.

KLOTZSCH, JOHANN FRIEDRICH.—*Beschreibung des Cynoches chlorochilon.* 4to. Berlin, 1838. *Allg. Gartenz.,* vi.

KLOTZSCH, JOHANN FRIEDRICH.—*Cyclosia Kl. eine neue Orchideen-Gattung aus der Sippe Vandeae.* 4to. Berlin, 1838. *All. Gartenz.,* vi.

KOENIG, JOHANN GERARD.—*Descriptiones Monandrarum; Epi-dendrorum in India Orientali.* Fol. Liepzig, 1783. *Fasciculus Observationum Botanicarun, III* (*Retzius*).

KRÄNZLIN, FRITZ W. L.—*Beiträge zu einer Monographie der Gattung Habenaria.* 8vo. Berlin, 1891 ; Leipzig, 1893. *Allgemeiner Teil. ;* and *Engl. Bot. Jahrb.,* xvi, *Bot. Pam. at R.H.S.*

KRÄNZLIN, FRITZ W. L.—*Beiträge zur Orchideenflora Südamerikas.* Illus., 4to. Upsala, 1911.

R

KRÄNZLIN, FRITZ W. L.—*Eine Neue Epidendrum.* 8vo. Geneva, 1895. *Bull. Herb. Boiss.*, III (*Bot. Pam. at R.H.S.*)

KRÄNZLIN, FRITZ W. L.—*Eine Neue Rodriquezia.* Illus., 8vo. Geneva, 1895. *Bull. Herb. Boiss,* III (*Bot. Pam. at R.H.S.*)

KRÄNZLIN, FRITZ W. L.—*Orchidaceae Africanae, II.* 8vo. Leipzig, 1895. *Engl. Bot. Jahrb.*, xxii (*Bot. Pam. at R.H.S.*)

KRÄNZLIN, FRITZ W. L., and PFITZER, F.—*Orchidaceae-Monandrae Coelogyninae.* 8vo. 1907. *Das Pflanzenreich*, 32.

KRÄNZLIN, FRITZ W. L., and PFITZER, F.—*Orchidaceae-Monandrae-Dendrobienae.* 1910. *Das Pflanzenreich.*

KRÄNZLIN, FRITZ W. L., and PFITZER, F.—*Orchidaceae-Pleonandrae.* Berlin, 1903. *Das Pflanzenreich*, 12.

KRÄNZLIN, FRITZ W. L.—*Orchidaceae-Monandrae-Dendrobünae.* 8vo. Leipzig, 1902, 1912. *Das Pflanzenreich*, 1 & 2.

KRÄNZLIN, FRITZ W. L.—*Orchidaceae-Monandrae-Pseuomonopodiales.* 8vo. Leipzig, 1923. *Das Pflanzenreich.*

KRÄNZLIN, FRITZ W. L.—*Orchidaceae-Monandrae, Tribus Oncidiinae-Odontoglosseae.* 8vo. Leipzig, 1922. *Das Pflanzenreich*, 2.

KRÄNZLIN, FRITZ W. L.—*Orchidaceae Papuanae.* 8vo. Vienna, 1894. *Osterr. Bot. Zeitschr.* (*Bot. Pam. at R.H.S.*)

KRÄNZLIN, FRITZ W. L.—*Orchidacearum Genera et Species.* Illus., 8vo. Berlin, 1897–1904. Only Vol. 1 and Part 1 of Vol. II published.

KRÄNZLIN, FRITZ W. L.—*Orchidaceen.* 8vo. Bremen, 1882. *Bremen Abh.*, vii; *Bot. Pam. at R.H.S.*

LINDEN, JEAN JULES—*Pescatorea : Iconographie des Orchidées.* Illus., col. plts., fol. Brussels, 1860.

LINDEN, JULES & LUCIEN (assisted by Em. Rodigas and R. A. Rolfe).—*Iconography of Orchids.* English Ed., illus., col. plts., fol. Ghent, 1891–1897.

LINDEN, JULES & LUCIEN.—*Lindenia.* Illus., col. plts., fol. Ghent, 1885–1901.

LINDEN, LUCIEN (assisted by Cogniaux, C. A. and Grignan, G.)— *Les Orchidées Exotiques et leur Culture en Europe.* Illus., 8vo. Brussels, 1894.

LINDLEY, JOHN and BAUER, FRANZ A.—*Illustrations of Orchidaceous Plants.* Fol. London, 1830.

LINDLEY, JOHN.—*A List of the Orchidaceous Plants Collected in the East of Cuba by C. Wright.* 8vo. 1858. *Ann. and Mag. Nat. Hist., Series,* 3, 1. (*Bot. Pam. at R.H.S.*)

LINDLEY, JOHN.—*Contributions to the Orchidology of India.* Illus., 8vo. London, 1857–1889. *Trans. Linn. Soc.*

LINDLEY, JOHN.—*Folia Orchidacea: an Enumeration of the known Species of Orchids.* 8vo. London. 1852–1855.

LINDLEY, JOHN.—*Genera and Species of Orchidaceous Plants.* 8vo. London, 1830–1840.

LINDLEY, JOHN.—*Orchidaceae Lindenianae.* 8vo. London, 1846 (*Bot. Pam. at R.H.S.*)

LINDLEY, JOHN.—*Orchidearum Sceletos.* Illus., 8vo. London, 1826.

LINDLEY, JOHN.—*Sertum Orchidaceum: Wreath of the Most Beautiful Orchids.* Illus., col. plates., large fol. London, 1838.

LINDLEY, JOHN.—*The Genera and Species of Orchidaceous Plants.* Illus., 8vo., London. 1830–1840.

LINDLEY, JOHN.—*The Orchidaceous Plants of Chile.* 8vo. 1827. *Brande Quart. Journ. Sci.*

LINDLEY, JOHN.—*West African Tropical Plants.* 8vo. London, 1862.

LODDIGES, CONRAD, AND SONS.—*Orchideae in the Collection of C. Loddiges & Sons.* 12mo. London, 1839.

L'ORCHIDOPHILE (*Journal des Amateurs d'Orchidées*). (*See* Godefroy-Lebeuf).

LOTHIAN, MARQUIS OF.—*See* Woolward, Florence.

LUDDEMANN, GUSTAVE ADOLPH.—*Catalogue de la Collection de M. Pescatore au Chateau de la Celle-St.-Cloud.* 8vo. Paris, 1849.

LYONS, JOHN CHARLES.—*A Practical Treatise on the Management of Orchidaceous Plants.* Illus., 8vo. Dublin, 1845.

LYON, JOHN CHARLES.—*Remarks on the Management of Orchidaceous Plants.* Illus., 12mo. Dublin, 1843. The first published book on Orchids.

MACKENZIE, J. S. F.—*British Orchids: How to Tell One from Another.* Illus., col. plts., 4to. London, 1918.

MAGNUS, PAUL.—*Kurze Notiz über dimere zygomorphe Orchideenblüthen und über ein montröses Cypripedium.* 8vo. Berlin, n.d. *Abh. Bot. Ver. Brandenburg,* xxi.

MARIE, THÉODOR and LORMOY, J.—*Les Orchidées et M. Georges Mantin.* 8vo. Paris, 1892[?].

MARTIUS, KARL FRIEDRICH PHILIPP VON, and EICHLER, AUGUST WILHELM.—*Orchidaceae.* Illus., fol. Munich, 1893-1906.

MASSEE, GEORGE E.—*The Spot Disease of Orchids.* 8vo. London, 1895. *Ann. Bot.* ix.

MASTERS, MAXWELL T.—*A Peloria and Semidouble Flower of Ophrys aranifera.* Illus., 8vo. London, 1865. *Journ. Linn. Soc.* (*Bot. Pam. at R.H.S.*)

MASTERS, MAXWELL T.—*Teratology of Orchids.* Illus., 8vo. London, 1894 (*Bot. Pam. at R.H.S.*)

MAYRHOFER, KARLE.—*De Orchideis in Territorio Vindobonensi.* 8vo. Vienna, 1832.

MEASURES, R. H.—*Collection of Cypripediums.* Oblong 24mo. Streatham, 1899. Printed privately.

MEASURES, R. I.—*Masdevallias.* 24mo. Camberwell, 1890. Printed privately.

MEASURES, R. I.—*Cypripediums.* Oblong 24mo. London. 1894. Printed privately.

MILLICAN, ALBERT.—*Travels and Adventures of an Orchid Hunter.* Illus., 8vo., 1891.

MINER, H. S.—*Orchids: The Royal Family of Plants.* Illus., col. plts. 4to. London, 1885.

MOORE, SPENCER LE MARCHANT.—*A Monandrous Cypripedium.* 8vo. London, 1879. *Bot. Pam. at R.H.S.*

MOORE, THOMAS (Ed.)—*Illustrations of Orchidaceous Plants.* Illus., col. plts., 8vo. London, 1857.

MOREL, CHARLES.—*Culture des Orchidées.* 8vo. Paris, 1855.

MUELLER, SIR FERDINAND VON.—*New Polynesian Orchids.* 8vo. London, 1882 (*Bot. Pam. at R.H.S.*)

MUTEL, AUGUSTE.—*Premier Mémoire sur les Orchidées.* 8vo. Paris, 1838.

MUTEL, AUGUSTE.—*Mémoire sur Plusieurs Orchidées Nouvelles* 4to. Paris, 1842.

NILES, G. G.—*Bog-trotting for Orchids.* Illus., col. plts., 8vo. New York, 1904.

OLIVER, FRANK WALL.—*On the Sensitive Labellum of Masdevallia muscosa.* Illus., 8vo. Oxford, 1888. *Ann. Bot.,* 1 (*Bot. Pam. at R.H.S.*)

ORCHIDOLOGIA ZEYLANICA.—*The Official organ of the Orchid Circle of Ceylon. Founded and Edited by Dr. E. Soysa.* Illus., sm. 4to. Ceylon. Still in progress.

ORCHID REVIEW.—*Founded by R. Allen Rolfe in 1893 and Edited by him until 1920; Edited by Gurney Wilson, 1921–1932; Edited by Charles H. Curtis since 1933 ; still in progress.*

ORCHID WORLD.—*Edited by Gurney Wilson.* Illus., col. plts., 4to. Haywards Heath, 1911–1916.

OUDEMANS, CORNELIUS ANTON J. A.—*Ueber den Sitz der Oberhaut bei den Luftwurzeln der Orchideen.* Illus., 4to. Amsterdam, 1864.

PFITZER, ERNST.—*Beobachtungen über Bau und Entwicklung der Orchideen.* 8vo. Berlin, 1884 (*Bot. Pam. at R.H.S.*)

PFITZER, ERNST.—*Beobachtungen über Bau und Entwicklung der Orchideen.* 8vo. Heidelberg, 1880 (*Bot. Pam. at R.H.S.*)

PFITZER, ERNST.—*Beiträge zur Systematik der Orchideen.* 8vo. Leipzig, 1894. *Engl. Bot. Jahrb.,* xix.

PFITZER, ERNST.—*Grundzüge einer vergleichenden Morphologie der Orchideen.* Illus., 4to. Heidelberg, 1882.

PRILLIEUX, EDOUARD.—*Coloration de Bleu des Fleurs de quelques Orchidées sous l'Influence de la Gelée.* 8vo. Paris, 1872. (*Bot. Pam. at R.H.S.*)

PLAUSZEWSKI, (?).—*Orchidées et Plantes de Serres.* Illus., fol. Paris, 1899.

PUCEL, A.—*Les Cypripedium et Genres Affines.* Cr. 8vo. Florence, 1891.

PUYDT, E. DE.—*Les Orchidées, Histoire Iconographique.* Illus., col. plts., 8vo. Paris, 1880.

RADDI, GIUSEPPE.—*Descrizione di una Nuova Orchidea Braziliana* (*Cyrtopodium glutiniferum*). 4to. Modena, 1833. *Mem. Soc. Ital. Sci.,* XIX.

RAMSBOTTOM, JOHN.—*Orchid Mycorrhiza.* In Messrs. Charlesworth & Co.'s *Catalogue of Orchids.* 4to. Haywards Heath, 1922.

RAND, EDWARD SPRAGUE.—*Orchids : A Description of the*

Species and Varieties grown at Glen Ridge, near Boston. Illus., 8vo. New York, 1876.

REICHE, KARL.—*Orchidaceae Chilensis: Ensayo de una Monografia de las Orquideas de Chile.* 4to. Santiago, 1910. *Annales Museo National de Chile.*

REICHENBACH, HEINRICH GUSTAV.—*Beiträge zur Orchideen-kunde.* Illus., 4to. Jena, 1869.

REICHENBACH, HEINRICH GUSTAV.—*Beiträge zur Orchideen-kund Central-Amerikas.* Illus. 4to. Hamburg, 1866.

REICHENBACH, HEINRICH GUSTAV.—*De Pollinaris Orchidearam Genesi ac Structura et de Orchideis in Artem ac Systema Redigendis.* Illus., 4to. Leipzig, 1852.

REICHENBACH, HEINRICH GUSTAV.—*Enumeration of the Orchids Collected by the Rev. E. C. Parish in the Neighbourhood of Moulmein, with descriptions of the New Species.* Illus., 4to. 1874. *Trans. Linn, Soc.,* XXX *(Bot. Pam. at R.H.S.)*

REICHENBACH, HEINRICH GUSTAV.—*Katalog der Orchideenzammlung von G. W. Schiller zu Ovelgönne.* Illus., 8vo. Hamburg, 1857.

REICHENBACH, HEINRICH GUSTAV.—*Orchideae in Flora Germanica Recensitae.* Illus., col. plts., 4to. Leipzig, 1850–1851.

REICHENBACH, HEINRICH GUSTAV.—*Orchideae quaedam Lansbergianae.* 8vo. Leyden, 1859. *(Bot. Pam. at R.H.S.)*

REICHENBACH, HEINRICH GUSTAV.—*Orchideae Splitgerberianae Surinamensis.* 8vo. Leyden, 1859. *(Bot. Pam. at R.H.S.)*

REICHENBACH, HEINRICH GUSTAV.—*Über einige Garten-Orchideen.* 8vo. Hamburg, n.d. *(Bot. Pam. at R.H.S.)*

REICHENBACH, HEINRICH GUSTAV.—*Xenia Orchidacea.* Illus., col. plts., 4to. Three Vols. Leipzig, 1854–1900. Continued by F. Kränzlin.

RICHARD, ACHILLE.—*Monographie des Orchidées des Iles de France et de Bourbon.* Illus., 4to. Paris, 1828.

RICHARD, ACHILLE, and GALEOTTI, HENRI.—*Monographie des Orchidées Recueiles sur la Chaine des Nilgherries par M. Perrottet.* 4to. Paris, 1841. *Ann. Sci. Nat., Series II,* 15.

RICHARD, ACHILLE, and GALEOTTI, HENRI.—*Orchidographie Mexicaine.* 8vo. Paris, 1845. *Ann. Soc. Nat., Sér.* 3.

RICHARD, LOUIS CLAUDE.—*De Orchideis Europaeis Annotationes.* Illus., 4to. Paris, 1817.

RIDLEY, H. N.—*Enumeration of all Orchideae from Borneo.* Illus., 8vo. London, 1896. *Trans. Linn. Soc.*

RIDLEY, H. N.—*Monograph of the Genus Liparis.* Illus., 8vo. London, 1886. *Trans. Linn. Soc.*

RIDLEY, H. N.—*The Orchideae and Apostaciaceae of the Malay Peninsula.* 8vo. London, 1896. *Trans. Linn. Soc.*

ROGERS, R. S., and WHITE, CYRIL T.—*Contributions to the Orchidaceous Flora of Queensland.* Illus., 8vo. Brisbane, 1920.

ROGERS, R. S.—*Introduction to the Study of South Australian Orchids.* Illus., col. plts., 8vo. Adelaide, 1911.

ROLFE, ROBERT ALLEN.—*See Orchid Review.*

ROLFE, ROBERT ALLEN, and HURST, CHARLES C.—*The Orchid Stud Book.* Illus., 8vo. Kew, 1909.

ROLFE, ROBERT ALLEN.—" *New Garden Orchids,*" I-VII. *Kew Bulletin,* 1891–1894.

ROYAL HORTICULTURAL SOCIETY.—*Awards to Orchids from* 1889. 8vo. London, 1906, 1910, 1913, 1916, 1926.

ROYAL HORTICULTURAL SOCIETY.—*List of Orchids used in the Fertilization of Hybrids which have received either First Class Certificates or Awards of Merit.* 8vo. London, 1910, 1913.

ROYAL HORTICULTURAL SOCIETY.—*Report of the Orchid Conference,* 1885. 8vo. London, 1886. *R.H.S. Journal,* vol. VII, No. 1, 1886.

SANDER & CO., F.—*Sander's Orchid Guide.* 8vo. St. Albans, 1902.

SANDER & SONS, *Sanders' List of Orchid Hybrids.* 8vo. St. Albans, 1915.

SANDER, HENRY FREDERICK CONRAD.—*Reichenbachia. Orchids illustrated and Described.* Col. plts. from Paintings by F. Moon. Folio, four vols. in Two Series. St. Albans, 1888–1890, 1892–1894.

SANDERS (ST. ALBANS), LTD.—*Sanders' Complete List of Orchid Hybrids, to January* 1*st,* 1946. 4to, pp. 308. St. Albans, Hertfordshire, 1947.

SCHILLER, G. W.—*Catalog der Orchideen—Sammlung.* Illus., 8vo, several Editions. Hamburg, 1850(?)–1861.

SCHLECHTER, RUDOLF.—*Die Orchideen: ihre Beschreibung, Kultur und Züchtung (Handbuch für Orchideenliebhaber, Kultivateure und Botaniker).* Illus., 8vo. Berlin, 1914. 2nd ed.; Berlin, 1927.

SCHLECHTER, RUDOLF.—*Neue Orchidaceen der Flora des Monsun-Gebietes.* 8vo. Geneva, 1906. *Bull. Herb. Boissier.*

SCHLECHTER, RUDOLF.—*Orchidacées de Madagascar.* Illus., 8vo. Marseilles, 1913. *Ann. Mus., Marseille.*

SCHLECHTER, RUDOLF.—*Uber eine neue Bifrenaria.* Illus., 8vo. Berlin, n.d. *Orchis* I.

SCHLECHTER, RUDOLF.—*Uber eine Neue Orchidaceen.* 8vo. Berlin, n.d., *Orchis* I.

SCHÖNICHEN, W.—*Die Orchideen.* Illus., col. plts., 8vo. Osterwieck n.d. *Die Natur,* vol. 4.

SCHULZE, MAX.—*Die Orchidaceen Deutschlands, Deutsch-Oester-reichs und der Schweiz.* Illus., col. plts., 4to. Gera-Untermhaus, 1892-94.

SCOTT, JOHN.—*Orchidaceae.* 8vo. Calcutta, n.d. *Journ. Agr. and Hort. Soc., Ind.* II. *(Bot. Pam. at R.H.S.)*

SCOTT, JOHN.—*The Individual Sterility and Cross-impregnation of Certain Species of Oncidium.* 8vo. London, 1865. *Journ. Linn. Soc.,* VIII.

SMITH, JOHANNES JACOBUS.—*Die Orchideen von Ambon.* 8vo. Batavia, 1905.

SMITH, JOHANNES JACOBUS.—*Die Orchideen von Java.* Illus., atlas. Leiden, 1908-1914. *Flora de Buitenzorg.*

SOYSA, DR. E. (Ed.).—" *Orchid Culture in Ceylon.*" Orchid Circle of Ceylon, 1943.

SOYSA, DR. E.—*See Orchidologia Zeylanica.*

SPLITGERBER, FRIEDRICH LUDWIG.—*Notice sur une Nouvelle Espèce de Vanille.* 8vo. Paris, 1841.

SPRENGER, C.—*Orchidee di Seme.* 8vo. Florence, 1907.

SPRENGER, C.—*Sulla Concimazione delle Orchidee.* 8vo. Florence, 1906.

STEIN, BERTHOLD.—*Orchideenbuch.* Illus., 8vo. Berlin, 1892.

STENZEL, KARL GUSTAV WILHELM.—*Abweichende Blüten heimischer Orchideen, mit einem Rückblick auf die der Abietineen.* Cassell and Stuttgart, 1902.

STEVENS, JOHN CRACE.—*A Catalogue of Various Valuable*

Orchids, which will be sold at the Chiswick Gardens. 4to. London, 1855.

STEVENS, JOHN CRACE.—*The Loddiges Collection of Orchids.* 4to. London, 1856.

STEVENS, JOHN CRACE.—*A Catalogue of a Collection of Orchids, that has Ranked for Some Years past as one of the Finest in the Kingdom.* 8vo. London, 1851.

SWARTZ, OLOF.—*Genera et Species Orchidearum.* Illus., 8vo. Erfurt, 1805.

THOUARS, AUBERT DU PETIT.—*Histoire Particulière des Orchidées recueilles sur les trois Isles Australes d'Afrique.* 8vo. Paris, 1822.

TIMBAL-LAGRAVE, EDOUARD.—*Memoires sur quelques Hybrides de la Famille des Orchidées.* 8vo. Toulouse, 1854.

TODARO, AGOSTINO.—*Orchideae Siculae.* Illus. 8vo. Palermo, 1842.

TRUFFAUT, GEORGES, and HÉBERT, ALEXANDRE.—*Étude de la Dégénérescence de Certaines Espèces d'Orchidées et en Particulier du Genre Cattleya.* 8vo. Paris, 1897.

VEITCH & SONS, JAMES.—*A Manual of Orchidaceous Plants.* 8vo. Chelsea, 1887–1894.

VERMEULEN, P.—*Studies on Dactylorchids.* Illus., 8vo. Utrecht, 1947.

VRIESE, W. H. de.—*Illustrations d'Orchidées des Indes Orientales.* Illus., fol. Hague, 1854.

WARNER, ROBERT.—*Select Orchidaceous Plants.* Illus., col. plts., fol. London, 1862 ; second series, 1865–1875 ; third series, n.d.

WARNER, ROBERT, and WILLIAMS, BENJAMIN S. (Botanical Descriptions by THOMAS MOORE).—" *The Orchid Album.*" Illus., col. plts., by J. N. Fitch. 4to, XI vols. London, 1882–1897.

WATSON, WILLIAM, assisted by BEAN, W. J.—*Orchids, Their Culture and Management.* Illus., col. plts., 8vo. London, 1890.

WEBSTER, ANGUS D.—*British Orchids.* Illus., 8vo. Bangor, 1886 and 1898.

WEISS, FREDERICK ERNEST.—*Seeds and Seedlings of Orchids.* Manchester, 1916. *Anns. Rep.* and *Trans. Manch. Micros. Soc.*

WILDEMAN, EMILE DE.—*La Revision de la Nomenclature chez les Orchidées*. 8vo. Ghent, 1896.

WILLIAMS, B. S.—*The Orchid Growers' Manual*. Illus., 8vo. London (several Editions), 1852–1885.

WILLIAMS, HENRY.—*Orchid Growers' Manual*. Illus., 8vo. (enlarged edition). London, 1894.

WILSON, GURNEY.—*See Orchid Review*.

WOOLWARD, FLORENCE H.—*The Genus Masdevallia (chiefly from Plants in the Marquis of Lothian's Collection at Newbattle Abbey)*. Illus. by Miss Woolward, with notes by F. C. Lehmann. Fol. London, 1890–1896.

GENERAL INDEX

INDEX OF GENERA, SPECIES AND HYBRIDS

ABBREVIATIONS

Batem Orch.	*The Orchidaceae of Mexico and Guatemala* (1837–43) by James Bateman.
Benth.	George Bentham (1800–84), British botanist.
Bot. Mag.	*Curtis's Botanical Magazine*, begun in 1787 by William Curtis and continued to the present day. W. J. Hooker edited it 1845–64, his son, J. D. Hooker, 1865–1904. It contains coloured figures with descriptions and observations on the botany, history and cultivation of new, rare or little-known plants. The Royal Horticultural Society of London now publishes it.
Bot. Reg.	*The Botanical Register* (1815–49), edited by John Lindley, 1829–47.
F. Muell.	Sir Ferdinand Jakob Heinrich von Mueller (1825–56), German botanist, who settled in Australia and became her leading botanist.
Fl. Gard.	*Paxton's Flower Garden* (1850–53) by John Lindley and Sir Joseph Paxton.
Hemsl.	William Botting Hemsley (1843–1924), British botanist, keeper of Kew Herbarium 1899–1908.
Hook.	Sir William Jackson Hooker (1785–1865), director of the Royal Botanic Gardens, Kew, 1841–65.
Hook. f.	Sir Joseph Dalton Hooker (1817–1911), director of the Royal Botanic Gardens, Kew, 1865–1911.
Hort.	Of Gardens.
Jacq.	Baron Nicolas Joseph Jacquin (1727–1817), Dutch botanist, who became director of the Vienna botanic garden.
Lindl.	John Lindley (1799–1865), British botanist and horticulturist, a founder and first editor of *The Gardeners' Chronicle*, in his day the leading botanical authority on Orchidaceae.
Linn.	Carl Linnaeus (1707–78), Swedish botanist, whose book *Species Plantarum* (1753) is the starting point of modern botanical nomenclature.
Lodd.	Messrs. Conrad Loddiges & Sons, Hackney nurserymen of Dutch origin, who published *The Botanical Cabinet* (1818–33).
Mag. Bot.	*Paxton's Magazine of Botany* (1839–49), edited by Sir Joseph Paxton.
Miq.	Frederik Anton Wilhelm Miquel (1811–71), German botanist, who became professor of botany at Utrecht.
Mongr. Odont.	*A Monograph of Odontoglossum* (1864–74) by James Bateman.
N. E. Br.	Nicholas Edward Brown (1849–1934), British botanist, assistant in Kew Herbarium, 1873–1914.
Orch. Alb.	*The Orchid Album* (1882–97), conducted by Robert Warner and others.
R. Br.	Robert Brown (1773–1858), British botanist, keeper of botany at the British Museum.
Rchb. f.	Heinrich Gustav Reichenbach (1823–89), German botanist, director of the Hamburg botanic garden, after Lindley's death the leading botanical authority on Orchidaceae ; he bequeathed his herbarium to the Vienna Hofmuseum on condition that it was kept sealed for twenty-five years to prevent other orchid specialists consulting it. He was the son of H. G. L. Reichenbach (1793–1879).
Sel Orch.	*Select orchidaceous Plants* (1862–91) by Robert Warner and Benjamin Samuel Williams.